A. W. Küchler, Ph. D., University of Munich, is Professor of Geography at the University of Kansas. He is a member of the Association of American Geographers, the American Geographical Society, the Ecological Society of America, the UNESCO Working Group on Vegetation Mapping, and other national and international professional organizations. Dr. Küchler has prepared many outstanding vegetation maps and has written widely on the subject; he is also editor and co-author of the *International Bibliography of Vegetation Maps*.

VEGETATION

MAPPING

August Wilhelm

A. W. Küchler

UNIVERSITY OF KANSAS

THE RONALD PRESS COMPANY · NEW YORK

Library of Congress Catalog Card Number: 66–21857

PRINTED IN THE UNITED STATES OF AMERICA

Preface

The time for vegetation mapping has arrived. On all continents vegetation maps are now being prepared, and it is interesting to see how a field of knowledge can become prominent almost overnight just because a certain phase in the long history of science has been reached. Less than a century ago vegetation maps were largely unknown, but the stage was set, and by today the attained heights of achievement are spectacular.

The intimate intercourse between two or more fields of knowledge often bears interesting and valuable fruit. Vegetation maps are such fruit, resulting from the union of botany and geography. The work of botanists can be comprehensive only if it includes a consideration of plants in space, i.e., in different types of landscapes. At this point, the work of geographers becomes important through the development of maps as tools to determine and to analyze distributions in space. Our highly developed knowledge of vegetation is matched by the refinement of cartographic techniques, and maps can now be made that will show the geographical extent and distribution of vegetation anywhere on the surface of our planet with a remarkable degree of accuracy.

Indeed, so much energy is now being spent on vegetation maps, and so great is the need for more and better maps, that it seems the time is at hand for a publication such as this, in which the relevant information on vegetation maps and their preparation is brought together. This, it is hoped, will clarify the thinking of those interested in vegetation maps, particularly if they lack the facilities to acquaint themselves with the many intricate problems involved. It is also hoped that future vegetation mappers may find here the help and guidance that at times are difficult to obtain.

In this book some basic considerations must necessarily precede the more technical aspects of vegetation maps and their preparation. Once these have been discussed, the reader will more fully appreciate the presentation of various mapping methods and techniques. When the basic features of vegetation mapping have thus been clarified, the section on what might be termed *applied vegetation mapping* can reveal the wide variety of uses which vegetation maps are serving today. Some questions have been answered in this book, but many more problems await solution. If bringing together the numerous facets of vegetation mapping will stimulate scientists to expand their research, making new vegetation maps more profitable to a wider variety of users, then this book will have served its purpose.

If the reader wishes information on a given topic, he should find it all in one chapter. This implies that certain aspects may be mentioned more than once although in different contexts. For instance, the use of color is discussed in the chapter on "Patterns, Colors, and Symbols." In this chapter, the basic ideas on the use of color on vegetation maps are thoroughly discussed. Later, in the chapter on GAUSSEN's ecological method, colors are again, and necessarily, discussed, because this method is entirely based on them. Of course, it was sometimes more practical to refer the reader from one section to another, i.e., wherever a second discussion would have been no more than a repetition of what had been said before. Technical terms are explained and defined wherever they are used for the first time.

The reader will become aware of a large number of European sources quoted in the book, whereas the number of American authors is relatively modest. So far, the latter have contributed little to the theoretical aspects of vegetation mapping compared with their European colleagues, who have discussed the whole field often and exhaustively. Hopefully, this book may help a wider audience benefit from the European ideas and experiences.

An effort has also been made to help the reader find relevant material in the world literature. The Bibliography has therefore been enriched over and beyond the actual citations in this book to provide a rich source and guide for vegetation mappers who wish to penetrate more deeply into the thought of their colleagues.

As will be seen from a perusal of these pages, the whole field of vegetation mapping is in flux, evolving rapidly. New ideas, new methods and techniques, are characteristic of our times, and the spectacular advances of science and technology are matched by social upheavals of unprecedented dimensions. In such turbulent periods it is not always easy to see the guidelines, even within one's own limited sphere of activity. The author hopes, therefore, that this book will help vegetation mappers keep their bearings when charting their courses, even though these lead into regions as yet unexplored.

A. W. KÜCHLER

Lawrence, Kansas
January, 1967

Contents

V APPLICATION OF VEGETATION MAPS

VI CONCLUSION

I

HISTORICAL SKETCH

1

Five Centuries of
Vegetation Cartography

Vegetation maps were not invented by one man at one time like the steam engine or the electric light bulb. The evolution of vegetation maps is characterized by a very slow tempo matched by an equally slow acceleration during most of its long history, a regionally spotty development and, finally, a much-increased acceleration and spread especially after the first quarter of the twentieth century. The highly sophisticated vegetation maps of the mid-twentieth century evolved from beginnings that are far removed in time and in character.

When maps came into more general use during the fifteenth and, particularly, the sixteenth century, vegetation (*sensu lato*) was frequently shown on them. FONCIN (1961) reports on maps I, V, and VI in the *Cosmographia* of Ptolemy, published in Bologna, Italy, in 1447, on which named forests are indicated by showing little groups of trees in perspective. In the second edition (Rome, 1478) this practice is extended, and the Ardennes Forest is shown on the map of France. These are serious efforts to reveal the geographical location and extent of known vegetation types. However, simultaneously with these maps and for long afterward as well, many maps were published on which vegetation in one form or another was shown largely for decorative purposes or in order to fill in the empty spaces of unexplored regions.

In the sixteenth century forests were recognized as items of significance in military matters, as hunting reserves, timber resources, or obstacles to communications. Forests were therefore shown on maps with growing frequency and accuracy. Thus MRAZ and SAMEK (1963) report on a map by CLAUDIANUS (1518) and another by CRIGINGER (1569) which they consider forerunners of modern vegetation maps. At the very end of the century (1599), three maps were published in widely separated areas: Nürnberg, Germany (FONCIN, 1961); Trokavec, Bohemia (MRAZ and SAMEK, 1963; and Muscovy, Russia (FONCIN, 1961). The Nürnberg map shows the distribution of forests and even some cultivated fields. On the Bohemian map PODOLSKY uses tree symbols for his forests and distinguishes four tree genera: oak, hornbeam, birch, and willow. The Russian map separates forests from grasslands. The maps in the famous atlas by BLAEU (1640–1654) also show little tree symbols, but they do not seem to indicate the distribution of forests accurately; they appear unrelated to the landscape. In the course of the seventeenth century, cultural vegetation is shown, occasionally at first, but with increasing frequency; its symbolization is established remarkably soon: stippling for meadows, lines (furrows) for ploughed fields, vines for vineyards, etc. FONCIN (1961) describes the map of some Mediterranean coastal regions in France by PERELLE (1680), who shows vineyards, orange groves, olive groves, pines, myrtle, and strawberry trees (*Arbutus unedo*).

Topography and Vegetation

The purpose of these maps is above all geographical, i.e., to show the location of places, administrative districts, rivers, mountains, etc. Information on vegetation is incidental. As cartography developed, especially in the form of detailed topographic maps with a high degree of accuracy and reliability, the symbolization of vegetation evolved, too. The first real success in a modern sense came with the famous topographic map of France at 1:80,000 by CASSINI in the late eighteenth century. On these sheets, broadleaf deciduous forests were consistently distinguished from needleleaf evergreen forests. In addition, some sheets showed remarkable detail. Thus a sheet of the lower Rhône region included forests of (1) *Quercus ilex*, (2) *Quercus pubescentis*, (3) *Populus alba*, and (4) *Pinus pinea*; scrub of *Quercus coccifera* and *Rosmarinus officinalis*; swamps of *Scirpus* and *Phragmites*, stands of *Salsola*; and finally vineyards. On the topographic sheets of many European countries the actual vegetation is now shown to the extent of indicating needleleaf evergreen forests, broadleaf deciduous forests, shrub formations (heath), meadows and pastures, marshes, swamps and bogs, vineyards, orchards, and similar items. In the United States this advanced state of mapping has unfortunately not yet been attained, and it is considered a step forward if forests (*sensu lato*) are shown at all—even if only by a flat green color.

However, topographic maps are not vegetation maps, even though many of them show some kinds of vegetation. In spite of the excellence of many modern topographic maps and of efforts to include vegetation on them as an integral part of their content, topographic maps are vegetation maps only in a limited sense, if, indeed, vegetation is shown on them at all. In many instances, it is not. It is therefore important to distinguish between maps such as these and vegetation maps *sensu stricto*, i.e., maps whose primary purpose it is to show the geographical distribution of various vegetation types in a given area.

Early Vegetation Maps

SENDTNER (1854) mapped the geographical distribution of "Sphagnetum with *Pinus pumilio*." Even though this map is quite limited in scope, it is nevertheless interesting because it builds on CASSINI's approach to vegetation: it is a map showing the extent of a defined vegetation type and thus pioneering in a new direction. Soon afterwards, MARTIUS (1858) published a map of the *Florenreiche* of Brazil. This is the first successful attempt to portray the vegetation of an entire country. The name implies the approach to floristic areas used by his famous predecessors, SCHOUW (1823) and HUMBOLDT (BROMME, 1851). But the five floral realms of Brazil as transcribed by HUECK (1957) reveal that MARTIUS showed in fact the physiognomic formations he had already described in 1824.

In the meantime, HARPER (1857) published his map of The Prairies above Tibley Creek, and with it started the United States on a development that remained unmatched for many decades. CURTIS' (1860) vegetation map of North Carolina was followed by maps of New Jersey (COOK and SMOCK, 1878) and of Colorado (HAYDEN, 1878). Then came two maps of parts of Wisconsin (SWEET, 1880; WOOSTER, 1882) leading to the important vegetation map of the whole state of Wisconsin (CHAMBERLIN, 1883), which was unsurpassed for detail and completeness. Only one year later the development became almost explosive when, under the editorship of SARGENT (1884), the tenth census of the United States published vegetation maps of North America and of more than a dozen states from Maine to Florida and westward to Texas and Minnesota. Nothing like it had ever been attempted before, and the vegetation of a larger area at similar scales elsewhere was not mapped until decades later. Then McGEE (1889) added his map of northeastern Iowa and LEIBERG (1899) his map of Montana to the already impressive score and, by the turn of the century, the area of vegetation mapped in the United States corresponded to nearly all of Europe west of the Adria and the Baltic. From then on, a steady stream of vegetation maps issued forth from various sources and while its volume fluctuated, it never ceased. This period of American vegetation mapping culminated in the well-known vegetation map of the United States by SHANTZ and

ZON (1923), the manuscript of which was already completed in 1912. This map was a truly remarkable achievement, considering the amount of information available at that time. For more than a generation, it remained the only significant vegetation map of the United States.

Simultaneously with the rapid progress of vegetation mapping in the United States, a similar though more modest development took place in Argentina, as reported by HUECK (1950–1951). The first map of that country was published by P. G. LORENTZ in 1876, accompanied by a more detailed map of the northwestern part. Then BRACKEBUSCH (1893) presented another map of the Argentinian Northwest which HUECK considers an extraordinary achievement even for today. The census of 1895 included a vegetation map of the whole country not unlike SARGENT's earlier efforts in the United States, and KURTZ presented his vegetation map of the province of Córdoba in 1905. The early introduction of vegetation maps into Argentinian school books was unequalled anywhere. In the United States, for instance, vegetation maps in school books are rare even today.

The spectacular development of vegetation mapping in the United States during the last decades of the nineteenth century was not matched by a similar evolution in Europe. Thus the bibliography of German vegetation maps by TÜXEN and HENTSCHEL (1954) does not contain a single entry for the nineteenth century or earlier. No bibliography can hope to be complete, and SENDTNER's map seems to have escaped the authors' notice; even so, this bibliography reveals what is characteristic for Europe, not just Germany.

Nevertheless, there were notable achievements, and prominent among these is the world map by GRISEBACH (1872). This was an advance from SCHOUW and HUMBOLDT, for the map shows such physiognomic formations as the Hylaea (the tropical rainforest of the Amazon Basin), prairies, pampas, etc. But the old floristic practices lingered on in items like the "arctic flora," the "Chinese-Japanese region," or the "Californian region"; they do not reveal the character of the vegetation. Presumably, these items are due to a lack of adequate information. Basically, however, GRISEBACH's map is the first attempt to prepare a genuine vegetation map of the world.

GRISEBACH's map revealed a scientific recognition of formations and their relations to the environment, especially the climate. Ecological relations had long been known to exist, especially since LINNÉ (1707–1778) and a few scientists had shown concern for them. However, at the end of the nineteenth century the time was ripe for an ecological approach, and SCHIMPER (1898) presented a new vegetation map of the world, the first that may be considered "modern," as is indicated by its legend:

Distribution of the Most Important Types of Formations on the Earth,
at an Equatorial Scale of 1:120,000,000

1. Tropical rainforests	9. Thornforests and scrub
2. Subtropical rainforests	10. Savannas
3. Monsoon forests	11. Steppes and transitions between
4. Temperate rainforests	steppes and deserts (semi-deserts)
5. Summergreen broadleaf forests	12. Heaths
6. Needleleaf forests	13. Dry deserts
7. Sclerophyll woods	14. Tundra
8. Savanna forests	15. Cold deserts

Haltingly at first but with slowly increasing momentum, vegetation maps gained recognition as bases for research and as instruments for the formulation of problems and for finding solutions to them. Toward the end of the nineteenth century, FLAHAUT (1894) presented a vegetation map of the area around Perpignan in southern France at the medium scale of 1:200,000 and discussed the possibilities of preparing similar maps for all of France. SCHRÖTER (1895) published his large-scale vegetation map of the St. Antöniertal, which provided an extraordinary stimulus to the development of vegetation mapping in Switzerland. The century closed with the publication of a vegetation map of Russia by Tanfilev (SOCHAVA, 1958).

The Twentieth Century

The new century did not at first bring about any radical change in vegetation mapping. However, the handwriting was already on the wall. Phytocenology and ecology as sciences were making great strides, and the formulation of principles for a systematic analysis and classification of vegetation advanced rapidly. Inevitably the new ideas were expressed cartographically. Thus DRUDE (1907), on parts of three topographic sheets (1:25,000), mapped the vegetation of the eastern Ore Mountains in Germany and showed physiognomic-ecological formations, subdivided floristically into units of similar-species combinations.

As the world recovered from the catastrophe of World War I, vegetation maps began to appear in more rapid succession. By then the situation had changed profoundly and the days of nineteenth century mapping were gone forever.

The new situation found its expression in at least three ways. First, the difference between the United States and Europe had changed. This country no longer led the way but shared the honors of being a major producer of vegetation maps with Europe and the Soviet Union. Second, the European phytocenologists placed heavy emphasis on mapping at large scales. Third, the development of schools of thought in phytocenology found its expression also on vegetation maps (KÜCHLER, 1953a). The contending schools of thought were at times engaged in very spirited debates, and a greater harmony seemed highly desirable. In fact, however, these debates were most fruitful, resulting in an ever-greater refinement of methods and an increasing solidity of the scientific foundation of the more recent vegetation maps. The Europeans took over the leadership based on a strictly scientific approach, reasoning that a vegetation map can be fully exploited only if it is based on the scientific method. Vegetation maps that are originally prepared for some utilitarian goal are not only limited in applicability, but rarely permit a later diversification of their uses.

European Mapping Institutes

The extraordinary success of European vegetation mappers rests on very clear and precise definitions and classifications of phytocenoses. This observation applies to all European schools of thought. Gradually, it was recognized that each of these had its own merits and should be promoted. Swiss phytocenologists were particularly active. Many governments, too, realized the value of vegetation maps and established special agencies devoted to vegetation mapping. Thus the Centre National de la Recherche Scientifique, the French equivalent of the National Science Foundation in this country, sponsored two institutes for vegetation mapping, above all in France but also overseas, and with their own journal, the *Bulletin du service de la carte phytogéographique*. These institutes are the Service de la carte de la végétation de la France au 1:200,000ᵉ at Toulouse founded by GAUSSEN and, since his retirement, directed by REY, and the Service de la carte des groupements végétaux de la France au 1:20,000ᵉ at Montpellier, founded and directed by EMBERGER.

The Toulouse institute is devoted above all to mapping all of France at the uniform scale of 1:200,000 according to the method developed by GAUSSEN (cf. Chapter 20). On the other hand, the Montpellier institute maps the vegetation of specified critical areas at 1:20,000 or larger; no effort is made to map the entire nation. In the past, these maps were based on the classification by BRAUN-BLANQUET, but important modifications in the approach now give these maps a more ecological character (cf. Chapter 19) and the institute has been renamed Centre d'études phytosociologiques et écologiques. In Switzerland, the Geobotanical Research Institute at Zürich is the chief center of phytocenological research and mapping, now directed by LANDOLT. A new and different method served the vegetation map of Switzerland by SCHMID, whose method is discussed in Chapter 23. The German Federal Republic established the Bundesstelle für Vegetationskartierung (Federal Institute for Vegetation Mapping), founded and directed by TÜXEN until his recent retirement. This institute still uses the classification by BRAUN-BLANQUET in its classical form (cf. KÜCHLER, 1957a).

Belgium now has its Centre de cartographie phytosociologique where the whole country is being mapped at 1:20,000. The Netherlands and Austria also have agencies devoted to vegetation mapping at large scales. Government-sponsored vegetation mapping is also well developed in several East European countries. Vegetation maps of the German Democratic Republic (SCAMONI, 1958a, b), the Romanian People's Republic (DONIŢA, LEANDRU, and PUSCARU-SOROCEANU, 1960), and northwestern Yugoslavia (HORVAT, 1958) exemplify the techniques and high standards achieved in these countries.

In the Soviet Union, the Geobotanical Institute of the Academy of Sciences of the U.S.S.R. has two establishments for mapping vegetation; their maps are superb (KLEOPOV and LAVRENKO, 1938; LAVRENKO and RODIN, 1956; LAVRENKO and SOCHAVA, 1956; cf. KÜCHLER, 1957b). SOCHAVA (1958) reviewed the development of Soviet vegetation mapping. Upon inspecting the exhibit of vegetation maps at the Toulouse Colloquium, FOSBERG (1961b) had this to say: "The most impressive exhibit was that of Professor SOCHAVA, of small-scale maps of the U.S.S.R. and of various of its component parts. The walls of a large room were covered and a stack of sheets for which there was no room on the walls were available for examination on the table. The careful detail of this work must be seen to be believed. This was the product of the small-scale mapping institute, headed by Professor SOCHAVA, manned by ten scientists plus the necessary technicians and draughtsmen. Another institute, not represented at the meeting, handles large-scale mapping. Russian supremacy in the field of vegetation mapping is not a matter of conjecture after this demonstration."

The usefulness of scientific vegetation maps turned out to be so great that after World War II considerable sums of Marshall Plan (E.R.P.) funds were devoted to mapping vegetation. This seemed surprising to many Americans, but the European logic proved to be sound; the funds were well spent, serving the local economy and its reconstruction (e.g., BUCHWALD, 1954; KRAUSE, 1954a).

FOSBERG (1961b) studied European vegetation mapping and concluded: "The most significant generalization from the observations made during this visit to Europe is that most of the maps seen, as well as the Montpellier system, deal with the basic scientific aspects of ecology. Although the ultimate objectives for which such large sums of money are being spent are certainly practical, it is an accepted assumption that the most economical way to serve a wide variety of practical purposes is by the production of the best possible scientific maps. From these, it is assumed that many different sorts of practical correlations and special maps may be made very readily. The major effort, however, is put into the basic work. In this way, not only are the foreseen practical ends served, but there are likely to be frequent extra dividends of unanticipated practical consequences. Also, these maps can serve as bases for practical maps of subjects that, though not of present importance or urgency, may become important in the future. They also serve as reference points for measuring environmental change and for detecting unfavorable tendencies or deterioration in the environmental complex. Hence they can serve the entire growing field of conservation and research on natural resources. It seems clear enough that here is an area of basic scientific research in which we in the United States are lagging seriously, if not dangerously, behind the European countries on both sides of the 'Iron Curtain.'"

Developments in the United States

In the meantime, vegetation mapping in the United States took a different road which, as it turned out, was beset with serious obstacles to progress. Whereas the phytocenological ideas and methods of any European country were promptly tested by its neighbors and modified or adapted to new situations, leading to an ever greater refinement and sophistication, the American phytocenologists drifted under the influence of CLEMENTS. The basic difference between CLEMENTS and his European counterparts was, for vegetation mappers, that his widely accepted classification of vegetation lacked a precisely defined terminology for describing individual phytocenoses. The development toward scientific vegetation maps was therefore seriously retarded and emphasis was placed on immediate applicability and utility. Not all American phytocenologists succumbed to the spell of CLEMENTS: such eminent scientists as SHANTZ and SHREVE stand out among the exceptions. But they were too few in number and too often preoccupied with other problems. Furthermore, Europe was remote and the urgently needed exchange of ideas was distinctly underdeveloped.

Nevertheless, the rapid growth of ecological thought brought the realization that vegetation maps can serve a useful function. As a result, the production of vegetation maps continued to grow. Notably, the U.S. FOREST SERVICE became interested in mapping its vast holdings. Fortunately, a good deal of freedom was permitted to the various regions, leading to a number of different systems. The Forest (and Range) Experiment Stations became important mapping centers and the vegetation of large areas under their jurisdiction was mapped. The station at Portland, Oregon, mapped Washington and Oregon on eight sheets, four for each state, at 1:250,000 and with a common legend. All non-forest vegetation was ignored, and the forest units included only trees, never the entire phytocenoses. Some of the commercially more valuable stands were presented in different age classes. In addition, burned areas were shown but without indicating what type of forest had been burned. Considering how close the vegetation of the Northwest is to climax conditions, this information would have enriched the maps appreciably.

The station at St. Paul, Minnesota, mapped the forests of Minnesota and Michigan at 1:250,000. The maps did not cover the entire states and their vegetation units were somewhat oversimplified. The same can be said of the South, where the stations at New Orleans, Louisiana, and at Asheville, North Carolina, used the same approach. All southern states were mapped at 1:1,000,000, one map for each state, but the scale was not fully exploited.

The CALIFORNIA FOREST AND RANGE EXPERIMENT STATION at Berkeley was the only one where large-scale mapping was carried on under the leadership of WIESLANDER. It was also the only one where the success of the program led to its continuation down to the present. The large scale, not unlike those used in Europe, permitted a much more accurate and detailed grasp of the character of the vegetation and its relation to soil, fire, and other features, and vegetation units were not limited to trees. WIESLANDER's system therefore offered major advantages: the large scale permitted detail, and the detailed description of the vegetation permitted the recognition of ecological relations. It is the only system sponsored by the Forest Service that can conceivably be developed into a scientific method for analyzing and mapping vegetation. Its use has spread beyond the borders of California and is now employed by private corporations as well (cf. Chapter 22).

The value of the earlier vegetation maps of the Forest Service may be debatable. But these maps are expressions of the trial-and-error approach and it is to the credit of the Forest Service that it continued to map and to raise its standards. Much mapping is now done on planimetric maps at 1:31,680 (2 inches = 1 mile) and, considering the vast areas involved, the extent of mapping already accomplished is impressive.

The Forest Service is by no means the only organization to publish vegetation maps. Both federal and state agencies became aware of their usefulness and, as the years passed, the number of vegetation maps grew enormously. The Bureau of Land Management, the Soil Conservation Service, fish and wildlife agencies, river basin authorities, planning agencies, state geological surveys, the National Park Service, and others realized the need for vegetation maps of the plant communities in the areas under their jurisdiction.

At the same time, vegetation mapping aroused more interest among the scientists at universities and colleges. These men focused their attention on basic research and gradually became more intimately acquainted with European techniques. As a result, they learned to appreciate the value of vegetation maps as research tools. New vegetation maps were prepared in all parts of the Union, eventually leading to a new map of the whole country by KÜCHLER (1964). There is today no longer any reason for producing medium- or large-scale vegetation maps in the United States that are in any way inferior to the European products because there is now ready access to the available knowledge everywhere. The recent bibliography of North American vegetation maps (KÜCHLER and McCORMICK, 1965) is already surprisingly rich in content, and a measure of optimism for the future development of vegetation mapping in the United States is surely justified.

Future Prospects

Europe, the Soviet Union, and the United States are by no means the only areas where vegetation maps are published in considerable numbers. All other continents are now sharing in this progress (cf. KÜCHLER, 1960b). The volume of published vegetation maps may not be large, but it is growing steadily. The increasing use of vegetation maps in developing countries was discussed by LEBRUN (1961) and the coming decades are likely to see everywhere a greatly expanded use of vegetation maps prepared with increasingly refined methods.

Many mappers, in many countries, necessarily have many different ideas, and as a result develop different techniques. Their circumstances and their goals vary greatly and their maps reflect this heterogeneity (KÜCHLER, 1960a). But the evolution continues. At national and international botanical and geographical congresses, the vegetation mappers exhibit their latest works and discuss their problems. There have already been two international congresses devoted exclusively to vegetation mapping: in Germany, the Stolzenau Symposium of 1959 (TÜXEN, 1963a); and in France, the Toulouse Colloquium of 1960 (GAUSSEN, 1961a). The exchange of ideas has been very fruitful indeed. If vegetation mapping had its childhood diseases, it has grown not only beyond them but into a healthy maturity. Slowly but perceptibly, the evolving ideas are converging toward the most rational and the most practical methods. This by no means weakens the originality of individual vegetation mappers, but it does replace the more dubious techniques of the trial-and-error period with the latest and most up-to-date methods. The need for mapping large areas in great detail has led almost inexorably to the use of punch cards on which a vast amount of information on both phytocenoses and their sites can be stored (GOUNOT, 1957, 1959). This "mechanized" form of phytocenology promises a number of important possibilities, notably standardization, diversification, speed, and detail. The experiments continue and as the methods are improved it becomes clearer what the basic information is that must always be available, what supplementary information may be useful or necessary under given circumstances. With such a large number of details recorded, it becomes a simple matter to extract a great variety of features and combinations of features of both phytocenoses and their sites and their interrelations can be studied much more effectively. The speed with which information can be extracted from IBM cards is already well known, and there is no doubt at all that modern computers will reveal a kind of detailed information that was undreamed of only a decade ago. As a result, the quality of vegetation maps can improve steadily. While an enormous amount of phytocenological research remains to be done, the cartographic possibilities are beginning to be realized and the growing utility of vegetation maps keeps in step with the advance of knowledge and the progress of technology.

II

SOME BASIC
CONSIDERATIONS

—

2

On the Nature of Vegetation

A vegetation map is a map which shows the vegetation of an area. Therefore it is important to know the meaning of the word "vegetation." According to Webster's New International Dictionary, "vegetation" is "the sum of vegetable life." In the Oxford English Dictionary it is defined as "plants collectively." Such definitions are not useful to one who wishes to map vegetation; a definition is necessary which suits the purposes of vegetation mappers. Accordingly, *vegetation* is here defined as *the mosaic of plant communities in the landscape.* This definition implies that vegetation consists of various more or less distinct mappable units. The word "mosaic" in the definition reveals that there may be many individual units corresponding to the tesserae, and possibly arranged in definite patterns. The patterns actually exist in the landscape and are portrayed on the vegetation map. The term "plant community" must here be understood in a neutral and broad sense, and definitely not as a unit of any particular classification of vegetation. A "plant community" may be defined as "a part of the vegetation that is relatively uniform in structure and floristic composition, consisting of competing plants which depend on the environment and affect it, too."

The floristic composition of the vegetation changes gradually from one region to another. The site characteristics change, too, often within very short distances. Conditions change with time as well. As a result, the number of species combinations can be vast, nearly infinite, because the species are not linked to one another. And yet, the independence of the individual organisms, their keen competition, and the variations of the sites do not lead to chaos. Instead, there evolves an order which becomes all the more amazing, the more it is investigated. Given species are consistently grouped together in plant communities which can be clearly identified.

Phytogeocenoses and Phytocenology

If vegetation consists of plant communities then this implies only plants. But it is not always useful to separate plants from their environment; the combination of a plant community and its environment may have to be treated as a unit. TANSLEY (1935) called such a combination an "ecosystem," and the term has found wide acceptance in English-speaking countries. In the Soviet Union, SUKACHEV (1947, 1960) uses "biogeocenose," which is essentially synonymous with "ecosystem." SUKACHEV's term has certain advantages in spite of being more cumbersome. "Bio-," derived from *bios* (life), refers to both plant and animal life; "-geo-," derived from *ge* (earth), relates the biota to their environment, and "-cenose," derived ultimately from *koinos* (common), by way of "-coenosis," shows that the biota form a community. The biogeocenose consists therefore of the ecotope or the abiotic environment on one hand, and of the biocenose on the other. SUKACHEV distinguishes three divisions of the biocenose: (1) the phytocenose; (2) the zoocenose; and (3) the microbiocenose. A phytocenose is therefore not so much a unit by itself. It is rather an integral part of the biogeocenose, or ecosystem. This was well demonstrated by ROWE (1961). However, within such a biogeocenose, the phytocenose is of such an essential and dominant significance that it usually expresses not only its own character but that of the entire ecosystem as well. While "phytocenose" thus implies "ecosystem," the two are by no means synonymous and their true relationship must always be kept in mind.

The "biogeocenose" therefore shrinks to "biocenose" if only the biotic community is considered and the physical environment is treated separately or not at all. "Phytocenose" and "zoocenose" simply stand for "plant community" and "animal community," respectively. A phytocenose may be one particular concrete stand, or else it may be an abstraction of many stands which are more or less alike. SUKACHEV calls the latter a "phytocenose type," but the distinction is of modest importance. The observer may, for instance, collect a plant and call it *Andropogon scoparius*. The name is correct for the particular collected specimen; it also applies to all members of that species, regardless of their individual variations. The same point holds for phytocenoses.

On the basis of our definition of "vegetation," it follows that the study of vegetation, or vegetation science, is termed *phytocenology*. Similarly, a student of vegetation is termed a "phytocenologist." The term "phytocenology" is etymologically and philosophically more correct than "phytosociology" and should therefore be preferred. GAMS has emphasized this for many years and is supported by ELLENBERG, SCHMID, the Russian students of vegetation, a number of French scientists, some

Americans, and many others. In the United States, "phytocenology" is generally recognized as a valid term but is rarely employed. Its use should be promoted, especially at universities and colleges. There are even a number of followers of BRAUN-BLANQUET who agree that "phyto-cenology" should be given preference over "phytosociology," but they persist in a habit that is more difficult to justify than to break.

The vegetation mapper is called upon to map plant communities or phytocenoses. However, attempts to show more are not at all unusual, and phytogeocenoses have been shown on many maps and in various forms (e.g.: ELLENBERG and ZELLER, 1951; GAUSSEN, 1948; PINA, 1954; TROLL, 1939). A phytogeocenose is, of course, a plant community and its physical environment. On most vegetation maps with phytogeocenoses, the plant communities are not related to the entire complex of environmental factors but only to a particularly prominent one, such as a climatic or topographic feature. In general, it is difficult to map biogeocenoses, unless these can be implied in phytocenoses.

The following two statements apply without exception anywhere on earth:

1. *All phytocenoses consist of life forms.*
2. *All phytocenoses consist of taxa.**

As plant communities are composed of various species, a number of phytocenologists were thereby led to approach the study of vegetation only from a floristic point of view, ignoring the other main avenue to a detailed analysis of the vegetation: physiognomy. In *physiognomy*, the emphasis rests on the appearance of the vegetation, regardless of its floristic composition. The vegetation mapper must realize that his work can be a lasting success only if he is thoroughly familiar with both the physiognomic and the floristic features of the vegetation and constantly endeavors to combine them. On maps at a very small scale, the use of taxa may not be feasible, and on very large-scale maps there may be little or no need to describe the physiognomy of the vegetation. But in preparing any vegetation map, the mapper should always be acutely aware of both.

Just as a phytocenose consists of individual species, so does it also consist of individual *life forms* (trees, shrubs, etc.), a term coined by WARMING and of great importance in ecological considerations. Indeed, life forms are responsible for the physiognomy of the community, i.e., its outward appearance and its structure. The floristic composition of a phytocenose has its counterpart in the physiognomic composition, i.e.,

---

* By international agreement since 1950, a systematic (taxonomic) unit without reference to its rank is termed "taxon" (plural: "taxa").

the community's total assemblage of life forms. As the floristic composition implies a listing of all species present in the plant community, so the physiognomic composition enumerates all life forms that occur in the community.

Synusias

The grouping of certain life forms within a community results in physiognomic divisions of a phytocenose. Such a division is referred to as a *synusia,* a term introduced by GAMS (1918). A "synusia" is defined as "a group of plants of one or several related life forms, growing under similar environmental conditions." It may consist of few or many species, but its over-all floristic composition is quite uniform. The synusias often correspond to horizontal layers of a community, such as a tree layer, a shrub layer, a ground layer of forbs,* a moss layer, etc. The stratification of phytocenoses is very common, even in grasslands, and the recognition and distinction of the individual synusias is of fundamental importance in analyzing a phytocenose.

Synusias are not limited to a vertical arrangement; they may also occur side by side and even interpenetrate one another without surrendering their identity. For instance, in the northwest European heath, a synusia of mosses will often develop under the protection of the heather (the synusia above it). But where the dwarf shrubs of the heather plants stand far enough apart to permit more sunlight and wind to reach the ground, a synusia of lichens takes the place of the moss synusia. In sections of the tundra, a graminaceous synusia will frequently develop in addition to the dwarf shrub synusia, as is well known in Alaska and other regions of high latitude.

The over-all appearance of a phytocenose is referred to as its *physiognomy.* The division of a phytocenose into synusias and the distribution of the various life forms in each of these is termed the *structure* of a phytocenose. The structure is, therefore, the spatial distribution pattern of life forms in a phytocenose, especially with regard to their height and density or coverage within each individual synusia.

Vegetation Maps vs. Area and Land-Use Maps

A vegetation map, in order to deserve its name, must show vegetation. Vegetation consists of plants, i.e., of various plant species. But maps which show the geographical extent of one or of several plant species are not vegetation maps. Such "area maps" (HANNIG and WINKLER, 1926 ff.;

---

* The term "forb" signifies a broadleaf herbaceous plant in contrast to a narrowleaf or graminoid (grasslike) plant.

MEUSEL, 1943; HULTÉN, 1950) refer only to floristic regions. The difference between "flora" and "vegetation" is that "flora" is concerned with individual taxa (genera, species, etc.). For instance, a "flora of Kansas" implies a book in which "all species occurring in Kansas" are listed and described. No more can legitimately be expected. "Vegetation," on the other hand, deals with plant communities. The area maps led to the well-known floristic regions, and terms like the Neotropic Realm, the Malagassy Region, the Atlantic Province, the Macaronesian Sector, and the like, are based on ideas that go back to WALLACE (1876) and beyond. In Europe and parts of Africa, these regions have been mapped in great detail, which permits a considerable subdivision of these areas. One need only view the beautiful map of France by GAUSSEN (1945a), or the map of Thiès (ROBERTY, GAUSSEN, and TROCHAIN, 1950) to see how far this work has advanced. An attempt to map the United States on such a regional basis was published by DICE (1943). Generally speaking, these are not vegetation maps; they rather indicate the areal affinities of the flora. Maps of floristic regions or of the areas of species therefore fall into a different category and will not be further considered here.

However, a map may show here pine, there oak, and elsewhere beech. In such instances, the pine area is not equivalent to the geographical extent of the genus *Pinus*. The map rather implies a vegetation characterized by pine forests in all their complexity, and similarly for the oak and beech forests. Such maps are considered vegetation maps because pine forests, oak forests, and beech forests are phytocenoses.

A vegetation map must not be confused with a land-use map. A different approach is used on the latter. A land-use map shows such items as dairying, lumbering, sheepherding, etc. On a vegetation map of the same area, the types of vegetation are shown instead. There are, of course, instances in which the types of vegetation and types of land use are nearly synonymous, e.g., vineyards, but this does not imply that the maps are alike in method or in goal.

Vegetation Types vs. Landscape Types

It is obvious that vegetation can be approached from several aspects. The vegetation mapper must know this and must be quite clear about the meaning and the implications of his particular choice. For instance, a vegetation map of Europe may show such items as heath, moor, meadows, steppe, forest, tundra, etc. A large number of such terms can be collected from all over the world (KÜCHLER, 1947b). HUMBOLDT and GRISEBACH have given these common words scientific meaning; they can be regarded as types of vegetation. But they can also be interpreted as types of geographical landscapes (REGEL, 1949). In the latter case, the vegetation may be better described in other ways in order to avoid confusion. Because most of such terms as heath are frequently linked to particular types of vegetation, landscape types and vegetation types have seemed synonymous to many people. But in fact, these terms are very broad and sometimes include various types of vegetation, rather than only one. The vegetation map should therefore be free from such terms whenever these can lead to doubt in the mind of the reader. In a geographical sense, vegetation is an integral part of the landscape,* often the dominant one, and usually there is little danger that vegetation types and landscape types will be confused, especially when the scale of the map is large.

Stability

An important feature of vegetation is the degree of its stability. A high degree of stability occurs often in natural vegetation (see below). But the natural vegetation can also be unstable, depending on local circumstances. Stability in cultural vegetation (see below) occurs primarily in regions that have been occupied by man for many centuries. In such instances, the people have learned through trial and error which types can be expected to sustain the highest yields over long periods without damaging the land unduly through erosion, floods, or other calamities.

Unstable vegetation implies that a change is taking place. A change may be brought about by natural phenomena, as when lightning ignites a forest or a prairie, or perhaps when a melting glacier or a landslide exposes a fresh surface, unoccupied by vegetation. Unstable plant communities succeed one another in series in the altered environment, eventually leading to a type of vegetation that is in harmony with the prevailing environmental features. Such a type will have the highest degree of stability and retain it until a new change leads to further succession.

Actual, Original, Natural, and Cultural Vegetation

In the field, the mapper finds himself surrounded by a variety of plant communities. This vegetation is termed the *actual vegetation*. The actual vegetation is therefore that vegetation which actually exists at the time of observation, regardless of the character, condition, and stability of its component communities.

---

* The geographical landscape is defined by TROLL (1950, p. 165) as "*ein Teil der Erdoberfläche, der nach seinem äusseren Bild und dem Zusammenwirken seiner Erscheinungen sowie den inneren und äusseren Lagebeziehungen eine Raumeinheit von bestimmtem Charakter bildet, und der an geographischen natürlichen Grenzen in Landschaften von anderem Charakter übergeht.*"

A distinction must be made between "original vegetation" and "natural vegetation." The latest and most advanced ideas on these terms were evolved by Tüxen (1956b, 1957b), on whose work the following paragraphs are based. His examples, all taken from northwestern Germany, are also used here because they are most illustrative.

The *original vegetation* exists in a landscape before man affects it significantly. As much of the surface of the earth has been populated for a long time, the original vegetation is often chiefly of historical interest. This is especially true of many parts of Europe and of southern and eastern Asia.

The *natural vegetation* is the vegetation which exists in the landscape unaffected by man. It is in balance with the abiotic and the biotic forces of its site. The biotic forces include man, as long as his activities do not alter the vegetation basically. As of when such a change is basic can be determined only in an arbitrary way or by agreement.

There are parts of the world where the original natural and the actual natural vegetation coincide. This implies that man has never been a serious factor of the environment there. It is especially true of some arctic and antarctic regions, high-altitude and high-latitude areas, certain sea shores and river banks, etc. But relatively well-populated regions may also contain many types of actual natural vegetation. For instance, in many Californian forest areas the vegetation is the same as that of the original virgin stands (CALIFORNIA FOREST AND RANGE EXPERIMENT STATION, 1958, p. 22).

The original natural vegetation can only be compared with the natural vegetation of today. In most parts of the world, the latter no longer exists, for various reasons. Usually, man has become very active, destroying natural plant communities, changing them or replacing them with others. Hence we can speak only of the *potential natural vegetation*. This, however, is most important, and in order to obtain it, two assumptions are necessary: (1) that man be removed from the scene, and (2) that the resulting succession of plant communities be telescoped into a single moment in order to exclude the effects of climatic changes. This, then, is the potential natural vegetation of today. In it, man's past activities may remain a factor. It is essentially the same as the climax vegetation, provided the term "climax" is not used in the original Clementsian sense but rather in the modern and more realistic way.

The original natural vegetation can differ appreciably from the potential natural vegetation of today. This is especially clear in areas where irreversible changes have taken place. For example, in the lower valley of the Weser River in northwestern Germany, the flood plain consisted during Roman times and much later of sands and gravel occupied by a natural vegetation of oaks and willows. In subsequent centuries, the forests around the headwaters of the Weser River were cleared and the resulting heavy erosion led to the deposition of a clay layer several meters thick on the flood plain of the lower valley. The natural vegetation of this clay, however, is not oak or willow but ash and elm (Tüxen, 1957). Irreversible changes may also take place where forests of spruce or pine replace broadleaf deciduous forests for more than three successive generations. They can also be induced by continuous heavy grazing, the artificial lowering of the water table, and in many other ways. Some parts of the world have been populated for a long time, at least since the last interglacial period. Climate and topography have changed significantly since then and so, of course, has the vegetation. The original vegetation and the potential natural vegetation of today have therefore little or nothing in common.

It is obvious that there exists the closest relationship between the various phytocenoses of the potential natural vegetation and the sites on which they occur. This is reflected in the terminology by the introduction of the term *biotope*. A biotope ("place of life," from *bios*, life, and *topos*, place) is an area of relatively uniform physical features (climate, soil, etc.) and is therefore occupied by one particular phytocenose of the potential natural vegetation. A given kind of biotope and a given phytocenose of the potential natural vegetation always go together. In other words, a biotope is the site type of a phytocenose of the potential natural vegetation.

All anthropogenic vegetation is termed *cultural vegetation,* as contrasted with natural vegetation which develops when human influences are at their minimum. The cultural vegetation can be subdivided into (1) cultural vegetation, *sensu stricto,* and (2) *semi-natural* vegetation. The former consists of the cultivated wheat fields, apple orchards, truck gardens, vineyards, rubber plantations, etc.; this is the *messicol vegetation* (from *messis,* crops harvested or to be harvested, and *coltura,* culture, as in "agriculture," i.e., cultivation). It includes the communities of weeds which are associated with the crop plants. The semi-natural vegetation is a more indirect result of human activity. It may be remarkably stable, and develops where certain types of land use have been more or less uniform over long periods. Such semi-natural vegetation types include the Corsican macchia, the Spanish tomillares, certain types of pastures, even the hedges that are so characteristic of the northwest European landscape (Tüxen, 1952a). A vegetation map may show the natural vegetation, actual or potential, with or without the semi-natural and other cultural types, or indeed only the latter.

The natural order of the landscape as expressed by the pattern of plant communities is not removed by man's activities, no matter how deliberate these may be. Actually, man is not free to decide when confronted with nature. Even his most modern techniques do not permit him to cultivate any crop anywhere; for instance, he cannot grow coffee in Kansas or coconuts in Minnesota. He must always select appropriate sites for them, and these appropriate sites are nothing but the sites or biotopes of certain natural plant communities. For instance, in northwestern Germany, the typical oak-hornbeam forest can be turned into excellent cropland but not into hayfields or pastures that can compete economically with the cropland. On the other hand, the moist variety of oak-hornbeam forest will make good grassland but not reliable cropland. Such relations between natural and cultural vegetation recur with great regularity, implying that only given cultural communities will take the place of given natural communities. The cultural communities have therefore been termed *substitute communities.* These substitute communities include not only all cultural communities (*sensu stricto*) but all semi-natural communities as well (KRAUSE, 1952). The entire cultural vegetation (*sensu lato*) therefore consists of substitute communities. But the mapper must understand that each particular type of natural vegetation can have only a definite and limited number of substitute communities, and these only.

The relation between the potential natural vegetation and the actual vegetation of our economy-dominated landscapes is remarkably close, and it is for this reason that the potential natural vegetation is an important object of study. Due to various human activities, such as ploughing, cultivating, mowing, fertilizing, burning, irrigating, draining, grazing, and planting native and introduced species, the actual vegetation consists of substitute communities which have replaced the phytocenoses of the potential natural vegetation to varying degrees. Should man cease to exist, the various substitute communities would promptly evolve toward the potential natural vegetation of that day.

Man likes to consider himself a free agent who can establish any plant community he wishes. And yet, it has become quite clear that every phytocenose of the potential natural vegetation has only a limited number of substitute communities. This is so because of their economic character, that is, only a few substitute communities will be among the most economical. Times and techniques change, and with them the substitute communities, but their number always remains quite limited.

TÜXEN (1957b) illustrates this with the following example from the areas around the southern North Sea, which were glaciated during the earlier part of the Pleistocene, leaving large areas covered with sandy moraines, others with heavy clay. On the sand, the potential natural vegetation consists primarily of forests of birch (*Betula pendula*) and oak (*Quercus robur*). Today the substitute communities give the landscape its peculiar character, featuring pine plantations above all, relatively few cultivated fields, mostly with rye and potatoes, and their respective weed communities: the Teesdalio-Arnoseretum and the *Panicum crus galli–Spergula arvensis* association. Hay meadows of the Molinietalia type and pastures of the Lolieto-Cynosuretum are fairly common. Occasionally, there are fragments of *Calluna* heath (the Calluneto-Genistetum). The country roads are lined with birches, leading through heath and forests where the most common native tree is again this birch.

In contrast to the sandy sites, the potential natural vegetation on the river terraces or on ground moraines with heavy clay soil consists primarily of a forest of beech (*Fagus silvatica*) and oak (*Quercus petraea*). As a result, the substitute communities are quite different, too. The pine plantations have disappeared as, indeed, have most forests. There are a few spruce plantations, but the few remaining forests of vigorous oaks and beeches remain characteristic. Pastures and hay meadows are less common, too, but by no means absent. On the other hand, turnip fields are frequent with their specific weed communities of *Alchemilla arvensis*, *Matricaria chamomilla*, and *Chrysanthemum segetum*. The country roads are lined with apple trees, linden, and maple.

The important point here is that every given plant community of the potential natural vegetation, such as the oak-beech forest or the oak-birch forest, will have its own variety of specific substitute communities which may lie side by side in any order, as dictated by economic considerations; and, because any one of them may contact any other one of these, they are referred to as *contact communities*. Contact communities are therefore substitute communities of one particular phytocenose of the potential natural vegetation. The contact communities of one natural phytocenose will not lie next to those if another natural phytocenose unless there is a break in the environmental features, such as a change in rock or soil, topography, water conditions, or microclimate, etc. The contact communities of one natural phytocenose will not intermingle with those of another.

The actual vegetation consists of some pioneer communities, some seral phases, a host of more or less permanent substitute communities, and a very few types of natural vegetation. Even these are probably not entirely free from human influences. The actual vegetation which the mapper observes is therefore the result of the integrated effects of natural and man-made conditions which control the order of all phytocenoses in space and time, and give direction to their evolution. Hence the actual vegetation consists of a mosaic of phytocenoses which make up the natural vegetation of an area, or else of substitute communities, consisting of various sets of contact communities, with each such set corresponding to a particular phytocenose of the potential natural vegetation.

Physiognomy

A phytocenose is composed on the one hand of life forms and on the other of taxa. The latter are determined according to the binomial classification of Carl von Linné, which is accepted throughout the world; it requires no comment. In contrast, the life forms of the individual plants and the resulting physiognomic and structural features of the vegetation lack such a uniform approach and need some elaboration.

From the very beginning of the history of modern plant geography, the appearance of plants has attracted the attention of the investigators (HUMBOLDT, 1807), but it was almost a century later before SCHIMPER (1898) put physiognomy on a sounder basis. More recently, his monumental work was revised and modernized by VON FABER (SCHIMPER and VON FABER, 1935). Others, too, have formulated and used physiognomic classifications, especially in the course of the last three decades. This resurgence of physiognomy may at first be astonishing. Fine and very detailed vegetation maps have been published in Europe for years, and many of them show a very advanced standard in every respect. But is physiognomy not a rather primitive method, to be used at best in an unexplored region? It is becoming increasingly evident that physiognomy offers a means of mapping vegetation which is far more valuable than once anticipated.

Under the impetus given by CHIPP (1926), physiognomy was once again pushed into the foreground and is now used increasingly. SALISBURY (1931) strongly promoted it, saying "physiognomy is the most important of the features to be defined in describing a plant community," and emphasized very justly the fundamental need for comparative studies of vegetation and the significance of physiognomy in such investigations. British foresters like CHAMPION (1936) used physiognomy successfully in India, and BEARD (1944) in the American tropics. The latter even goes so far as to say: "The physiognomic classification of vegetation meets all the essential requirements for the treatment of tropical formations. First, structure and life forms are capable of exact measurement and record in the field and secondly, on the basis of actual types so recorded, structure and life form of any desired formation can be mathematically defined." BURTT-DAVY (1938) sought to make his approach applicable throughout the tropics. His work was closely followed by that of RICHARDS, TANSLEY, and WATT (1939), who state that "vegetation should be primarily characterized *by its own features*, not by habitat, indispensable as is the study of habitat for the understanding of its nature and distribution. It is the *structure* and *composition* of a plant community that we must first ascertain and record as the secure basis of all subsequent knowledge."

The important conclusions to which a clear presentation of the physiognomy of vegetation may lead, especially in ecological and historical studies, the value of this approach for comparative studies, and the relative ease with which the pertinent data can be compiled all help to give physiognomy an important place in the study of vegetation. Furthermore, the physiognomic method enormously extends the preparation and use of vegetation maps as it does not presuppose a taxonomic knowledge of the vegetation. It is therefore not astonishing that physiognomy is increasing in popularity. On the other hand, the physiognomic description can only be a beginning, perhaps the safest beginning, but only that. Physiognomy thus becomes the starting point which can and should lead to the further and deeper investigations of floristic composition, environmental influences, and historical development. Whereas the study of physiognomy and structure is thus considered methodologically as the first step in phytocenological investigations, to be followed by floristic analyses, DANSEREAU (1961) places these two approaches qualitatively on the same level when he says: "The application of this [physiognomic] system to very different types of vegetation from the humid tropics to the Arctic has convinced me that structure characterizes vegetation quite as significantly as does the floristic composition. . . . I have never thought that one could do without the other."

Life forms have been classified by many phytocenologists. All these classifications are based on the general appearance of the plants. Only RAUNKIAER (1934) presented a novel approach, his reasoning going somewhat as follows: All climates show a seasonal rhythm, but some seasons are more favorable to plant growth than others. It follows that one of the seasons must be the least favorable. In the hot and wet climates of what HUMBOLDT called the "equinoxial regions," the character of the least favorable season does not differ noticeably from any other season but everywhere else the least favorable season is such as to result more or less in a period of dormancy in the plants. The protection afforded the meristematic tissues during this critical season of drought or frost led RAUNKIAER to select the location of the perennating buds as the basic criterion for his classification. Accordingly, he divided all plants into the following major classes:

1. Phanerophyta   Buds more than 25–30 cm above the ground
2. Chamaephyta   Buds above the ground but less than 25–30 cm
3. Hemicryptophyta   Buds at the surface of the ground
4. Geophyta   Buds below the surface of the ground
5. Therophyta   Buds in the seed: annuals

The simplicity of RAUNKIAER's approach at once captured the imagination of phytocenologists everywhere, and his terms have been adopted universally. The system was elaborated partly by RAUNKIAER himself, partly by others. Du Rietz (1931) treated life form classifications exhaustively, reviewing all major past achievements in addition to his own original contributions. Today it is, in fact, difficult to be a competent phytocenologist without a thorough acquaintance with at least some of the more recent physiognomic systems presented by Du Rietz (1931), Ginzberger and Stadlmann (1939), Küchler (1949, 1950), Ellenberg (1956), Dansereau (1957, 1961), the Yangambi Conference (Trochain, 1957, 1961), and Fosberg (1961c), in addition to the British foresters mentioned above.

One of the problems a vegetation mapper must always face is the manner in which he presents the vegetation types on the map. It is important to be as clear and comprehensive as possible, and the reader of the map must be in a position to visualize the vegetation. The mapper must, therefore, have at his disposal a method that permits him to meet all eventualities; this requires that his method must be very flexible. An *a priori* fixed number of vegetation types as proposed by Rübel (1930) is primarily useful for small-scale maps because the enormous variety of phytocenoses cannot be pressed into such a system without sacrificing too many variations and details.

A solution lies in the use of symbols, each of which describes a particular feature of the physiognomy of the vegetation or of its component life forms. The symbols can be combined in formulas and the possible combinations are very numerous; this assures a very high degree of flexibility. A system to describe vegetation with the help of symbols is presented in Chapter 9.

3
Classification of Vegetation

The scientific method requires that observed phenomena be described, classified, and explained. In the case of vegetation as an object of scientific investigation, this requirement has caused considerable difficulty; and with regard to classification, no agreement has been reached. Vegetation is heterogeneous, the approaches to its classification numerous, the purposes served by classifications manifold, and the personal attitudes of the phytocenologists perhaps equally varied. There are, therefore, different avenues to an orderly arrangement of the vegetational mosaic, and each of these avenues may lead to success in certain regions or for certain purposes, but may be less satisfactory under different circumstances. It is of fundamental importance that the vegetation mapper is aware of these aspects of classification because he must be sure to select the correct classification for any given region and purpose. He cannot ignore the point that the quality, and hence the value, of a vegetation map rest more heavily on the selected system of classification than on any other feature.

Every map that shows differences of vegetation implies a classification, and one might argue that every vegetation map is an application of the classification which a particular author happens to choose. This leads to the conclusion that the relation between classifying and mapping vegetation is that of a sequence in which the first item (classification) is arrived at more or less arbitrarily, whereas the second item (vegetation map) expresses the first one cartographically.

A vegetation map presupposes that a number of vegetation categories can be established. These categories can be arrived at in two ways, both of which have been used frequently. One of these is to view the vegetation of the earth as a whole and consider a variety of methods to divide this total into meaningful parts, which may then be repeatedly subdivided until one arrives at units so small that further division becomes undesirable. The result of this process is a classification of vegetation in which all classes are abstractions of the actually occurring vegetation types; a number of such classifications has been developed (e.g., RÜBEL, 1930). This *a priori* classifying is illustrated by the well-known map of Angola (GOSSWEILER, 1939). But the marvelous variety of forms which plant life assumes on all continents has been a major stumbling block to the development of a simple and universally accepted classification, and the problem of classifying vegetation remains an unending one.

Many scholars have therefore taken to the field and proceeded on the basis of direct observation: one sets down on a map what one sees and thus accumulates data which can be sorted and organized. Because mapping implies observation, this other way has been used in the case of many vegetation maps. This *a posteriori* mode of classifying differs fundamentally from the first, or *a priori*, method by its direct approach and, at least theoretically, its freedom from preconceived notions. One maps first, and classifies later. The results can be very graphic, as in the case of the Patuxent map (STEWART and BRAINERD, 1945). WAGNER (1961a) is concerned with large-scale vegetation mapping and observes that an important condition for the determination of local details consists first of all in renouncing all types of classificatory units of vegetation established elsewhere and by different methods. The vegetation mapper must begin with conditions just as they actually exist in his area. The entire vegetation is divided into broad physiognomic divisions such as forests, grasslands, and cultivated fields. Within each of these divisions, all stand samples are brought together in a single table. In WAGNER's particular instance, the stand samples are arranged ecologically, from dry to wet, i.e., according to increasing soil moisture.

WALTHER (1957) proceeds similarly when he calibrates phytocenoses for a specific aspect of an environmental factor, for instance, the seasonal fluctuation of the water table (see also KNAPP's examples of calibration in Chapters 24 and 30). He analyzes and records the vegetation in a conventional fashion, using stand samples. Then he relates them to the chosen factor and arranges them in the sequence of growing or declining effects of this factor. In this manner, he can establish remarkably close relations between the phytocenoses and the environmental factor, and the indicator value of the phytocenoses can reach a high degree of accuracy. His map of the Elbe Valley near Damnatz has become a classic in this respect. But he emphasizes that the phytocenoses which indicate a given degree of intensity of the environmental factor are not at all equivalent with any rank in the classification of vegetation by BRAUN-BLANQUET, and the vegetation mapper is warned against confusing the two. While the units of vegetation fall within an association, they are basically different from subassociations or variants (WALTHER, 1960, p. 67). Such a flexible approach to classifying vegetation is highly desirable and more likely to assure the best results.

Similarly, Zonneveld (1963) reports on the vegetation-mapping activities in the Biesbosch (Netherlands) and says: "We deliberately chose not to use any existing system of classifying vegetation. This was done in order to recognize without prejudice those differences in the vegetation which are most significant in this landscape, i.e., which are directly related to the specific combination of environmental factors of this area." The success of Wagner, Zonneveld, and others and the practical usefulness of their results demonstrate that mappers will find it worth their while to experiment more often with *a posteriori* classifications.

Most authors, however, reveal the powerful influence that existing classifications can exert. The postmapping classifications show in most instances a distinct affinity to the *a priori* classifications, more or less modified as local circumstances and the author's originality dictate. The *a posteriori* method can be highly descriptive. It is more flexible and, hence, can be more readily adapted to local conditions. But maps based on *a posteriori* classifications are sometimes difficult to compare because what is important in one area may be irrelevant in another. This is especially so when the regions to be compared are widely separated or ecologically quite unlike.

The classification of vegetation, the author's observations, and the purpose of the map combine to control the character of the map. Observation and purpose are the less debatable factors: the former can be checked in the field as to accuracy, and the latter is predetermined. On the other hand, whether an author develops his own classification or employs one already in existence, with or without modifications, the result is always open to question, no matter how carefully devised, how clearly defined, or how well proved. As a result, vegetation maps show a great variety of classifications, of which the older ones sooner or later give way to more modern ones or are revised to meet changing standards. The following paragraphs essentially follow Ellenberg (1956), who recently summarized the relevant material.

Abstract Vegetation Units

Certain considerations are basic to all classifications of vegetation; one of these is the distinction between concrete and abstract groups of plants. Phytocenology often deals with abstract types such as associations, sociations, and others. These are hardly realities, even less so than the species. Among the individuals of the latter there is a real relationship through their common ancestry. On the other hand, the "relationship" of vegetational units consists only of a graded similarity of the plant combinations and the causes of their origin. They are simply the result of comparisons. Hence the establishment of abstract vegetation units is nothing but a matter of convenience and agreement, albeit a necessary one for scientific progress.

The vegetation mapper always finds three aspects common to his observations. First, he notices how remarkably similar plant communities can be under similar environmental circumstances. But in making detailed comparisons, he becomes aware of the fact that similar plant communities are never quite equal and that communities may differ more or less even though they are close to each other and apparently experience the same environmental conditions. Finally, if he studies his plant community over larger areas, he finds that its floristic composition changes more or less continuously, as does the regional flora. Obviously, the floristic composition of a community is controlled by its environment; but it is variable, and in principle, this variability is limitless because essentially a plant community is not an organism.

These three observations, which are confirmed again and again, outline the possibilities and limits of a systematic order of plant communities. Without doubt, it is feasible to arrange the wealth of different plant communities in some order. But such an order is possible only by abstracting from the peculiarities of the individual stands. Even then, the order is valid only within a limited region and may not necessarily be adoptable elsewhere without modification.

It is necessary to distinguish clearly between abstract and concrete vegetation types in order to avoid confusion. Terms like "association," "sociation," "plant society," and so on should be used exclusively to denote abstract entities, and not for any particular stand of plants. In discussing the latter, terms like "plant community," "phytocenose," or "biocenose" are preferable; they refer to concrete as well as abstract units. Unfortunately, there has been semantic confusion in the phytocenological literature, especially because different authors have given the same terms different meanings.

Classification Systems

For the vegetation mapper, as for all phytocenologists, it is imperative that the vegetation be studied in the field, thoroughly and without bias; such a study should include the plant communities, their evolution, and the conditions under which they exist. Plant communities have so many characteristic features that it is not possible to use them all in devising a classification of vegetation. By being selective, however, authors necessarily emphasize some features and neglect others, according to their individual purposes. Table 1 presents all important characteristics of plant communities, from which authors may choose their own combinations as they see fit.

The various classifications of vegetation have emphasized one or the other of these features. The best-known systems are the following:

1. Physiognomic systems
2. Ecological systems
3. Physiognomic-ecological systems
4. Areal-geographical-ecological systems
5. Dynamic-floristic systems
6. Physiognomic-floristic systems

Each of these systems has advantages and disadvantages. A classification based strictly on any one concept of Table 1 can be clearer and simpler than a classification based on a combination of concepts. If, on the other hand, more than one basic concept is introduced, the scope of the map can be extended a great deal. The mapper's best approach to vegetation is to be adaptably diversified in order to suit individual cases, and to avoid rigidity. It is desirable to begin in physiognomic-ecological terms, without which a world-wide comparison is impossible. Floristic features gain in emphasis as the study of vegetation becomes areally more restricted and intensified. But in any case, the guiding principle should always be to base a vegetation map and the classification used on it directly on the facts as observed in the field.

Many of the best-known phytocenologists now recognize the importance of life forms and physiognomy. BRAUN-BLANQUET (1951) devotes ample space to life forms and life form communities, although later in his book he attempts to play down the significance of physiognomy. However, AICHINGER (1954) states categorically: "*In erster Linie müssen wir auch in der pflanzensoziologischen Forschung vom Erscheinungsbild (Physiognomie) ausgehen und dieses floristisch, pflanzengeographisch, ökologisch und syngenetisch, unter besonderer Berücksichtigung der menschlichen Einflüsse untermauern.*" This demand that phytocenological research start with physiognomy agrees well with the statements quoted in Chapter 2; but there are phytocenologists who are as yet too unaware of the significance of a careful physiognomic and structural analysis of the vegetation. The modern vegetation mapper should make every effort to avoid this pitfall.

Most botanists study vegetation by analyzing it floristically. The floristic composition becomes the basis of procedure and the units shown on the maps are plant communities characterized by certain species combinations. The great advantage of such a floristic approach is that it permits a high degree of detail and accuracy. It is therefore often preferred on large-scale maps.

Table 1. Criteria for the Classification of Phytocenoses *

A. *Features of Plant Communities*
    I. Physiognomic Criteria
        a. Life forms
            1. The dominant life form(s)
            2. The combination of life forms
        b. Structure
            1. Layers of different life forms and their height
            2. Density within layers
        c. Seasonal periodicity

    II. Floristic Criteria
        a. An individual taxon† (rarely 2–3 taxa)
            1. The dominant taxon (or taxa)
            2. The most frequent taxon (or taxa)
        b. Groups of taxa
            1. Statistically established groups
                α. Constant taxa
                β. Differential taxa
                γ. Character taxa
            2. Groups that are independent of statistics
                α. Taxa of similar ecological constitution
                β. Taxa of similar geographical distribution
                γ. Taxa of similar dynamic significance

    III. Numerical Relations (community coefficients)
        a. Between different taxa
        b. Between different stands

B. *Features Outside the Present Plant Communities*
    I. Final State of Vegetation Evolution (climax)
        a. As a physiognomic unit
        b. As a floristic unit

    II. The Site
        a. Geographical location of the site
        b. Individual site factors
            1. Physical factors
            2. Chemical factors
            3. The water factor
            4. The human factor
        c. The site as a whole

---

* After ELLENBERG (1956), slightly modified.
† "Taxon" is here used in order to avoid terms like "genus" or "species" because the kinds of plants involved here may be of any taxonomic rank.

One of the major limitations of floristic methods rests on the fact that the number of important species in a given area may be so large as to make it impossible for the mapper to convey an adequate idea of the vegetation. This is especially true of many tropical and subtropical regions where even very large map scales cannot overcome this difficulty.

SEIBERT (1954), who accurately mapped a very small segment of the relatively simple vegetation in central Germany—and on the large scale of 1:15,000—nevertheless shows as many as 134 different categories of vegetation! One can easily visualize the problems one would encounter in humid equatorial regions. According to CAIN and CASTRO (1959) in their discussion of the tropical rainforest, WARMING found 2,600 species of vascular plants on 3 square miles, WHITFORD observed 120 tree species over 3 meters tall on only 0.3 acre, and they themselves recorded 173 tree species of more than 10 centimeters' diameter on 2 hectares. Not all tropical rainforests are so diverse; nevertheless, in many areas with a complex vegetation a purely floristic method of mapping is not always likely to produce the best results.

A further problem arising from the floristic approach to mapping is the frequent lack of familiarity with the flora of many regions. Even well-trained systematists rarely know the species of more than a few limited areas, and the majority of the users of vegetation maps have little taxonomic training, if any. In addition, in many regions, especially in the tropics, our knowledge of the flora is still far from complete. In all such cases, a detailed analysis of tropical vegetation, especially forests, should be based on the proposals by RICHARDS, TANSLEY, and WATT (1939), or as outlined in Chapter 21 of this book.

A number of vegetation classifications have been presented which attempt to be all-inclusive and thus apply to the vegetation of every region on our planet. They all have in common an *a priori* fixed number of categories. Obviously, a classification with a small number of such categories permits less detail on a vegetation map than one with a larger number. The classifications by DRUDE (1913), RÜBEL (1930), and FOSBERG (1961c) are given in the Appendix for the purpose of comparison and experimentation.

Environmental Aspects

As the study of vegetation developed, it was observed that, inevitably, certain plant communities occur in certain types of environment. HUMBOLDT's (1805) diagrammatic map of the Andes of Ecuador was a forerunner to SCHIMPER's (1898) ecological world vegetation map. Such maps show formations like deserts, savannas, etc., always with the implication that their occurrence and extent is based directly and perhaps exclusively on environmental conditions.

In itself, the recording of environmental aspects is not equivalent to mapping vegetation. But the physical, chemical, and biotic features of the environment have such a strong effect on the distribution of plant communities that attempts continue to incorporate them into vegetation maps. It is therefore common to find vegetation maps on which the various categories show one or more ecological aspects directly or by implication.

In the United States, the vegetation map of southern Florida (DAVIS, 1943) illustrates an ecological basis for a vegetation map: the vegetation is directly related to the geology of the area. All so-called phytosociological maps, as for instance those published by the Bundesstelle für Vegetationskartierung under the direction of REINHOLD TÜXEN, imply an ecological interpretation, but the full extent of this is usually not evident on the maps. Excellent ecological maps have been published by ELLENBERG and ZELLER (1951), FRIEDEL (1956), GAMS (1927, 1936), GAUSSEN (1948), PINA (1954), and TÜXEN (1956a). The classifications on these maps differ widely from one another but every one has its merits and should be studied with care by any vegetation mapper planning to prepare an ecological vegetation map. On ecological vegetation maps, the scale and the organization of the map content require special attention.

If physiognomic features are to be related to the environment, care must be taken not to generalize the interpretation of the classification beyond the mapped region. For example, dwarf-shrub formations occur in much of arid Nevada, in the humid moorlands of Great Britain, above timberline in the Alps, and in the arctic tundra. In each of these regions the ecological explanation of the dwarf-shrub formation is quite different. It is also possible that a single species can dominate two or three vegetation types that vary physiognomically according to changed ecological conditions. Here a change in the environment does not lead to different dominant species but to different life forms of the same species! BEADLE and COSTIN (1952, p. 66) have reported good examples of this phenomenon from Australia with regard to *Eucalyptus woolsiana*. Vegetation mappers in this country may be acquainted with the tree form and shrub form of the alpine fir (*Abies lasiocarpa*) below and above timberline, respectively.

What has been said about the regional limitations of physiognomic-ecological classifications applies to floristic-ecological classifications as well. SHANTZ (1923) observed long ago that the ecological attitudes of species vary from region to region as physical environment and competing species change. This was later demonstrated experimentally by ELLENBERG (1954a). The interpretation of ecological vegetation maps should therefore not be extended unduly beyond the borders of the mapped region.

Choosing a Classification System

The vegetation mapper must be familiar with a variety of approaches and classifications. Only then is he in a position to make an intelligent choice. He may usefully remember that all types of vegetation throughout the world have only two basic features in common: structure and floristic composition. The vegetation mapper may well employ these two features together as the foundation for his work. He will find it particularly rewarding to experiment with two or more classifications. The results will clarify his thinking and, in addition, assure the best choice when he selects a classification for his particular area and purpose. Thus OZENDA (1963) compared the classifications by GAUSSEN and BRAUN-BLANQUET for the purpose of mapping the vegetation of the French Alps; he also considered the classification by SCHMID. Once he was thoroughly familiar with each of these three classifications and could express the observed vegetation in the terminology and categories of each, he chose the one by GAUSSEN as best adapted to his purpose. His work is highly instructive.

If the mapper works in a thoroughly studied region like western Europe, he may well select a strictly hierarchical classification like that by BRAUN-BLANQUET (1951). Elsewhere, a non-hierarchical approach is more advantageous. EMBERGER of the Zürich-Montpellier (BRAUN-BLANQUET) school of thought stresses that there is often no need to show plant communities as members of a hierarchy as only some specialists are interested in this. Usually, it is preferable to establish and map all plant communities as equals, without regard to rank in some hierarchical scheme, and the result will be more practicable for most purposes. ELLENBERG (1956, p. 67) and WAGNER (1961a) have had the same experience.

The relation between classifying and mapping vegetation is very intimate, and each strongly affects the other. Mapping is a method of portraying nature, and the classification must permit the mapper to approximate the true conditions as closely as possible. Actually, a vegetation map is the meeting ground of two poles: an author's systematic classification and nature's kaleidoscopic arrangement of plants. The degree to which these poles meet depends on the imagination, insight, and skill of the mapper.

4

Site Qualities

A vegetation map is a map which shows the *vegetation* of some area. This has led some authors to the point of view that a vegetation map ought to show *nothing but* vegetation; they frown on vegetation maps with supplementary information on site qualities, such as soils, ground water, and climate. This attitude is easily defended. The vegetation of almost any area is so complex and so few features of the vegetation can be shown on any one map that an author of vegetation maps should give all available space to the vegetation. If he had planned to present certain characteristics of the vegetation and finds while preparing the map that he can show more, then he should show additional features of the vegetation rather than some aspects of the environment. In this manner, the strictly vegetational character of the map is maintained and all available space is well utilized.

Climatic Indicators

However, even if nothing but vegetation is shown on the map, much environmental information is given by implication. If the vegetation of an area is to be presented on a map, the author obtains a base map with an outline of this area, the coastlines, if any, and the rivers, in addition to the parallels and meridians giving latitude and longitude. All this is entirely legitimate and, indeed, quite necessary. But every phytocenologist knows, too, that the grid shows more than the geographical location, and that a change in latitude often results in vegetational changes also. Nobody would expect to find the same plant communities in Ohio and in Florida, or perhaps in Scotland and on the Riviera. The longitude often reveals the location of a place with regard to oceans and seas to the east or west, and as the great wind belts of our planet often extend west-east or east-west rather than along the meridians, an indication of the longitude immediately betrays significant climatic information. The courses of rivers and coastlines at once reveal a series of environmental features: the high atmospheric humidity along the sea shore, the high water table on flood plains, and others.

Topography

Many vegetation maps have contours, too. This topographic information is so useful that it should be given on all maps of large or medium scale, possibly as far as 1:1,000,000. The altitude above sea level, and the exposure to light, heat, and wind, especially rain-bearing winds, are all features of fundamental significance in explaining the character of the vegetation. A splendid example is the vegetation map of the Nanga Parbat group in the northwestern Himalaya Mountains (TROLL, 1939) or the two Grossglockner maps (GAMS, 1936; FRIEDEL, 1953).

The importance of topography is revealed especially in the relation that exists between the vegetation on the one hand and the water economy of the soil and the features of the microclimate on the other. Convex surface features differ markedly from concave ones even though the contrast is ever so slight, and perhaps hardly noticeable at first sight. Even the slightest rise will occasion an increased runoff and an erosion of the finest soil particles. More pronounced elevations nearly always result in a localized microclimate with its own contrasts. In depressions, on the other hand, no matter how shallow, soil and water accumulate, promoting growth, but snow and cold air accumulate as well, retarding growth.

The topographic effect is well illustrated by the "cove forests" of the Great Smoky Mountains. The narrow ravine-like valleys are well protected against high winds; they are humid and relatively rich in soil, especially when compared with the exposed flanks and bluffs. The result is an unusually rich flora, the cove forests contrasting sharply with the much simpler plant communities on the less favorable sites. SCHARFETTER (1932, p. 147) stated the need for contours quite bluntly when he said: "A good vegetation map clearly expresses the organic connection between a plant community and the local topography; the absence of contours results in an unmotivated side-by-side of color splashes." A vegetation map is therefore usually not free from ecological information in any case.

Environmental Relations

It is important to realize the intimate relationship between vegetation and the site on which it grows because here is the key to a veritable treasure of information. The innumerable features of the environment are so intricately interwoven that it is quite impossible to unravel them, and in spite of the vast amount of ecological research we still lack the means to measure a site in all its complexities. BILLINGS (1952) tentatively enumerated seventy-one factors of the environment, but it is not difficult to add to his list. In most ecological studies only a few of the more obvious features are singled out for investigation, but the inadequacy of this method is well known. As an example, it may be pointed out that in order to establish the hydrogen ion concentration (pH) of the soil, "the" pH is measured by conventional means. Less often, the investigators remember that the pH may not be the same in all soil horizons; and that the pH may fluctuate appreciably in the course of the seasons (Figure 1) is ignored all too often.

Another point in this connection is that many observers measure the environmental factors that come most readily to mind (e.g., soil acidity or precipitation) although the composition of the plant community is actually determined by quite different factors of which the observer is unaware. The following example from ELLENBERG (1956) illustrates this point.

A comparison of the weed communities on fields of small grain and on fields of row crops revealed that the crop plants bore only a minor part of the responsibility for the consistent combinations of crops and weeds. It was found that the same weed communities can be obtained without the crop plants, if only the soil is cultivated at the same time and in the same manner as with small grains and with row crops. But even this cannot be the determining factor. Many weed species typical for row crops, e.g.,

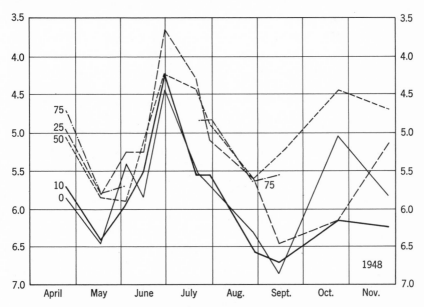

Figure 1. Seasonal changes of pH-values in different soil depths (0.5, 10, 25, 50, and 75 cm) under winter wheat. (After Ellenberg, 1950.)

Solanum nigrum and *Chenopodium polyspermum*, are more sensitive to cultivation (as it is commonly practiced with row crops) than *Matricaria chamomilla, Scleranthus annus*, and other small-grain weeds. The row crop weeds thrive best when the soil is cultivated only once and in the summer, when it is not too dry. If this one cultivation is shifted toward early spring or late fall, only small-grain weeds will germinate, besides the numerous indifferent species common to both crop types. Actually, it is the time of germination or, rather, the temperature prevailing at the time of germination that decides the composition of these weed communities. If quantitative measurements are to be made, they should therefore begin in this case with the germination temperatures.

Actually, the environment is dynamic and every change produces chain reactions which may be of great consequence. As an example of a chain effect, let us assume that, through a period of years, the precipitation at a given site is appreciably less than the average. This means first of all that less water is available. A drier soil heats and cools faster and the temperature fluctuations grow more extreme. If a moist soil helps to keep the relative humidity of the soil air and of the air layer immediately above the ground rather high, a drier soil means a drier air about it. The higher daytime soil temperatures combined with the reduced atmospheric humidity result in a more vigorous evaporation; this further aggravates the drought conditions. The increased evaporation at the soil surface draws more capillary soil water to the surface, enriching the surface horizons with solutes from below, possibly raising the pH. This is just the reverse process of what goes on during rainy years when the surplus water leaches the top soil and carries the solutes to lower horizons. It is easy to see that a change in precipitation, evaporation, temperature extremes, atmospheric humidity, and chemical composition of soil and soil water must necessarily affect the biota of the site. Many species, from vascular plants to soil bacteria, react more or less sharply to changes in any one of these factors. In the given example, the effect may well be that the production of dry matter is reduced; indeed, some species may vanish altogether. Such a disappearance may then result in the invasion of the area by species from more arid regions. As a result, the competitive relations among the species are altered as well as the amount and kind of humus produced. This, in turn, again affects the chemical and physical character of the soil, which in turn reaffects the biota and the microclimate. These chain reactions will continue until, over a period of years, everything is adjusted to the lowered precipitation and its effects.

The foregoing example of a chain reaction due to a change in one environmental factor (the amount of precipitation) may seem farfetched to readers who know only humid regions such as the northeastern United

States or western Europe. Desert dwellers may have a similar reaction. But to readers in the great grasslands of the world, be they in Kansas or the Sudan, in the pampa of Argentina or the steppes of Russia, the given example is realistic because periodic droughts with the resulting profound effects on the character of the vegetation have been experienced all too often. Careful studies of the phenomenon have been published by AL-BERTSON and his collaborators (1957), COUPLAND (1959), and others. Striking illustrations were submitted also by KÜCHLER (1964, Fig. G and Fig. 65). But one of the most outstanding vegetation mappers of north-western Europe with its equable climate noted the example above and commented that, undoubtedly, the vegetational fluctuations are mostly physiognomic. His remark is characteristic of many phytocenologists who fail to appreciate the extent of the *floristic* fluctuations that can occur in climax vegetation. Actually, the environment is not a constant and the annual deviations from a mean can be considerable. Rainfall fluctuations and their effects are usually at a minimum in very humid or quite arid regions but assume major proportions in subhumid and semiarid climates.

The purpose of the foregoing example of an environmental change and (only some of!) its consequences is to show how intimately all climatic, edaphic, and biotic features in the landscape are interrelated. At the same time, phytocenologists must be aware of the fact that theories evolved and tested in one region may not be practical in others.

Ecological Research and Site Analysis

When ecology first became a field of study, ecologists hopefully studied the individual factors of the environment, thinking thereby to solve the ecological problems (e.g., LIVINGSTON and SHREVE, 1921). But as knowledge increased and information accumulated, the confidence waned. TANSLEY (1935) introduced the ecosystem. EGLER (1951) insisted on holism and argued that splitting the environment into factors is misleading and indeed erroneous.

These ideas evolved simultaneously with the recognition of the need for more detailed knowledge of site qualities. As the world's population is growing rapidly, the most intelligent use of the land becomes ever more imperative. This implies that the land be devoted to those crops, pastures, or forests which are most in demand at a given time; it implies that the productivity of the land be sustained indefinitely at the highest possible level. This requires that the capability of the land be known in detail; but this is precisely the major unsolved problem.

Here the vegetation comes to our rescue and gives us the needed clue because it permits us as nothing else does to recognize the critical features of a site. The basic consideration for this is relatively simple; it is that all plant species have a limited tolerance for every feature of the environment. Plants are rooted in the soil and grow into the lower atmosphere. They must be able to withstand all aspects of the dynamic environment, or perish. Where the tolerance of a species is exceeded, as for instance when the temperature falls below a certain point or the water table comes too close to the surface of the ground, the species dies. This is the reason why the species are not world-wide in their geographical distribution but are restricted to particular areas. Actually, tolerance is a complicated matter. Not only has each species its own tolerances but even for a given species these tolerances may vary from one ecotype or geographical race to another, and with the seasons or the ontogenetic phases of the individual or with both. One example may suffice to illustrate this: The minimum temperature which *Pinus cembra* can tolerate in the Alps lies at about −47° C in January but at only −7° C early in July (Ulmer, quoted in WALTER, 1951, p. 57).

Certainly, the seasonal aspects of the vegetation are basic in understanding the nature of the landscape. The preparation of phenological maps was therefore an important step forward in the direction toward site analysis. GAMS (1918) pointed out that "phenology must be employed where climatology always fails, i.e., in determining the total ecology of every site. Thereby phenology becomes a full-fledged member of ecological research." The limits of tolerance may lie close together or far apart, but the narrower this range between the limits is, the more valuable is a species as an indicator of a given site quality. But a small range of tolerance for one site quality is not reflected in a similarly small range of tolerance for all other environmental features. At any rate, the ranges of tolerance of a species are usually so wide that the indicator value of one species is too coarse to be of much use.

Another important feature is that a species will find that its optimum growth conditions, and indeed, its chances for survival, depend not only on the physical and chemical nature of the site but quite as much on the species with which it must compete. For this reason individuals of the same species will grow on quite unlike sites because of the different plant communities in which they find themselves. In one plant community, for example, the given species may grow best at a certain pH but finds its optimum growing conditions in a different plant community at quite a different pH. ELLENBERG (1953) spoke of the "physiological behavior" of a plant when grown by itself and distinguishes from this the "ecological behavior" of plants grown under natural conditions, including competition. The ecological behavior is not fixed, because it depends not only upon the character of the species under consideration but also on the character of all competing species. If these competitors are quite different in different parts of the area of our species, then its ecological behavior will vary accordingly. The ecological behavior of all species examined has deviated from the physiological behavior. With regard to a given environmental factor, it is possible to distinguish a number of such possible deviations; they are shown in Figure 2.

1. Physiological and ecological optimum coincide:
   a. The ecological amplitude is barely restricted (e.g., *Fagus silvatica*).
   b. The ecological amplitude is strongly reduced (e.g., *Senecio silvaticus*).

2. The ecological optimum is shifted unilaterally from the physiological optimum:
   a. Close to the minimum (e.g., *Deschampsia flexuosa* and *Spergula arvensis*).
   b. Slightly toward the minimum (e.g., *Alopecurus pratensis* and *Raphanus raphanistrum*).
   c. Slightly toward the maximum (e.g., *Arrhenatherum elatius* and *Sinapis arvensis*).
   d. Close to the maximum (e.g., *Tussilago farfara*).

3. There are two ecological optima, located near the physiological extremes:
   a. The ecological optimum is more pronounced near the minimum (e.g., *Festuca rubra*, var. *fallax*).
   b. Both ecological optima are approximately equivalent (e.g., *Pinus silvestris*).
   c. The ecological optimum is more pronounced near the maximum (e.g., *Convallaria majalis, Legousia speculum veneris*).

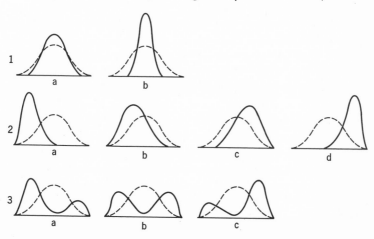

Figure 2. Types of ecological behavior. Schematic presentation of the physiological optimum (dashed) and the ecological optimum (solid) curves resulting from competition as related to a given factor. (After Ellenberg, 1956.)

The above examples refer to the pH factor and are valid only in central Europe.

The same species may behave very differently with regard to the various site qualities. The ecological behavior must therefore never be related to the entire site complex but only to a single quality.

Site Quality	pH	Water	Nitrogen
Bromus erectus	2d	3a	2a
Briza media	3c	3b	2a
Arrhenatherum elatius	2c	2c	2c

The numbers in the foregoing tabulation refer to Figure 2.

The importance of these observations for phytocenology can hardly be overstated. But the necessary experiments are time-consuming and not easy to perform; hence our relevant knowledge is still very incomplete.

The observations concerning competition and the ranges of tolerance reveal clearly that one species is inadequate to portray the qualities of a site and that it is imperative to rely only on the plant community as a whole. Vegetation is exposed to all ecological factors and their totality is more likely to be appreciated when studying phytocenoses rather than individual taxa. This is especially true because a given species will occur on a variety of site types. On the other hand, a given type of phytocenose will occur only on a given site type. This is particularly obvious in mountainous regions. In the United States, the indicator value of phytocenoses has been recognized and, indeed, employed for a long time, thanks to the observations of SHANTZ (1911, 1923), CLEMENTS (1920), SHANTZ and PIEMEISEL (1924), and others.

If the indicator value of an entire plant community is employed, instead of that of individual species, the results can be remarkably accurate. In Figure 3, the solid lines may represent the ranges of tolerance of eighteen species concerning the pH of the soil. Some species have a much narrower tolerance than others, but all have a range so wide as to preclude the accurate determination of the pH by a single indicator species. However, the degree of soil acidity must lie between the values of x and y. This becomes clear when the plant community is taken as a whole, because a higher pH would result in the disappearance of species No. 4, 8, and 13, whereas a lower pH would force out species No. 2, 6, and 12.

Throughout the area of a biotope the ecological potential is relatively uniform. WALTHER (1960) concludes quite correctly that a comparison of biotopes therefore reveals qualitatively the controlling factors that are responsible for floristic differences among the phytocenoses. This also permits an insight into the intimate relationship between the phytocenoses and their sites.

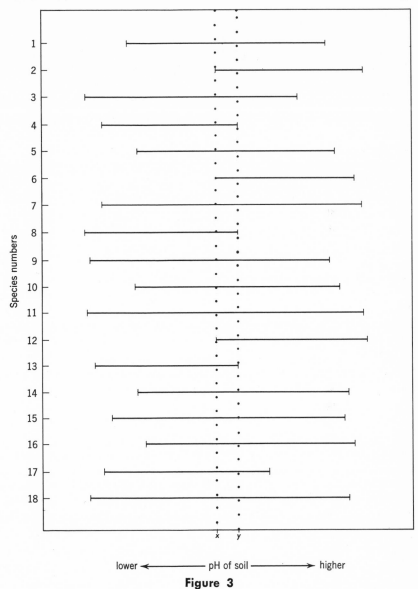

lower ◄─────── pH of soil ───────► higher

Figure 3

"Site" is here understood to mean the total of all physical and chemical factors and influences of the environment, and biotopes are types of sites characterized by specific phytocenoses of the potential natural vegetation. If a given feature of the environment is not a part of the biotope, then the phytocenose will not indicate anything about it, as, for instance, in the case of rock strata deep below the surface and beyond the reach of all roots. On the other hand, the site analysis can be refined wherever measurable site qualities are of significance for the vegetation.

This sort of consideration applies to all site qualities, not just the pH of the soil or the depth of the water table. Of course, the tolerances of the species must be known in order to make full use of the indicator value of a plant community. As time progresses, more and more such information will become available, but already it is the plant community rather than the individual species which can and must be used for a worthwhile analysis of site qualities. The community taken as an entity reveals the nature of a site more accurately and more comprehensively than anything else known to man. Detailed vegetation analyses have made it possible to relate several phytocenoses to one feature of the environment. As they react differently to such a feature, it is now feasible to calibrate them. As a result, a series of such calibrated phytocenoses can indicate the increase or decrease of an environmental feature or its effects with considerable accuracy (see also Chapter 24).

The effects of the environmental influences are not limited to the floristic composition of the plant communities. They find their expression also in the life forms of the species and the resulting appearance or physiognomy of the vegetation. The following observations by CARL TROLL (1951, p. 37) illustrate this: "For me it was one of the greatest scientific experiences to become acquainted with the tropical and subtropical vegetations of the Old and New Worlds with their convergent life forms in all variations from the desert to the rainforest and from the lowlands to the highest mountains. There were not only the well-known convergences of particular life forms (trunk-succulent cacti and Euphorbias; leaf-succulent aloes, *Sansevaria* and agaves, bromeliads; trunk-forming Espeletias and Senecios; *Usnea barbata* and *Tillandsia usneoides*, etc.) but also the life form communities of whole formations, e.g., the caatinga type of South America also in Africa, the African Miombo type also in South America, the monte formation of South America in the Karroo of South Africa, the tropical cloud forests of both continents, etc."

Of course, it is well known that similar ecological conditions often result in vegetation types of strikingly similar physiognomy, and it is not difficult to add examples of such homologous types of vegetation to TROLL's list: the Californian chaparral and the Corsican macchia, the Dakota prairies and the southern Russian steppes, the Nevada sagebrush and the Aralo-Caspian wormwood formation, etc. The observation of homologous vegetation types logically led to the conclusion that particular combinations of ecological features find their expression in particular types of vegetation.

The convergent evolution of life forms under analogous environmental conditions must not lead to the conclusion that the physiognomy of vegetation by itself is an adequate indicator of these conditions. For instance, WELLS (1962) shows in the mountains of the California Coast Range that "both in pure form and in complex mixture, all physiognomic types often occur in close proximity on the same substratum, and on the same slope, and at the same elevation and distance from the ocean. Since these coincidences were encountered repeatedly on a wide variety of substrata, it is difficult to avoid the conclusion that the physiognomic end-members are not segregated primarily on the basis of climatic or edaphic factors in this area." Later in the same paper, WELLS says: "Since grassland, shrubland and forest occur on almost all geological substrata in the San Luis Obispo area, it is obvious that the nature of the substratum has little direct influence on the physiognomy of vegetation under this range of climate, except when considered in connection with fire. But if the vegetation is regarded from the floristic standpoint, then the nature of the geological substratum has a pronounced effect."

This is a good illustration of the fundamental rule that the phytocenose must always be considered both *physiognomically and floristically* if it is to help in the interpretation of a site and its potential.

The study of vegetation types offers the added advantage of revealing long-term phenomena, such as are hidden from direct observation, e.g., fluctuations in the water table. Those trained to interpret the nature of the vegetation can therefore often tell at a glance what conclusions to draw from their observations. Not only is the vegetation the most sensitive site indicator, but the vegetation map is therefore the most comprehensive, the most reliable, and the simplest tool in analyzing the site qualities of the landscape (KRAUSE, 1955, p. 11).

Mapping Site Characteristics

A number of scientists have endeavored to express the physical environment with the help of vegetation maps. At small scales, such maps can imply only a few broad features, as is perhaps best illustrated by PINA (1954) on his map of Portugal. Such a map may be considered an introduction to a country. KRAUSE (1952) published an excellent study in which he presents his *Gross-Standort*, a term which extends certain site characteristics over large areas, retaining nevertheless a considerable degree of unity in the basic features; it may be translated as "[vegetational] site region." TROLL (1941, 1943, 1955, 1956) in a series of imaginative papers presents world-wide relations between vegetation and sites; the basic thought of appreciating the quality of a site or of site regions is fundamentally the same as that of the other authors even though his approach is different. Small-scale maps usually cannot show individual plant communities but are limited to more or less abstract generalizations. However, they do reveal the regional correlations of which the mapper loses sight all too readily.

Close acquaintance with the features of the landscape is achieved by focusing attention on a restricted region. GAUSSEN's (1948) maps are particularly original; they are veritable regional geographies and perhaps the most comprehensive pictures of an area that can be produced cartographically at the scale of 1:200,000. TROLL (1939) shows great detail on his map of the Nanga Parbat. The purpose of this map is to show the three-dimensional distribution of vegetation types, and in addition, he succeeded in organizing his material in such a fashion that the more outstanding site qualities are always apparent and indeed an integral part of the individual legend items. TROLL's map deserves therefore much more appreciation than it has received in the past.

More recently, a number of efforts have been made to bring site qualities into a sharp focus. Although the aims of the various authors overlap greatly, their methods and results vary considerably. At this point, vegetation maps become particularly valuable because they permit the recognition and clear formulation of phytocenological problems. They sharpen the phytocenologist's power of observation appreciably and permit him, first, to take note of what seems obvious, and then to advance from here to observe the finer, more delicate, and much less obvious relations between the plant communities and their sites. The basic advantage of a vegetation map, according to KRAUSE (1950), is that it reveals not only the mosaic of plant communities in the landscape but also the orderly fashion of the spatial distribution of the mosaic's tesserae.

The vegetation maps of Schlitz (SEIBERT, 1954) and of Leonberg (EL-LENBERG and ZELLER, 1951) attempt to give a very intimate insight into the landscape. It is not necessary here to discuss the usefulness of these maps; both are examples of the highest and most advanced levels in analyzing and mapping site qualities. However, it is useful to compare the maps. SEIBERT uses BRAUN-BLANQUET's phytosociological method. The map, at a scale of 1:16,000, is remarkably detailed and therefore can point out very fine variations in the vegetation. It shows the site qualities by various vegetation types, i.e., by implication. This is, of course, the usual approach; it is quite justified because vegetation reacts so neatly to environmental variations and change.

In contrast, however, ELLENBERG and ZELLER (1951) present a vegetation map which shows the character of the sites directly rather than by implication only and thereby depart from the more traditional practice. They even do this at a smaller scale (1:50,000) than the map of Schlitz. Their professed goal is a description of the natural conditions controlling agricultural production, and they emphasize that this description must be based on the requirements of the plants. In this, ELLENBERG's thinking follows WALTER (1951), who rejects the conventional anthropocentric approach to ecology, and who sees the plant as the center from which to view the environment.

SEIBERT's map of Schlitz shows phytosociological associations and their subdivisions; ELLENBERG and ZELLER show site types. The latter's way is therefore more immediately revealing of what the former only implies. Both maps require elaborate reports and techniques to utilize them to the greatest benefit. Somewhat later, TÜXEN (1956a) goes beyond implications and reveals site qualities to a marked degree on his vegetation map of Baltrum.

A vegetation map should show site qualities as comprehensively as our present state of knowledge and the map scale permit. Therefore, such a site classification as the one used by many foresters is sometimes insufficient; it is based exclusively on the annual increment of one or very few tree species. "Site class or site quality for pine is indicated by the average height of dominant or uncrowded trees at 50 years of age" (U.S. FOREST SERVICE, 1952, p. 25). The great advantages of this system are its simplicity and the cheapness of its execution. Its crudeness is justified by the extensive nature of forestry as practiced in this country and many other nations. DUNNING (1942) attempted a refinement of this method while retaining its basic ideas, and McARDLE (1949) adjusted it to the conditions of western Oregon and Washington (Table 2). It is used in Cali-

Table 2

Site Class Symbol	Site Index (height in feet of dominant and codominant trees at 100 years)
I	200
II	170
III	140
IV	110
V	80

fornia as well but in most regions of the world even the tallest trees do not generally exceed 100 feet appreciably. This table therefore demonstrates clearly how limited the areal applicability of any such system must be. In essence, this type of site classification attempts to evaluate site qualities by the annual growth of one or a few given tree species, assuming that the latter expresses the former; and within varying limits, this is so, but the system is not reliable. HILLS (1952) studied the

problem of site characteristics and mapping in Canada, whereas WEST-
VELD (1951, 1952, 1954) sought to apply some of the Finnish ideas to site
mapping in New England. Ultimately, they all map vegetation and describe the sites through it.

At times, there have been doubts concerning the efficiency of vegetation
maps in studying site qualities. Such doubts almost invariably arise from
insufficient information or inadequate exploitation of mapping techniques.
In all such cases, additional checking is necessary before any conclusions
can be finalized.

A detailed vegetation map will reveal the site qualities to a remarkable
degree. But a detailed map is possible only at a large scale; necessarily,
therefore, it portrays only a small area. The question then arises as to
how far the information on the vegetation map is applicable beyond the
borders of the map. Theoretically, the answer to this question is that it is
applicable insofar as the same ecological conditions prevail. However,
these conditions may change imperceptibly yet steadily, and the user of
vegetation maps must exercise discretion. The safest method is perhaps to
relate the site to the vegetational site regions (*sensu* KRAUSE's *Gross-
Standort*). Within such a region, ecological conditions are related and
sufficiently alike to permit their interpretation with reasonable accuracy.
But the information on the vegetation map should not be applied to other
areas of the same vegetation site region without considering the variations
of the ecological conditions, and it should not be applied at all to sites in
a different region. TROLL (1950, p. 170) discusses the geographical methods of landscape analysis and concludes that the landscape is a complex of
ecotopes. Geographical research and biological research therefore meet at
this important junction, as "site" and "ecotope" are largely synonymous.
Site portrayal and site analysis are among the most important tasks and
contributions of the field of vegetation mapping, and probably will be for
a long time to come for, as GAUSSEN (1957a) put it, the vegetation map is
a means of integrating all environmental factors.

5

Relating Classification
to Purpose

How good is a vegetation map? What criteria may be applied? The numerous aspects of vegetation permit a series of unlike approaches to the study of plant life, and as a result, the interpretations of vegetation differ widely. How, then, can vegetation be recorded meaningfully on maps? Vegetation, obviously, consists of plants. Their character, number, height, density, and usefulness, their relation to the environment, to the past (that is, the long history of both the individual species and the environment), and to man, are some of the features that concern the phytocenologist.

Actually, a vegetation map does not really show the vegetation in all its aspects. This observation throws a new light on the character and usefulness of vegetation maps. It implies that their usefulness must necessarily be restricted, that any individual map serves only a small number of purposes, because it can show only a limited number of features of the vegetation.

These considerations lead to two conclusions: (1) there are different types of vegetation maps; and (2) there are different purposes that these maps serve. When the two conclusions are brought into relationship, they give rise to a new question: Which type of vegetation map serves a given purpose best?

There are two recognizable attitudes among authors of vegetation maps. The first reveals a groping toward a clearer recognition of what is involved in making vegetation maps for a given purpose. Lack of background often results in inferior maps, and the author may or may not be aware of their weaknesses. The other attitude is that of the author who "believes" in the superiority of his "system" and applies it for all purposes. The wiser among these authors limit themselves to the purposes to which their methods are most relevant, but is not every author confident that his particular work will be the long-sought contribution? Alas, the solution is not so simple: vegetation is too complex to be shown in all its aspects on one map, and as in the past, particular maps will serve particular purposes, even though the techniques will almost certainly be greatly improved.

The question then remains: What type of vegetation map should be selected for any one of the many given purposes? It may be asked whether it is at all possible to answer this question, and at first sight the task does indeed seem hopeless. Happily, the situation is more encouraging than it appears to be. In fact, in an oversimplified form, the answer is to analyze every vegetation map in the light of all purposes. This is obviously a tortuous way, but it leads in the right direction. Many curves can be straightened out by grouping both the maps and the purposes into types; many pitfalls can be avoided by *comparing* map types in the light of a given type of purpose, instead of trying to evaluate each map by itself. SCHARFETTER (1932) stated quite categorically: "Nothing contributes more to phytocenological cartography than the presentation of vegetation of one and the same area according to different points of view." The solution to our problem consists therefore in making comparative analyses of types of vegetation maps, the criteria to be based on the requirements of given types of purposes. We have now answered our two initial questions: (1) How good is a vegetation map? A vegetation map is good if it serves its purpose well. (2) What criteria may be applied? An evaluation of the map in terms of the requirements of the purpose will tell to what extent the map serves this purpose. We have not yet found an answer to the third question (which type of vegetation maps serves a given purpose best), but we know now where to look for it.

The comparative method is old and has been used many times. But attempts to compare vegetation maps are frustrated all too often. In fact, one of the lessons learned in making such comparisons is that many vegetation maps simply are not comparable. Differences in scale and resulting differences in generalization are disturbing. Frequently it is difficult to compare vegetation maps of different areas because of the unlike characteristics of the areas. Authors may disagree in their interpretations of vegetation, and even contradict one another.

These difficulties can be overcome by the preparation of a set of maps, all by the same author, on the same scale, and of the same area, but each based on a different classification of vegetation. The differences in approach and interpretation usually find their basic expression in the classification, and the classification is therefore the critical feature of vegetation maps. With the classification taken as the only variable, comparison becomes feasible. KÜCHLER (1956a) and MOOR and SCHWARZ (1957) have made such comparative studies. KÜCHLER's work is described in the following paragraphs.

The decision to prepare a set of comparable vegetation maps produces problems of its own: What scale, what area, what classifications should be selected?

Scale

The scale has a direct bearing on the size of the area to be mapped. It also affects the classification to be selected, because not all classifications lend themselves to all scales. The fundamental difference between large and small scales is the degree of generalization. As the purpose of this project involves a scrutiny of classifications, a small scale seems to hold out less promise for satisfactory results than a large scale, which permits the presentation of many details on the map as they occur in nature, and hence a minimum of generalization. Further, the area covered is correspondingly small. The time available for field work is usually limited, and only a fairly small area can be adequately mapped. In view of these considerations, small or medium scales are ruled out, and a relatively large scale becomes a necessity.

Area

The selection of the area to be mapped presents the next problem. For practical purposes, the area has to be small. On the other hand, illustrating a classification of vegetation demands that a reasonably large number of vegetation types be present. The choice fell in this case on southeastern Mount Desert Island, Maine. The dimensions of the area are about 11 by 11 kilometers; the elevation ranges from sea level to 466 meters on the summit of Cadillac Mountain. The topography and vegetation are heterogeneous: low, flat, swampy places; steep, rocky cliffs; freshwater lakes; forests and bush and grasslands. There are only a few urban places. Part of the vegetation was destroyed by the disastrous fire of 1947, which became known throughout the United States as the "Bar Harbor fire." The regeneration of vegetation in the burnt sections has resulted in many different types because of variations in the destructiveness of the fire and in the ability of species to resist fire or to produce new sprouts from undamaged roots. The differences in the pre-fire vegetation and in the degree of soil destruction by the fire or by subsequent erosion have also contributed to the complexity of the present vegetation. The larger part of the area is located in Acadia National Park, and, thanks to the efforts of Mr. John D. Rockefeller, Jr., and the National Park Service, the entire area is covered with a dense network of good roads and trails. This is an important consideration in selecting an appropriate area, since ready accessibility saves an enormous amount of time during field work and permits an accuracy of field mapping that would be impossible in a nearly trackless region.

Classifications

Not all classifications can be used in a study such as this. For example, all classifications requiring a medium or small scale are eliminated.

ECOLOGICAL MAPS

We begin with the so-called "ecological" vegetation maps. These include the famous works by GAUSSEN, RÜBEL (with BROCKMANN-JEROSCH), and TROLL, and at first it seems a matter of course that they should have to be considered. Two arguments decided against their inclusion. The first one is philosophical: vegetation maps should be strictly limited to vegetation. Some authors feel strongly about this. There is, indeed, logic in this argument and it presents a defensible point of view, although it is not the only valid one.

The second argument is practical and carries more weight than the preceding one. It is based on the character of ecological vegetation maps. On such maps the geographical distribution of vegetation types is related to the kind of environment in which they occur. But the environment is quite as complex as the vegetation itself, if not more so, and, as with vegetation, only one feature of the environment is shown on ecological vegetation maps, or at any rate very few. Further, different authors naturally select different environmental features. For example, TROLL (1939), on his beautiful map of the Nanga Parbat, relates the vegetation to exposure and height above sea level. GAUSSEN introduces temperature and precipitation; WIESLANDER incorporates aspects of the soil. RÜBEL includes various environmental features, but not consistently, and some of his legend items indicate no relation to the environment. The problem is further complicated by the fact that a given species will grow here in rather acid soils, there in more alkaline ones, or behave equally inconsistently with regard to other environmental relations, depending on the combination of other species with which it must compete. Obviously, the ecological comparisons are hazardous. It is a real challenge to correlate the geographical distribution of vegetation with the many facets of the environment. But, for the present project, it is clear that ecological maps do not lend themselves sufficiently to comparative study. How, for instance, can a vegetation-exposure relation be compared with a relation of vegetation to soil acidity?

FLORISTIC MAPS

There are two basic approaches to the study of vegetation. The first begins with a description of the appearance of the vegetation or its physiognomy and structure. A more detailed discussion of the physiognomic approach has been given elsewhere in this book, including a method for portraying the physiognomy and structure of vegetation cartographically (cf. Chapters 15 and 21). This method is used here to represent the physiognomic vegetation-map type.

The second of the two basic approaches to the study of vegetation considers the kinds of plants of which the vegetation consists. Because it deals with individual species, it is called floristic. On a floristic vegetation-map type, therefore, the emphasis is on the characterization of phytocenoses by species combinations.

In most parts of the world the vegetation consists of so many species that it is not possible to show all of them on one map, and various methods have been developed to overcome this difficulty. There is, however, a great difference between the group of physiognomic map types and that of floristic map types. No matter what method is used, physiognomic maps always describe the appearance of the vegetation, but a variety of floristic maps can show very different aspects. EMIL SCHMID, for instance, uses large continent-wide "belts," identified by certain genera or species and their affinities. This is an interesting way to portray vegetation on maps, but it is better adapted to medium or small scales.

It is likewise possible to describe the vegetation by those species which by their mass and number dominate all others. This is, of course, an incomplete description of the vegetation, and even of its floristic character, but if the dominants are judiciously selected, they can convey a good picture. Although this method has been employed by many authors, few have produced such satisfactory maps as KURT HUECK. His method has therefore been selected to represent the floristic vegetation-map type in this study.

COMBINATION MAPS

Of all basic types of vegetation maps, e.g., physiognomic, floristic, regional, and ecological (KÜCHLER, 1951a), only the physiognomic and the floristic types can be tested in the present study. However, there is still another type which deserves consideration, and that is one which combines two or more of the basic types. Only the physiognomic-floristic combination is here feasible.

There are few examples of classifications that combine physiognomic and floristic features, especially because, in a study such as the present, only strictly and consistently organized classifications can be considered. It may, of course, be asked whether such a combination does not simply embody all the advantages and disadvantages of its component types. This need not be so.

Two combination methods, above all others, come to mind: one by A. E. WIESLANDER, and one by KÜCHLER. The latter's work has so far been demonstrated only on one small-scale map (KÜCHLER, 1953) but WIES-LANDER's numerous large-scale maps assure him first consideration. WIES-LANDER's work is affected by his need to serve forestry interests; also, his classification (JENSEN, 1947) was devised exclusively for California. However, among the officials of the United States government concerned with vegetation mapping, WIESLANDER has shown a particularly keen insight into the problems of vegetation mapping and used a scientific approach to their solution. It is not difficult to adapt his method to other parts of this country.

WIESLANDER has also developed a second classification of vegetation, closely related to the first, but it is partly ecological and relates vegetation types to soil types. Although WIESLANDER now uses the more recent method almost exclusively, it is the earlier one that has been adopted for this project.

Our comparative study is based, then, on three map types, as illustrated by KÜCHLER, HUECK, and WIESLANDER, respectively: (1) the physiognomic type, (2) the floristic type, and (3) the physiognomic-floristic combination type. The legends of the three type maps will be found in the Appendix (pages 450, 451) to assist the reader in his appreciation of the problems involved and the selections made on the basis of comparisons.

Purposes

If vegetation maps are to be related to purposes, it will be necessary to examine the latter, too, at least briefly. The number of human activities that may be served by vegetation maps is large, and, as in the case of the maps themselves, it is necessary to group the purposes into major types. Such types can be established from many points of view. And just as there are vegetation-map types that combine two or more of the basic approaches, so, also, it is possible for a purpose to combine aspects of more than one type. For instance, agriculture is surely an economic activity, but in some respects it is also applied science. Furthermore, it is not possible to disregard certain purposes as not fitting into the scheme of this project, as was done with some of the classifications of vegetation. On the contrary, every purpose is acceptable in testing vegetation maps. However, it is necessary that the purpose be stated clearly and in detail in order to permit the formulation of criteria that must be used in analyzing the maps. Ultimately, clarity in stating the purpose is necessary to permit the proper choice of vegetation map.

It would be tedious simply to enumerate a long list of purposes and test the suitability of the vegetation maps for each. The list must of necessity remain incomplete. To illustrate the method of comparative analysis employed in the present study, it has seemed preferable to select one or more examples from each of three types of purposes: scientific, economic, and military. The reader can then put the method to a test: he can formulate his own purpose for using a vegetation map and should be able to make a reasonable choice.

Example 1

Purpose. The Internal Revenue Service wishes to assess the value of extensive landholdings of lumber companies.

Criteria. The economic value of forest vegetation depends on several factors, notably the extent and condition of the forests and the floristic composition. Usually, only a relatively small number of species is of commercial significance. The distribution of the economically important species is, therefore, a prime consideration.

Analysis. Physiognomic Map. For a tax assessor a physiognomic map is useful because it tells him a great deal about the condition of the vegetation. He can see at a glance which land is forested and which is not, and he can easily distinguish different forest types. However, as there is no indication of the species, he cannot tell which forests are of value.

Floristic Map. A floristic map reveals the distribution of species, which to the tax assessor means species that are economically valuable. But it tells nothing about the character of the vegetation. A plant may be of a valuable species, but that does not mean it can be sold. The value of a spruce is potential rather than actual if it is only 1 meter tall.

Physiognomic-Floristic Combination Map. This map combines flora and physiognomy. But it omits many details of the physiognomic map, and the physiognomic and floristic units are grouped in a manner that must at once arouse the interest of the tax assessor. The map not only reveals which areas are wooded and which are not; it singles out the forests that have commercial value and gives the names of the species that compose these forests.

Comparison. Comparing the physiognomic, floristic, and combination maps, the revenue officer finds that all have merit but that the combination map serves his purpose best because it tells him clearly how much of the area is forested, which are the commercially most important trees, how they are distributed, and where they are concentrated. Thus he is able to evaluate the landholdings accurately.

Example 2

Purpose. A soil scientist has been assigned the task of mapping the soils of an extensive forested area at a large scale and as accurately as possible.

Criteria. The pedologist can make his map by taking soil samples systematically every few feet in a grid pattern throughout his area. The accuracy of his results will be in direct proportion to the density of the grid. But this is a tedious, slow, and expensive procedure. The pedologist knows that a close relation exists between soil types and vegetation types and that the vegetation changes with the soil. Aerial photographs are inadequate, and a detailed vegetation map thus becomes the most valuable tool.

Analysis. Physiognomic Map. The physiognomic map tells the pedologist where to find forests, and where the grasslands are, and such information is valuable; if some grass grows in wooded area, this knowledge, too, may be useful. But oaks, maples, beeches, and many others are all lumped together under the designation "broadleaf deciduous trees," and the pedologist cannot find the kind of detail that his purpose requires.

Floristic Map. The distribution of species in their various combinations is an excellent indicator of the distribution of soil types. A vegetation map that shows the extent of such plant communities can therefore tell the pedologist the extent of his soil types and the location of their boundaries. Usually one soil sample for each plant community or combination of species is then adequate, except perhaps where one community merges gradually into the next. The more accurately plant communities are portrayed, the more useful is the floristic map to the pedologist.

Physiognomic-Floristic Combination Map. The physiognomic map with floristic overprints presents several advantages to the soil scientist. Although the physiognomic features are of relatively little value to him, the indication of the dominant species is useful. But the organization of the map, the use of colors for physiognomy instead of for the flora, and the difficulty in seeing at a glance the distribution of the floristic communities reduce the significance of this map for his purpose.

Comparison. Comparison reveals that the floristic map is the most useful of the three for the pedologist because it indicates the features of the vegetation that respond most directly to variations in the soil. He can correlate the floristic combinations more readily with soil types than any other aspect of the vegetation, and therefore he requires a map that depicts the distribution of plant species and their communities in the greatest possible detail.

Example 3

Purpose. A geographical report with emphasis on the physical features of the landscape is to be prepared on an underdeveloped tropical area, and this report is to include a vegetation map. It is important to convey as graphic a picture of the vegetation as possible because the report is to serve as a basis for further investigations.

Criteria. The area is underdeveloped and not well known. The geographer requires descriptive categories of vegetation that he can identify in the landscape. He analyzes various vegetation-map types in order to determine what kind of map he can reasonably hope to prepare in his area.

Analysis. Physiognomic Map. The physiognomic map shows in great detail many different vegetation types and their combinations. All these types are readily observable in the landscape and can be described easily and with a high degree of accuracy.

Floristic Map. The floristic map presents major problems. It is not possible to describe the vegetation floristically unless the names of all or nearly all plant species are known. The geographer is not a botanist, and even most botanists would be baffled by the array of species in an area with which they are not familiar.

Physiognomic-Floristic Combination Map. Once again the geographer has a physiognomic map, at least as far as the colors are concerned. The floristic overprints are not so useful to him, and he may want to ignore them, but to do this would eliminate a significant part of the map and reduce its value accordingly.

Comparison. Comparing the three map types, the geographer soon concludes that the floristic map does not suit his purpose. The physiognomy of the vegetation is shown on both the physiognomic map and on the combination map. However, if on the combination map the floristic features are ignored, the physiognomic characteristics do not in any way match the distinctive and varied features of the physiognomic map. This latter, then, serves the purpose of the geographer best because it illustrates a method with which he can portray the vegetation of his area rapidly, accurately, and in detail.

Example 4

Purpose. An animal ecologist wishes to study the habitats of deer in order better to understand their life history; his interest is focused on their food and shelter habits.

Criteria. As deer are primarily browsing animals, their food and shelter come from the vegetation, and more especially the woody vegetation. The ecologist's attention is therefore directed primarily to the distribution of certain plant species that serve the deer as food and to the structure and density of the vegetation, because deer seek refuge from cold winds and carnivores in thickets and dense growth.

Analysis. Physiognomic Map. The physiognomic detail of this map reveals the height and density of the tree and shrub layers of the vegetation, and therefore the map is of considerable significance for the ecologist. Unfortunately, the lack of floristic data reduces its value, since the distribution of food plants is not shown.

Floristic Map. The distribution of plant species that serve the deer as food can be determined from this map, but the physiognomy and structure of the vegetation are ignored. Again, as in the case of the physiognomic map, the information is good in quality but inadequate in quantity.

Physiognomic-Floristic Combination Map. This combination of physiognomy and flora presents all the features of interest to the ecologist, that is, the density and distribution of shrubs, thickets, and trees, and the dominant species of each vegetation type; moreover, there is an emphasis on woody plants.

Comparison. Comparison of the three maps reveals at once to the ecologist that the combination map best serves his particular purpose. True, the physiognomic map shows the structural details of the vegetation better than the combination map and the floristic map shows the distribution of the plant species and plant communities more clearly, but neither the physiognomic map nor the floristic map give both types of the needed information, and the combination of the two types on the third map more than compensates for the lesser detail.

Example 5

Purpose. A commercial beekeeper plans to expand his business, and a certain area has been suggested to him as being rich in plants that produce nectar. Before embarking on his expansion, he plans to investigate the prospects.

Criteria. As a first-class apiarist, he knows the needs of his bees, what plants they frequent, what plants are useless to them, and so on. Thus he is able to determine whether or not the vegetation of the new area holds out enough promise for an adequate profit.

Analysis. Physiognomic Map. This map of the physiognomy and structure of vegetation reveals, among other things, the occurrence of meadows and forests, whether there are layers of shrubs and dwarf shrubs in the forests. But bees are not wild animals that seek protection in thickets, and the apiarist finds little of interest on this map.

Floristic Map. This map tells the beekeeper what species grow in the area, and he himself knows whether or not they are useful for his bees. It makes no difference to him whether a plant species occurs as a shrub or a dwarf shrub as long as it is nectar-producing and is present in sufficient quantities.

Physiognomic-Floristic Combination Map. Since the colors of this map refer primarily to the physiognomy of the vegetation, they are of only moderate value to the apiarist. The dominant species are shown by letter symbols, but it is difficult and tedious to discover the distribution of particular species because for each species it is necessary to examine the symbols of every vegetation type on the map.

Comparison. Comparison of the three maps reveals to the beekeeper that the floristic map serves his purpose best. It shows him what species grow where, and he can tell quickly and accurately which parts of the area (if any) are most promising for his expanded apiary, and how much they promise.

Example 6

Purpose. An army officer has to move men and their provisions through an area or occupy it, and this must be done in secrecy, that is, an enemy must not be able to observe the movement or occupation from the surrounding territory or from the air.

Criteria. The officer has orders to proceed in secrecy. His critical question, therefore, is what sort of vegetation map can show him best where and to what extent his troops can be concealed. He must discover whether the vegetation is dense enough to hide the troops and whether there is a continuous tree canopy under which the soldiers can find cover. He will want to know whether or not the vegetation is evergreen, since this may make a vital difference. The other important feature is the structure of the vegetation. A forest with many large trees per unit area and a thick shrub layer can seriously impede the movement of troops and their gear.

Analysis. Physiognomic Map. This shows the vegetation in the form of trees, shrubs, dwarf shrubs, grass, and so on. It shows combinations of these and such details as continuous layers of shrubs and patches of shrubs. It indicates which parts of the landscape to avoid because of open grasslands, dwarf shrubs, and similar low growth; troops would be detected here with ease. It shows where continuous tree cover exists, the proportion of evergreen to deciduous trees, of special importance during the winter and early spring, and where the closed forest gives way to scattered trees or patches of trees. An area with shrubs may offer excellent lateral concealment, but progress through it may not be easy, and cover from above may be wholly inadequate. Where evergreen and deciduous trees are mixed, the cover may be better than the proportion of evergreens would indicate, because the ground may appear sufficiently mottled when viewed from very high altitudes.

Floristic Map. If the officer happens to be acquainted with the species of the area, and knows their life forms, the floristic map may be helpful. But he cannot be relied upon to know them, and anyway the distinction between sugar maple and beech is not significant, since troops can hide under one as well as under the other. The map says nothing about the height, density, and other structural features of the vegetation, which, for cover, camouflage, concealment, and movement are of greater importance than the names of species.

Physiognomic-Floristic Combination Map. This map distinguishes between grasslands and forests, and so on, and therefore offers major advantages. But neither height nor density is revealed. Also, the distinction between woodland and commercial conifers is not useful; the officer is not selling timber, and the term "woodland" includes both broadleaf deciduous and needleleaf evergreen trees. To know what the woodland really is like, he must know the specific names of the dominants, and this can hardly be expected of a military man.

Comparison. By comparing the three maps, the officer clearly sees that the physiognomic map serves his purpose best because it shows directly and in greater detail those features of the vegetation which interest him most.

These examples illustrate the comparative method of relating vegetation maps to a purpose. All the questions posed earlier have now been answered, but the answer is not really complete. The examples were so selected that the comparison always resulted in a clear choice. But it may not have escaped the observant reader that, in some instances, the good choice would have been even better if the maps could have been modified. For instance, in Example 4, the purpose of the ecologist would have been better served if the floristic letter symbols of the combination map had been overprinted on the much more detailed physiognomic map. Whether, and to what extent, modifications are desirable or necessary must be decided independently in every case. Modification may be desirable but too expensive. Where funds are of no consideration, only the best choice should be made; in all other cases, compromise may be necessary. This means that the attempt should be made to produce the best map which circumstances permit; and the result depends largely on the judgment and experience of its author.

Another important point concerns the ecological maps. The difficulties in comparing ecological maps have been explained. Nevertheless, these maps happen to be among the most useful contributions in the whole field of vegetation mapping. If an author wishes to prepare an ecological vegetation map, it is best for him to inspect a large number of such maps, especially those that contain the type of information with which he is most concerned. The high production cost of colored vegetation maps does not justify a second-rate map. It would therefore be a wise investment for the prospective author to visit a good collection of vegetation maps in order to become familiar with as many ideas on his subject as possible. Scientific progress rests largely on the utilization of ideas that were developed by others, at other times and in other places. This applies also to the field of vegetation mapping, and an author will give his vegetation maps their strongest foundation by first making comparative evaluations of the works of others.

6

Standardization

It has long been recognized that the bewildering wealth of plant species all over the world makes the vegetation of the earth a chaotic mixture of individual specimens which cannot readily be described unless the many species are grouped according to some classification. Once this is done, the various groups and their divisions will permit a systematic scientific investigation of the vegetation which can result in valuable and interesting discoveries. Above all, the vegetational chaos will be resolved into orderly arrangements and geographical patterns. The plant communities or phytocenoses are the individual units which, in their totality, compose the mosaic of the vegetation in the landscape; they must somehow be circumscribed and defined so that they can be clearly identified in the field and distinguished from one another. Today, as in the past, vegetation mappers all over the world continue to look to Europe for inspiration and guidance, because many of the more important vegetation mappers reside on that continent.

Braun-Blanquet's Method

Of the many European vegetation maps, a sizable share is based on plant communities which were determined by employing the ideas and methods of Josias Braun-Blanquet. These ideas have become well established in many parts of Europe, especially France and Germany, Switzerland and Belgium, and others, and active research institutes in these countries continue to develop them. Indeed, an outsider, perhaps from overseas, who listens to the leading advocates of Braun-Blanquet's classification must come to the conclusion that it is only a matter of time before all phytocenologists and vegetation mappers throughout the world will employ only this method of describing and mapping vegetation.

This is indeed a happy thought, for it implies that a method has been discovered which can serve many purposes of mapping vegetation, which is applicable to many types of vegetation, and which permits an ideal degree of standardization on all continents. Such standardization is highly desirable because in a sense, all phytocenologists will be speaking the same language, and semantic confusion, one of the most difficult problems of our times, will cease to exist. BRAUN-BLANQUET's methods are already being tried and applied outside Europe, in Africa, America, and Asia, and the confidence of the users of this method seems justified.

However, an objective appraisal of many vegetation maps leads one to believe that the ideal degree of standardization is not likely to be achieved. If we compare the vegetation maps by BRAUN-BLANQUET and his followers, it becomes at once evident that this strict standardization used in classifying vegetation is not applied on vegetation maps. Men like EMBERGER, MOLINIER, LÜDI, TÜXEN, and even HUECK, the very leaders of European vegetation mapping, all profess to be followers of BRAUN-BLANQUET. And yet, their maps are not at all alike. One need only hold side by side such maps as that of Montpellier by BRAUN-BLANQUET and TCHOU (1947), of Aix by MOLINIER (1952), of Schlitz by SEIBERT (1954), of Baltrum by TÜXEN (1956a), and of the Riesengebirge by HUECK (1939). It would be difficult to speak of any degree of standardization.

It is not necessary here to make a detailed study of the differences. But it is important to observe that some of the finest examples of vegetation maps that emerged from the school of BRAUN-BLANQUET are quite unlike in character, leading to the conclusion that standardization on vegetation maps is not likely to be achieved simply because the intellectual approach to the classification of vegetation is the same.

Small-Scale Mapping

In addition to this divergence in method and approach, there is also the important limitation of scale. BRAUN-BLANQUET said in 1951 that his classification of vegetation is not adapted to mapping except at very large scales. And indeed, most major map productions of the BRAUN-BLANQUET school of thought are of large scale, usually somewhere between 1:5,000 and 1:25,000. EMBERGER's map (1939) of Morocco at 1:1,500,000 or HUECK's (1943) map of Germany at 1:1,000,000, of which unfortunately only one sheet has been published so far, are both of much smaller scales. As a result, a reader of these maps would find it difficult to guess that their authors are followers of BRAUN-BLANQUET. On the other hand, LONG (1954) demonstrated with his map of Sbeïtla at 1:200,000 that within limits it is feasible to employ this method on maps of medium scale, too.

The vegetation maps of the Soviet Union at 1:4,000,000 (LAVRENKO and SOCHAVA, 1956) or the vegetation map of Australia (WILLIAMS, 1955) at

1:6,000,000 could not have been published if vegetation mapping were limited to BRAUN-BLANQUET's method. However, it is obvious that small-scale maps have their value, too, and must be published with the same enthusiasm as their counterparts of larger scale.

Color

On looking through a collection of vegetation maps we find soon that other authors, too, have developed mapping methods, and indeed, promote them with similar determination. GAUSSEN's maps, which have been successfully executed in Europe, Africa, and Asia, come to mind. They too, are based on a well thought-out system; they, too, claim applicability throughout the world, but they, too, have their scale limitations. What gives GAUSSEN's maps their own particular character is the manner in which colors are manipulated. This original system for the use of colors enables GAUSSEN to show more than most of his colleagues do. But while the color system is the very strength of these maps, it is also their weakness. The colors represent environmental conditions, and the system was devised in a part of southern France where hot and cold and wet and dry conditions prevail side by side. The map of Perpignan at 1:200,000 (GAUSSEN, 1948) remains the finest expression of GAUSSEN's method. But it was an accident that GAUSSEN lived in southern France, and perhaps it was an accident, too, that he should have decided on the medium scale of 1:200,000. All this worked in his favor except that elsewhere environmental conditions may lack the contrasts they show in the Pyrenees. For instance, TÜXEN's map of Baltrum would have been rather meaningless had TÜXEN used GAUSSEN's system because the uniform climatic conditions imply one single color for the entire map. Large-scale vegetation maps of plains regions such as in Kansas are therefore more useful when they are based on a different method. Even GUINET's (1953) map of Béni Abbès, employing GAUSSEN's method at 1:200,000, has only a few tiny blue dots and otherwise the entire sheet is pink.

The Physiognomic Approach

If, then, such excellent methods as those developed by BRAUN-BLANQUET and GAUSSEN have a limited applicability imposed by the scale when we obviously need vegetation maps beyond these limits, the question arises if it is not possible to overcome this difficulty and find a manner of mapping vegetation which is independent of the scale. Such a possibility exists in the physiognomic approach to vegetation mapping, for the physiognomy of the plant communities can be shown in any desired detail and degree of generalization. Colored maps showing the physiognomic features of the vegetation at scales of 1:2,000 and of 1:100,000,000 have been published (KÜCHLER, 1950, 1951b), and in each case the purpose of the map was adequately served, demonstrating the wide range of applicability of a physiognomic method. The physiognomy of the vegetation is indeed most revealing, often much more so than some phytocenologists are willing to admit. But the fact remains that physiognomy alone places important limitations on the interpretation of the plant communities. In spite of its great usefulness and detail, therefore, it seems adequate as a basis for a world-wide standardization only for maps of relatively small scale.

Standardization permits vegetation maps to be appreciated quickly and widely. But standardization must be achieved in such a manner that it is, in effect, applicable everywhere. It seems, therefore, that a world-wide standard must be physiognomic. World vegetation maps and even vegetation maps of the larger continents imply such vast areas and hence such a small scale that the introduction of floristic features is not feasible. Of course, such a standardized approach can be applied in much more limited areas as well. But as smaller areas can be shown at larger scales, and hence with more detail, it is desirable to show more than the physiognomy and structure of the vegetation.

There cannot be much difference of opinion concerning the use of physiognomic types as standards on small-scale maps. But as soon as the scale is large enough to show appreciably more than structure, it will be much more difficult to find a general agreement on basic standards. ELLENBERG (1960) also proposes a physiognomic method, perhaps *sensu* BEARD or the Yangambi conference, for a broad world-wide approach. But he then suggests the method of BRAUN-BLANQUET as a basis for all work done at larger scales. This latter suggestion may be good but it will be much more difficult to have it generally accepted. Our mapping techniques are now so advanced and so much information is now available that vegetation maps at the scale of 1:1,000,000 can show both structural and floristic features, the latter at the species level (KÜCHLER, 1952). But that the method of BRAUN-BLANQUET should be the most desirable at this and somewhat larger scales remains an open question. It would be highly desirable to make more tests and comparative experiments.

In Resolutions No. 1 and 2 of the International Colloquium on Vegetation Mapping in Toulouse (GAUSSEN, 1961a), satisfaction is expressed at the unified physiognomic approach to the classification of tropical African vegetation. The Colloquium then expressed the hope that this standardization of physiognomic terminology can be extended from tropical Africa through the remainder of the tropics and eventually through all latitudes. The Colloquium recommended further that a standardized color system be used in presenting vegetation on maps.

Advantages of Divergent Approaches

The general trend of thinking among the world's leading vegetation mappers seems to be toward standardization. It may therefore seem regrettable that the vegetation maps of our time show no more uniformity than they do, i.e., practically none at all. Even one and the same author will employ different methods to map vegetation at different times or under different circumstances.

In fact, however, such divergence is to be welcomed rather than regretted. If the limitations of our methods to classify and map vegetation are liabilities, then let us turn them into assets. It may not be quite so desirable to attain the degree of standardization which at first appeared so attractive, because different approaches and different methods stimulate the imagination. They allow a much greater degree of originality; they also permit a greater flexibility with which to adjust a vegetation map to varying local conditions.

Authors of vegetation maps might well be encouraged to become thoroughly familiar with all major methods of mapping vegetation, and then to review critically their particular needs as dictated by the purpose of their vegetation maps. In the light of such considerations, they will be able to study the vegetation of their area and devise a method of mapping it which will do a maximum of justice to the readers of their maps, as well as to the mapped vegetation and their own originality. This may be done by utilizing one of the existing methods, as it has been developed or perhaps with modifications which local conditions make desirable. Or else it is possible to develop a new and different method incorporating the ideas of several other authors. Finally, the door is always open for an entirely fresh and original approach.

A particularly fruitful promise is held out by the collaboration of two or more schools of thought. The ideas and methods of one will supplement the other and the resulting vegetation map is greatly enriched. A fine example of such collaboration has recently become available when the Service de la carte de la végétation in Toulouse published the vegetation map of Tunisia at a scale of 1:1,000,000 on which some phytocenologists on the staff of the Service de la carte des groupements végétaux in Montpellier had collaborated (GAUSSEN and VERNET, 1958). The result is gratifying and shows that collaboration between two or more schools of thought should be explored further.

This is an important observation in view of the growing interest in a vegetation map of the world at the scale of 1:1,000,000 (GAUSSEN, 1949; KÜCHLER, 1952; TROCHAIN, 1961). Maps at this scale are becoming available in different parts of the world, as for instance those of Central Asia in seventeen sheets (Lavrenko and Rodin, 1956), European Russia in sixteen sheets (Kuznetsov, 1928), the southern United States in eight sheets (U.S. Forest Service, 1934–1941), France in four sheets (Gaussen, 1945b), Northern Rhodesia in two sheets (Trapnell, 1948), Germany (Hueck, 1943), Kwango (Devred, 1955), Tunisia (Gaussen and Vernet, 1958), and a number of others. It is therefore not astonishing that some authors should seek to achieve a more unified approach to this effort. A need for more uniformity is now recognized and attempts are being made to standardize the physiognomic types of tropical vegetation with a first success in Africa (Trochain, 1957; Aubréville, 1961). The map of Africa south of the Tropic of Cancer (Keay, 1959) is, within limits, based on this accord.

Similar efforts are being made in the middle latitudes for phytocenoses defined floristically (Weise, 1952; Tüxen, 1937, 1950; Society of American Foresters, 1954). But their success and acceptance varies within wide margins. A conference at Montreal, during the International Botanical Congress (Heikurainen, 1960), attempted to find a way toward a standardized world-wide forest classification and essentially failed.

Gaussen (1936), Trochain (1961) and, much earlier, Rübel (1916) have proposed special standardized symbols to be overprinted in black on the colored maps. Trochain's symbols stand for life forms and crop types; subscripts in the form of numbers can refer to floristic data, i.e., taxa of any desired rank, given in the legend. Rübel and Gaussen suggest symbols for species and are, therefore, geographically more restricted in their application. The principle, however, is applicable everywhere; it is used to advantage on the map of Central Asia (Lavrenko and Rodin, 1956).

Perhaps here is a way toward a more widely acceptable standardization: commonly agreed-upon symbols for species of individual regions. Thus Gaussen's symbols apply above all to western Europe, and Kosmakova (1960) reports on the regional system of symbols for Siberia and the Soviet Far East. The regions should be reasonably large, although their size depends at least in part on the number of vegetation types that may be found there, and their complexity.

Standardization is highly desirable because it greatly aids in communicating. It makes different vegetation maps comparable and facilitates their use and exploitation. It should certainly be promoted. But it should never be adopted to the exclusion of different, non-standardized methods. A new and original approach to mapping can reveal new problems and thus become highly stimulating. Anything that will aid in research and lead to new ways of progress must be given a fair chance to evolve. Ozenda (1961a, b) has recently expressed similar thoughts.

It is indeed fortunate for vegetation mappers that Braun-Blanquet developed his school of thought; it is even more fortunate that others developed their own contending schools of thought at the same time. The simultaneous evolution of challenging ideas has resulted in much valuable research and has enabled us to improve and refine the quality of our vegetation maps. Standardization in vegetation maps offers real advantages, especially with regard to communications. Standardization, however, in all its usefulness can also be stifling. Whenever certain standards in vegetation mapping are recommended, it should be done in such a manner that the proposed standards will not limit the imagination and creativeness of phytocenologists and vegetation mappers. For what good is a scientist without imagination?

III

TECHNICAL ASPECTS

7

Scales and Grids

The amount of detail that can be shown on a map is mostly a function of the scale; it diminishes with a diminishing scale, and information on a small-scale map is usually more generalized than on a map with a large scale. As the scale controls the detail of the map, it also has a strong bearing on the type of material that can be shown. Broad formations (*sensu* FLAHAULT and SCHRÖTER, 1910) are readily shown at small scales, whereas small plant communities usually require a large scale. Where phytocenoses gradually merge with others, an author may be tempted to show too much detail.

In compiling the data in the field, an author is quite easily impressed with unusual features of the vegetation, e.g., the occurrence of a rare species, or the relict of a formation which has long since migrated elsewhere. Such features, interesting as they may be, should not be shown unless the scale is sufficiently large to place them on the map without clutter, or if the organization of the material is worked out in such a manner that the unusual features can be fitted in as integral parts of the vegetation. In case of doubt, an author should always choose the simpler method and avoid complications. He must feel quite sure of the quality of his results before attempting to produce complex maps.

Even before the mapping work is started, the size and scale of the final version of the map should be determined, at least approximately. Whether the map is to be a wall map, appear on the page of a book or journal, or is produced as an individual sheet for research purposes, definitely affects the scale. To know the scale in advance of the mapping work may spell the difference between economy and waste in time, funds, and energy. On extensive plains with horizontal geological strata, e.g., in parts of Kansas, the vegetation can be remarkably monotonous for miles. In such an instance, a small scale is adequate. If, on the other hand, the vegetation to be mapped occurs in a region of alpine topography (e.g., the Olympic Peninsula) or in a region of great geological complexity (e.g., the

73

Coast Ranges of northern California), there will be many significant plant communities that must be shown on the map and the scale must therefore be large. WAGNER (1961a) has demonstrated this point in Austrian grasslands where a scale of 1:20,000 and even 1:10,000 may be inadequate to serve the purposes of the map. The vegetation maps of the Pasterze in the Alps (FRIEDEL, 1956) and of a part of the Elbe Valley (WALTHER, 1957) are classic examples of vegetation mapping at very large scales.

Purpose and Practicality

Only large scales permit an accurate presentation of the geographical distribution of phytocenoses. Wherever a high degree of accuracy is required, as for instance in detailed land-use studies, the map scale must necessarily be large. In this, vegetation maps parallel soil maps and geological maps. But this only underlines the need of the vegetation mapper to select a map scale which is in harmony with the purposes that his map is to serve.

It is therefore quite essential that the vegetation mapper is thoroughly acquainted with the purpose and its exigencies. If the purpose is complex, it will require a large scale. If, on the other hand, the purpose is very limited or the vegetation is simple and uniform over large areas, the scale can be reduced.

Maps of small scale are usually derived from maps of larger scale. Such small-scale maps serve the interests of government agencies that are in charge of large areas. They serve as a basis for over-all directives. Once such directives are to be translated into practical application on the local scene, the small-scale maps must be replaced by vegetation maps at large scales. The vegetation mapper will appreciate by now that it is to his advantage to select an appropriate scale before his mapping activities are begun.

Some authors distinguish between large, medium, and small scales, but these terms have no fixed values and are entirely relative. Usually, a scale smaller than 1:1,000,000 is considered small. A scale from 1:100,000 to 1:1,000,000 may be called medium, and a scale over 1:100,000 may be termed large. SOCHAVA (1961) reported on five scale classes used in the Soviet Union. MATUSZKIEWICZ (1963, p. 347) calls 1:37,500 a large scale whereas DOING KRAFT (1963, p. 308) speaks of a small-scale map at 1:25,-000! It is usually simpler, more accurate, and more effective to mention scales by their actual values than to refer to them as large, medium, or small.

There are maximum and minimum scales, and above all there is an optimum scale. It is not always feasible to choose the optimum, but the author must be aware of the limits within which he is free to operate, if the scale is to be selected intelligently.

It is not feasible to state categorically which is the "best" scale; nor is it possible even to suggest one optimum scale for vegetation maps. Where great detail is to be shown, a large scale becomes imperative; where broader vegetation units suffice, the scale should be correspondingly small. Ultimately, the selection of the scale depends on the purpose of the map; however, every purpose permits some flexibility.

The cost of production is often another controlling factor. If the map is to have several colors, a large scale may render the printing cost prohibitive. Unless there is no financial problem involved, the author must compromise between what is desirable and what is necessary.

It is customary to reduce a manuscript map to the desired size and scale of the printed map. Such a reduction is frequently influenced by financial considerations. The vegetation mapper must remember, however, that there are limits to which he can carry such a reduction. If he reduces his map below a minimum scale, he will sufficiently alter the character of the map so as no longer to serve its purpose. Where this minimum is reached depends largely on the organizational skill of the author and again, of course, on the purpose of the map.

Whereas the minimum scale is often a critical problem, the maximum scale presents no difficulty. A map shows the areal differences of the vegetation and, in the case of great uniformity, the scale may well be of modest proportions as a larger scale will result in too few variations on the map. Too large a scale implies waste.

To illustrate this, the reader is invited to compare the vegetation map of Germany at 1:1,000,000 (HUECK, 1943) with the Major Forest Types of Georgia at the same scale (U.S. FOREST SERVICE, 1934). It is not necessary to study the two maps at length in order to realize that the map of Georgia could have been published at half its scale (reducing its area to one quarter of its present size) without sacrificing a single feature and without cluttering the map. HUECK, on the other hand, adapted his information to the given scale and used the available space to capacity. It would, therefore, not be feasible to reduce HUECK's map without changing its character.

Another disadvantage of an unduly large map scale is the difficulty of observing the distributional pattern of the phytocenoses. A reader wants to see the pattern of vegetation and to compare it with those of other maps and areas. However, if the map scale is too large, the vegetational pattern is obscured and the value of the map is diminished.

Optimum Scale

The optimum scale varies only with the purpose of the map and the skill of the author in organizing the map content, but it has nothing to do with production cost. Ideally, all vegetation maps should be prepared at their respective optimum scale; prospective authors are urged to seek enough financial support to permit the optimum scale for their maps. Such funds are usually well spent, as the best scale greatly enhances the value of the map. Vegetation maps tend to be complex, and the optimum scale is therefore particularly desirable.

The problem which every author must face is to determine the optimum scale for his particular purpose. This depends largely on the individual case, but the following points should be remembered. The smallest units which are to be shown on the map should have a diameter of at least 1 millimeter if round in shape, and if the map is printed in color. If the item is long and narrow, less than 1 millimeter is permissible. In the case of galeria forests, the space should be wide enough to show the river between two narrow strips of forest.

In order to determine the optimum scale, the mapper must consider the size of the area to be shown on the map and the kind of detail that is required by the purpose of the map. By correlating one with the other and by selecting a fixed value for the minimum size of any area shown on the map (usually at least 1 millimeter), the determination of the optimum scale becomes a matter of simple arithmetic. The mapper must remember to base his calculation on the final version of his map as it will appear when it is printed. The manuscript map is, of course, done at a larger scale for a variety of compelling technical reasons. The accuracy and the legibility of a vegetation map depend *inter alia* on the dimensions of the smallest areas to be shown. If the map is to be printed in color and if the minimal area is to be at least 1 square millimeter, the mapper will find it useful to consult Table 3 for correlating the field work with the final map.

Exaggeration

There are times when, for scientific reasons, very small areas ought to be shown on a vegetation map even though their extent is well below the calculated minimum. In such cases it is permissible to exaggerate these small areas to such a degree that they can be drawn on the map. A small scale usually necessitates the suppression of many details to prevent the map from being cluttered. This procedure is a matter of expedience. But if it is justifiable at times to reduce certain items to nonexistence, it is

Table 3. Scale Relations

At the Scale of	1 Millimeter on the Map Equals	1 Square Millimeter on the Map Equals	
1:1,000,000	1,000 meters (1 km)	100	hectares (1 km²)
1: 500,000	500 meters	25	hectares
1: 250,000	250 meters	6.25	hectares
1: 125,000	125 meters	1.5625	hectares
1: 100,000	100 meters	1	hectare (10,000 m²)
1: 50,000	50 meters	2,500	square meters
1: 25,000	25 meters	625	square meters
1: 20,000	20 meters	400	square meters
1: 10,000	10 meters	100	square meters
1: 5,000	5 meters	25	square meters

At the Scale of	1 Millimeter on the Map Equals	1 Square Millimeter on the Map Equals (approx.)
1:1,000,000	3,280.90 feet	247.11 acres
1: 500,000	1,640.45 feet	61.77 acres
1: 250,000	820.23 feet	15.44 acres
1: 125,000	410.11 feet	3.86 acres
1: 63,360	207.88 feet	1.00 acre
1: 62,500	205.05 feet	0.97 acre
1: 31,680	103.94 feet	0.25 acre
1: 24,000	78.74 feet	6,200.00 square feet
1: 20,000	65.62 feet	4,306.00 square feet
1: 15,840	51.97 feet	2,700.88 square feet
1: 10,000	32.81 feet	1,076.50 square feet
1: 7,920	25.98 feet	675.22 square feet
1: 4,800	15.75 feet	247.00 square feet

At the Scale of	1 Inch on the Map Equals		1 Square Inch on the Map Equals (approx.)	
1:1,000,000		15.78 miles	249	square miles
1: 633,600	10	miles	100	square miles
1: 500,000		7.89 miles	62.25	square miles
1: 250,000		3.95 miles	15.6	square miles
1: 125,000		1.97 miles	3.88	square miles
1: 63,360	5280	feet (1 mile)	1.00	square mile (640 acres)
1: 50,000	4167	feet	398.62	acres
1: 31,680	2640	feet (½ mile)	160	acres
1: 24,000	2000	feet	91.82	acres
1: 15,840	1320	feet (¼ mile)	40	acres
1: 10,000	833	feet	15.93	acres
1: 7,920	660	feet	10	acres
1: 4,800	400	feet	3.67	acres

equally justifiable to enlarge some items in order to assure their presence on the map.

Largest Feasible Scale

Color permits the use of smaller areal units than do black and white patterns. In the latter case, the areas must be at least large enough to show the patterns clearly. When the vegetation types are shown by sets of letter and number symbols, it is important to keep the scale so large that the vegetation type of the smallest areas can still be identified.

If any uncertainty exists concerning the scale, one should be careful to choose the largest feasible scale, at least for the manuscript map. This permits the maximum amount of detail to be shown and to be relatively accurate. If it is found later that the scale is too large, the map can be reduced. This can be done by diminishing the size of the map photographically either without making any changes in the map content or by omitting some details, or by a certain amount of generalization, or both, but the relation of accuracy to scale can be maintained. The advantage of being able to make such adjustments is lost, however, if the original scale is found to be too small. The maps can, of course, be enlarged photographically, but one cannot thereby improve the refinement and accuracy of details which the larger scale calls for. For this, it is necessary to return to the field and map these vegetational details anew.

Rübel (1916, p. 3) suggested for Switzerland that a scale of 1:25,000 is the best, that 1:50,000 is all right, but that 1:100,000 is too small. Such a rigid approach cannot lead to good results. A good scale is good only for a particular purpose and may be poor for another purpose. Most maps made under Tüxen's direction are necessarily of a scale larger than 1:20,-000; Schmid's (1948) excellent map of Switzerland is at 1:200,000. Rübel's categorical statement is therefore without merit. Special purposes require special scales. For instance, Ellenberg (1950, p. 126) discusses the scales for mapping weed communities and finds that the scale should be very large, somewhere between 1:5,000 and 1:10,000 but surely not less than 1:25,000. For the cadastral manner of vegetation mapping by Kuhnholtz-Lordat (1949), Ellenberg's scales would appear distinctly too small.

Base maps at scales of 1:20,000 to 1:25,000 are now available in many countries, and their number is increasing. These are the largest scales that can be used conveniently for mapping sizeable areas. The scale is so large as to show adequate detail, and the widespread availability of maps at such scales permits a country-wide or region-wide terminology and methodology. A larger scale, however, focuses the attention on such a small area as to be largely of local interest. This permits the introduction of ideas and methods that are of local use only, especially in ecological considerations. WAGNER (1961a) gives some excellent examples of how he successfully modified the conventional procedures to serve local needs. His units of vegetation are ecologically controlled and their rank in the hierarchy of BRAUN-BLANQUET is largely irrelevant.

The scale of accurate and detailed vegetation maps is also affected by the local relief. A mountainous terrain usually calls for a larger scale in order to assure an appreciation of the three-dimensional character of the distribution of the phytocenoses.

MOLINIER et al. (1951) demonstrated the relation between the scale and the usefulness of a vegetation map with the help of the maps of the Forest of Sainte Baume. This forest was mapped at five different scales, thus permitting an illustrative comparison. The forest is 2 kilometers long and 800 meters wide and of historic interest.

> At the scale of 1:2,000, the map of the forest covers an area 1 meter long and 40 centimeters wide. At this large scale it is possible to show all details, even the exact location of some rare species.
> At the scale of 1:5,000 the map is only 40 by 16 centimeters. It is still possible to show most of the details that could be shown at 1:2,000 although it is necessary to use overprinted symbols to avoid cluttering.
> At the scale of 1:20,000 the forest measures only 10 by 4 centimeters. Only the major facies of the oak forests and the beech forests can now be shown, without any indication of their density. But all essential features of the vegetation can still be shown.
> At the scale of 1:50,000 the forest is no more than 4 by 1.6 centimeters. Only the oak forests and the beech forests can still be distinguished, with perhaps some adjacent communities. The boundaries are only approximate.
> At the scale of 1:200,000 the forest is reduced to 10 by 4 millimeters. The boundaries of the two major vegetation groups are now quite inaccurate and the reader can get no more than a general idea of the vegetation.

Interestingly enough, MOLINIER then concludes that a general idea is inadequate for practical purposes and that the very largest scales (1:2,-000) are the most useful for agricultural planning because conditions sometimes vary within a few meters. His conclusion reveals the extraordinary detail in which Europeans have studied their landscapes; it reveals also the constant pressure to improve the productivity of the land. In the end, however, and as a practical vegetation mapper, he adopts a scale of 1:20,000 for work on a nation-wide basis. This approaches the scale of 1:24,000 (1 inch = 2,000 feet) of the topographic sheets of the U.S. Geological Survey.

A problem arises if the map is to be done in a series of many sheets covering a large area. Unless the scale is predetermined the author should select the most complex area, often the one with the greatest relief, and establish the optimum scale for it. On the other sheets this scale may then appear larger than necessary but a smaller scale would clutter or oversimplify the more complex maps in the series.

Special caution should be exercised where manuscript maps are to be reduced to a scale which requires generalization of the vegetation features on the map. Again the purpose is the deciding factor. For instance, if the general appearance of the vegetation is wanted, the ground cover should be suppressed in favor of the forest trees. On the other hand, if a pasture map is desired, the ground cover must be emphasized, and the generalization should affect primarily the trees.

Legibility

Another concern arises with reducing the manuscript map to the final scale of the printed map: the legibility of the names, terms, numbers, etc., written on the manuscript map. It happens all too often that this point is overlooked; as a result, it is practically impossible to read anything on the map without a magnifying glass. The value of such maps is unnecessarily low and care should be taken when preparing the manuscript map that all types of writing are large enough to permit the desired reduction without endangering the legibility of the printed map.

Factors To Consider

GIACOMINI has given more thought to scale problems than perhaps any other phytocenologist. In reviewing the types of maps that have been prepared at medium and large scales, he concluded that there are at least eight factors that help to determine the scale of a vegetation map and that they should be considered in deciding on the final scale whenever a vegetation map is planned (GIACOMINI, 1961). These eight factors are discussed in the paragraphs immediately following.

AVAILABILITY OF TOPOGRAPHIC BASE MAPS

In the past, this was a more critical point than it is today because in the past good topographic maps were available for only a few areas. The new topographic maps at 1:24,000 of the U.S. Geological Survey, like those of other countries, are now so accurate that they can be enlarged and thus offer a base for a wide variety of scales. However, even today, there are vast regions where good base maps are either unavailable or of modest quality. Aerial photographs can help here a great deal to improve the less accurate base maps. Where only medium-scale maps are available, they will have to be enlarged photographically before they can be used for field work.

CLASSIFICATION OF VEGETATION

The various classifications, of course, permit a considerable range of scales; but the latest maps by GAMS attain their optimum at very large scales, for SCHMID's method the scale need not be larger than 1:100,000, and for the BRAUN-BLANQUET method the best scales remain at from 1:5,000 to 1:50,000 in spite of the wider range that has been employed. Obviously, differences in scale affect not only the amount of detail but the classification of vegetation, too.

PURPOSE OF THE MAP

There are many different uses to which vegetation maps are put and sometimes a vegetation map is prepared for narrow and sharply focused purposes. The astonishing variety of purposes for which vegetation maps are made is illustrated in Part V of this book. But it is quite obvious that different uses require different scales, and the vegetation mapper must fully appreciate the purpose of his map in order to select a scale that is best fitted for it.

SIZE OF THE AREA TO BE MAPPED

Large areas require, of course, a relatively small scale. However, if the mapping is done by a government agency so that many parts of the country can be done simultaneously and by a large staff, such a national effort permits a larger scale. In such cases, one uniform approach is needed. But if the areas are more limited and local considerations increase in importance, the scale must be adjusted to these changing circumstances; it must be enlarged accordingly.

CHARACTER OF THE PHYTOCENOSES

For instance, KÜCHLER (1954a) observed that if a forest which is 20 meters tall is mapped floristically at 1:100,000 then a corresponding scale for a map of grassland communities which are 1 meter high should be in the neighborhood of 1:5,000. The approach is a little schematic but the observation demonstrates that not all scales can do equal justice to all phytocenoses.

STRUCTURE OF THE PHYTOCENOSES

For instance, it may be that a multilayered forest must be shown at a scale that is even larger than that of grassland communities in order to properly reveal the internal structure of the vegetation. In other words, the scale is at least in part a function of the complexity of the structure.

LOCAL RELIEF OF THE MAPPED AREA

A rather small scale can present the essential features of the vegetation where a region consists of extensive and relatively uniform plains, as in parts of the United States or the Soviet Union. Frequently, however, the vegetation grows increasingly complex as the local relief increases and the topography includes ever greater differences in altitude and steepness. In mountainous countries it is therefore often necessary to map at very large scales in order to do justice to the complex features of the vegetation in the narrow confines of steep-sided valleys and similar microlandscapes.

CARTOGRAPHIC TECHNIQUES

For instance, the choice between colors and black and white greatly affects the scale. The black-and-white maps require a scale two to three times as large as that of colored maps in order to show the details with an equal degree of clarity.

These eight factors are not to be taken as rules or directives. They rather reveal some of the problems the vegetation mapper must face. He will also discover that it is difficult to consider these factors in isolation because they affect one another. The proper choice of a scale implies therefore a delicate balance between a whole series of considerations.

GIACOMINI then suggests five different scales for different types of purposes:

A scale of 1:200,000 to 1:250,000 for mapping the vegetation of a whole country.

A scale of 1:100,000 for a synthesis of several small regions or for forestry maps on a nation-wide basis.

A scale of 1:20,000 to 1:25,000 for synthesizing the natural vegetation of areas that can be selected for their scientific interest or their economic significance.

A scale of about 1:10,000 for correlating phytocenoses with the characteristics of their sites. At this scale, the vegetation maps can present so much floristic detail that they can also portray ecological conditions more effectively.

A scale of 1:5,000 or larger is preferable for all messicol vegetation as well as the structure of natural communities and their synusias. This seems reasonable because the features of cultivated crops and of synusias are apt to change and vary within very short distances.

Here again, as in the case of MOLINIER, the European origin of the proposals is evident, especially in the idea that a scale of 1:100,000 or 1:200,-000 should be used for mapping an entire country. What a great step forward it would be, for instance, if the vegetation of the fifty states of the

United States were mapped at 1:500,000 or even at 1:1,000,000! This is now feasible (Küchler, 1952) but also very expensive because of the enormous areas involved; the lack of properly trained personnel presents another problem.

Identifying the Scale

It is always of the greatest importance that the scale is clearly stated on the map, and it is equally important that the reader become aware of the scale before analyzing the map features.

There is more than one way to show the scale on a map (Figure 4). One method is to show the scale in the form of a fraction (hence, the *fractional scale*), e.g., 1:200,000. It means that every distance measured on the map is 200,000 times longer in the landscape, or conversely, that any distance measured on the map is 1/200,000 of the corresponding distance in the landscape. The great advantage of giving the fractional scale is that it readily permits the reader to compare map scales quickly and without having to take any measurements. One glance will tell him which scale is larger and how much. A map should therefore always bear the scale in the form of a fraction.

Another method of showing scales is to draw a straight line and on it mark off the scale equivalents of kilometers, miles, feet, meters, etc. This is called a *linear scale*. It permits the reader to make direct measurements of distances on the map without any calculations. Distances can, of course, be measured on maps with fractional scales, too, but some calculation is necessary. For instance, 3 inches measured on a map with a scale of 1:200,000 is, in the field, 3 × 200,000 or 600,000 inches. To convert this into feet or into miles, the total number of inches must be divided by 12 or by 63,360, respectively. The 3 inches corresponds therefore to 50,000 feet, or nearly 9.47 miles. For the benefit of the reader, the vegetation mapper should always show the scale of his map in both forms, i.e., as a fractional scale as well as a linear scale.

$$\text{FRACTIONAL SCALES} \quad - \quad 1{:}100{,}000 \text{ or } \frac{1}{100{,}000}$$

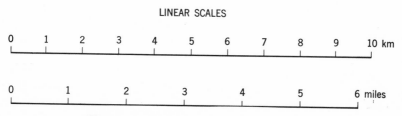

Figure 4. Methods of showing map scales.

The map scale reveals only the dimensional proportions. For a true and accurate orientation of the reader, the map must also have a grid. This is a network in which lines drawn west-east (called "parallels") indicate latitude, and lines drawn north-south (called "meridians") indicate longitude, and between them give a frame of reference for every point on the map. These parallels and meridians are all the more necessary, as vegetation maps from all over the world are now becoming available and the reader is often quite unfamiliar with the names of places and areas on some of these maps. The grid will reveal the exact location at once even though the names of the areas portrayed may be Kwango, Riverina, or Thiès. Some vegetation mappers and phytocenologists will, of course, recognize these names because of the important vegetation maps of these areas (DEVRED, 1955; MOORE, 1953; GAUSSEN *et al.*, 1950).

Many phytocenologists prepare vegetation maps but have little experience in cartography. The result is that they occasionally omit to show either a scale or a grid, or even both. If both are missing, it is impossible to make any measurements on the map, thereby reducing the value of the map seriously and unnecessarily. If the scale is missing but the map has a grid, this grid can serve as a scale because the distances between the parallels are known or can be determined. The reader need only remember that one degree of latitude very nearly equals 69.15 miles. Without a grid, a vegetation map cannot be compared with analogous maps because individual locations cannot be determined accurately where there is no grid. This is true even if the map is to be compared with other maps of the same area, if these are done on a different projection.

If an author objects to having a grid, he can do without it by marking the degrees of both latitude and longitude on the margin. He can, in addition, show the intersections of the parallels and meridians in the form of crosses of fine lines. This is an adequate substitute on a large number of maps.

Sometimes the scale is so large that the mapped area is very small, so small in fact as to fall between two parallels and between two meridians. This applies to maps of individual peat bogs and other vegetation types of small areal extent. But this is not an adequate justification for omitting a grid. Each degree of latitude and longitude is divided into sixty minutes and topographic sheets will readily permit the accurate placing of a grid by minutes in such a manner that at least two parallels and two meridians can be shown on the map. There is, of course, no excuse for having no scale, no matter how small the mapped area is.

The Toulouse Colloquium of 1960 (GAUSSEN, 1961a) recommends in Resolution 11 that every vegetation map have a grid, the scale in both the fractional and the linear form, and also the name of the projection.

8

Aerial Photographs

There are several reasons why vegetation mapping is progressing so rapidly during this midcentury period, and not the least of these are the fine technological devices that now permit us to do things which seemed unthinkable a generation or two ago. From the point of view of the vegetation mapper, the most useful and most significant of these modern devices is aerial photography. It is not a new idea to take photographs of vegetation, but the tremendous strides of photographic research, especially in the fields of emulsion chemistry, filter optics, and color photography, have permitted an unparalleled progress in mapping vegetation from the air. Like all branches of modern technology, photography is rapidly evolving at the present time and perhaps it is not difficult to forecast that the near future will see most vegetation mapping done with the help of aerial color photography.

There is no need to discuss here all the latest devices in the field of photography. Almost every year new devices are placed on the market, rendering older ones obsolete. Prospective authors of vegetation maps are advised to look into exactly when and how they want their vegetation photographed, especially with regard to season, weather, time of day, altitude, etc. They should then discuss their requirements with experts in aerial surveying companies or government agencies in order to arrange for the proper selection of cameras, films, filters, etc.

Rather than discuss the latest devices, this chapter will therefore be devoted to some of the more fundamental ideas which form the basis for mapping vegetation with the help of aerial photographs.

The pattern and the boundaries of the phytocenoses in the landscape can be observed and recognized better from a plane than from the ground. The bird's-eye view of the landscape permits a new insight into the landscape and the nature of its vegetation. This insight can be exploited now that aerial photography has become available, but an author of vegetation maps will soon discover that certain procedures must be followed in order to reap the greatest benefit from existing possibilities.

Vertical Photographs

The first observation is that photographs taken vertically downward should be preferred. Oblique photographs, i.e., those taken at an angle of less than 90° with the plane of the horizon, can be and often are much more picturesque than vertical photographs but their use in mapping creates such difficult technical problems that most authors find the solutions beyond practical reach. The first maxim is therefore that the author of vegetation maps will insist on aerial photographs taken vertically.

There are, however, other compelling reasons why vertical photographs should be used exclusively. First of all, only vertical photographs permit a correct grasp of the geographical distribution of the different vegetation types in the landscape. It is easy to see that this is quite important, but another reason is no less significant: only vertical photographs can be transferred to a topographic map without much difficulty. In areas where good recent topographic maps are available, this is a tremendous advantage and permits rapid progress with a high degree of accuracy. And, as a last argument in favor of vertical photographs, an author should not overlook the possibilities of composing a mosaic, i.e., piecing together several vertical photographs and thereby cover more territory, if not indeed the entire area to be mapped. Care must be taken to obtain a *controlled* mosaic, i.e., one in which the distances between any two points are correct in relation to each other. In order to achieve this, there must be control points on the ground and the author will find it necessary to leave the composition of a controlled mosaic to the surveying (photographing) organization. He should obtain a cost estimate before he orders one, in order not to tax his budget unduly.

Advantages and Limitations

COLWELL (1964) summarizes the advantages and limitations of aerial photographs as follows. The major advantages are: (1) reliability, (2) favorable vantage point, (3) minuteness of detail, (4) completeness of coverage, (5) ease of interpretation, (6) opportunity to extend limited ground observations, (7) ease of measurement, (8) ease of checking for sources of error, (9) opportunity for studying areas at any time of the year, (10) rapidity of obtaining data, (11) suitability for comparative studies, (12) suitability for the making of "discrete appraisals," and (13) economy. The major limitations are: (1) the photographs may rapidly become outdated or obsolete, (2) they may emphasize the wrong features,

(3) a single aerial photo may fail to show the entire area of interest, (4) aerial photography does not entirely eliminate the need for field work, and (5) prolonged training of the photo users may be required before their interpretations become of acceptable accuracy.

The most important aspect of aerial photography in vegetation mapping is the fact that it permits a rapid and accurate tracing of the boundaries of the individual vegetation units. The photographs thereby save so much time (and hence funds) and so increase the accuracy of the map (and hence its value) that the prospective author of vegetation maps should make every effort to obtain a good up-to-date set of aerial photographs that cover his entire area. The cost of such photographs is only a small fraction of the expenses which would be incurred in preparing a vegetation map of the same quality without aerial photographs, i.e., by field surveys only.

The rendering of accurate outlines of vegetation types is not the only advantage derived from the use of aerial photographs. Another one, often underestimated, is that the photographs indicate the exact location of the vegetation types. This not only permits an author to correlate them with the landscape but first of all to find them. By studying the photograph, he becomes aware of vegetation units that he might have missed. He is also enabled by the photograph to establish the most convenient route to one or several plant communities and so to save much time on his inspection trip. In countries which are developing only just now, it is often difficult or impossible to obtain accurate base maps. In all such regions, aerial photographs offer an excellent substitute. They permit the mapper to indicate the location of all vegetation types, their outline and their extent. But, as EMBERGER (1961) rightly emphasized, this does not take the place of necessary vegetation studies on the ground.

If at all possible, an author should have the photographs taken specially for his purpose and, as a corollary, he should avoid aerial photographs which are so old as to be obsolete. Just when a photograph is too old depends entirely on the local situation; but this problem does not arise when the photographs are specially taken, and preferably according to the instructions of the author.

Color vs. Black-and-White Film

The variety of technical devices in aerial photography make it desirable for an author of vegetation maps to become acquainted with the possibilities. There are different kinds of photographs, each of which offers particular advantages. These different photographic qualities are the result of different types of films, such as orthochromatic, panchromatic, and infrared films, each with its various modifications. The variety can be greatly increased by various combinations of films with filters. The quality of the various types of films and filters is now such as to permit the production of excellent black-and-white photographs. In spite of this, it is quite reasonable to assume that in the not too distant future their place will have been taken by color films. For a long time, colored photographs were expensive and difficult to produce. But their recent evolution has changed the situation. Where black-and-white photographs can range only through various tones of grey, color photographs permit a much wider variety of distinctions. Many different colors correspond to the same type of grey; it is inevitable that color photographs should therefore save much valuable time and effort in the correct interpretation of the photographs. Whenever these savings exceed the cost differential, color photographs will replace black and white photographs.

Altitude and Scale

The usefulness of aerial photographs depends in part on the height above the ground from which they were taken. The greater the height, the greater is the danger of interference by haze. This, however, is a minor consideration. Pictures can be made on clear days and a light haze can be overcome by the proper choice of films (e.g., infrared types) and filters. Much more fundamental than haze, of course, is the fact that the height above the ground directly affects the size of the object on the photograph: if the pictures are taken from too high an altitude, too many details of the vegetation become unrecognizable and are lost.

Standard photographs, as prepared by some agencies of the United States government, have a scale of 1:20,000, but there is no policy that requires this scale and it often varies from case to case. The Toulouse Colloquium (GAUSSEN, 1961a) recommends in its Resolution No. 8 that aerial photographs on a scale of 1:15,000 be used for the general purposes of systematic vegetation mapping.

Obviously, the larger the scale of the photograph, the more accurate and the more detailed is its interpretation. The scale is therefore governed in part by the purpose of the vegetation map for which the photographs are taken. If, for instance, no more is required than the distinction of broadleaf trees from needleleaf trees, perhaps with a few height and density classes, as on some Canadian forestry maps, then a scale of 1:20,000 and even smaller is entirely feasible. The smaller scale implies a smaller cost and speedier progress. Where very large areas are involved, this may be an important consideration.

SEIBERT (1958) mapped the Pupplinger Au, a small area (about 4 square kilometers, or 1.6 square miles) in southern Germany. He used aerial photographs at a scale of 1:5,000, which permitted him to maintain a high degree of accuracy and to identify vegetation units even if these were very small. He also had at his disposal older aerial photographs at smaller scales. These revealed surfaces of open water, sandbanks, and gravel deposits without vegetation. Among the vegetation units, pine forests could readily be distinguished from shrub types. The density of the canopy and the degree of coverage could be determined without difficulty. It was therefore possible to assign each stand to a given phase of a sere, but it was not feasible to determine on the photographs which particular seres were involved. The large-scale vegetation map, prepared in 1956, was used to solve that problem. Different scales therefore served different purposes: the smaller scales permitted a quick general view while the large scale revealed the details.

The first and foremost consideration in making aerial photographs must be that the mapper can distinguish the required details in such clarity that all sources of error are reduced to a minimum.

What details are required depends on the individual case; there is no point in having a scale larger than necessary, as this needlessly increases the cost. The prospective author of a vegetation map will find it useful to examine a variety of aerial photographs to determine which scale is best adapted to his particular needs. Ultimately, the scale of the aerial photographs is affected by the scale of the planned vegetation map, and a careful author will see to it that the scale of the photographs is at least twice as large as the scale planned for the printed map.

Stereoscopy

The usefulness of aerial photographs is so much improved by employing a stereoscope that this is really an essential tool. A single photograph is equivalent to viewing the landscape through one eye. There is then a serious lack of depth which often makes it difficult to recognize objects or to interpret them correctly. Often an appreciation of the various vegetation types is altogether impossible on a single aerial photograph.

This problem is solved by viewing the landscape three-dimensionally, which is achieved through the use of a stereoscope and by viewing through it two photographs simultaneously, rather than only one. The stereoscope not only reveals the landscape in its full depth, it somewhat exaggerates this depth and thereby enables the viewer to correlate the vegetation even with minor variations in the topography. The value of a stereoscope in interpreting aerial photographs is so great that a vegetation mapper can ill afford to do without one.

A lens stereoscope can often be collapsed and carried in a pocket; it is relatively inexpensive and is most useful during field work; but it has the disadvantage that only a small area can be viewed at a time. In the laboratory a mirror stereoscope is preferable. While its cost is higher, it permits an analysis of a large area.

It can readily be appreciated that a three-dimensional viewing of aerial photographs is of singular value for the vegetation mapper. What, on a single photograph, appears as a uniform grey without depth distinctions is resolved by a stereoscope into individual layers of the vegetation, especially in deciduous forests. The relative size of trees and shrubs is readily distinguished. The relative length of the shadows of all trees and shrubs is often useful in analyzing vegetation types, forming a valuable supplement to the three-dimensional quality of the photographs when viewed through a stereoscope. The three-dimensional quality also aids greatly in identifying species, or at least genera, of trees and shrubs. The task of describing or interpreting an unknown object from a considerable distance involves many variables which differ in character among themselves and from one region to the next. It is therefore not feasible to devise one method for the interpretation of all aerial photographs.

Timing the Flight

The phenological variations require that the time for taking aerial photographs be carefully chosen. Some trees are easily recognized at one time, often for a limited period only, whereas other tree species can be identified more readily at other times; such optimal times may, however, overlap. The most strategic period for taking aerial photographs occurs therefore when the optimal times for the greatest number of species overlap. Late spring and autumn are good times for recognizing many deciduous tree species. Even different climax types of vegetation can sometimes be distinguished on aerial photographs only when the seasonal coloration is at its optimum, as was well demonstrated by AYASSE and MOLINIER (1955). The best time for many herbaceous plants is when they are in bloom, provided the photographs are taken from a low altitude. The tremendous advantage of color photography in photo-interpretation is too obvious to be stressed again.

HORVÁT (1961, p. 135) reported on a series of flights in the Mecsek Mountains in Hungary during the spring. On the resulting photographs he observed the sequence in which various species of forest trees foliate. With the help of this information he could establish five phytocenoses on the serial photographs.

TÜXEN (1961, p. 135) had four flights made over the areas of selected quadrangles. In contrast to HORVÁT, he distributed the flights through the year with one flight per season. This ruled out the fine gradations that HORVÁT was able to observe. However, TÜXEN's results were quite as satisfactory because of the unlike behavior of the various phytocenoses in different seasons. Tüxen was able to distinguish the phytocenoses with great accuracy by comparing the four series of aerial photographs.

Interpretation

It is more useful, in a given area, to consider all possible aspects, such as vegetation, relief, soil, water, field patterns, settlements, roads, etc., in their mutual relationships. The goal should always be to recognize a given type of landscape as an integrated unit of a variety of sites and plant communities. If this is done, it will frequently be possible to identify individual biotopes of the landscape, not so much because of their particular features but because they are recognized as a part of a larger integrated entity. A given landscape with its various biotopes is always characterized by a given set of potential natural phytocenoses and their substitute communities. Therefore, the observant mapper will sometimes be in the position to conclude from landscape features what plant community grows there, and at other times he can derive the site qualities directly from the phytocenoses observed on the photographs. Knowing the substitute communities of a given landscape, he can eliminate all others from his consideration when he analyzes the vegetation on the photographs, and thus arrive more readily at a proper interpretation.

KRAUSE (1955) gives some good examples from Germany, two of which may here be quoted. (1) A swampy meadow in a landscape complex of the beech forest (Fagetum) can only be a *Trisetum* meadow whereas a similar meadow in the landscape complex of the oak-hornbeam forests (Querceto-Carpinetum) must be an *Arrhenatherum* meadow. (2) The country road which is lined with birch trees and leads through the landscapes of the oak-birch communities (Querceto-Betuletum) is not likely to be flanked by fields of sugar beets or wheat but rather of rye, potatoes, or oats. Even the weed communities along fences and the like fit themselves into these larger combinations.

The two examples show how an understanding of landscape complexes will help in identifying features of the landscape on an aerial photograph. However, it takes much patient study to appreciate all the fine details of these relationships.

If the aerial photograph portrays a more or less unknown landscape, detailed field work is needed to produce the necessary information. In the end, this will permit a reasoned interpretation of the aerial photographs over a wider area. The more comprehensive and accurate the field work, the more satisfactory will be the interpretation of the photographs with regard to the entire landscape complex. After all, the preparation of the vegetation map must serve a purpose, and hence the interpretation of the vegetational features on the aerial photographs is a vital aspect of the usefulness of the map.

In identifying particular vegetation types, the color of the individual plant community is of considerable significance and, once established on a given series of photographs, becomes a very useful aid. The color is important for both woody and herbaceous plants and varies, of course, with the seasons.

In the middle and high latitudes, it is the broadleaf deciduous trees which help most in identification, because the colors of their foliage vary much from genus to genus (often species) and also changes with the seasons. In areas with a continental climate like the interior of northern North America, even some needleleaf evergreen forests seasonally change their hues so much that the variation becomes clearly visible.

In a black-and-white photograph, the color of the vegetation is only some shade of grey. This is also true if infrared photographs are used. The various tones of grey help a great deal in identifying plant communities. Phytocenoses of simple floristic composition or with a pronounced dominance of at most one or two species can often be identified with relative ease, and more unequivocably, than communities of great floristic complexity. Any phytocenoses that consist of more or less pure stands fall into this category, be they beech forests or cattail communities. But the tones of grey may not be used alone for identification. The same species may have very different tones at different ages and, according to SPURR (1948), young stands of white pine (*Pinus strobus*) are sometimes so light in color that they cannot be distinguished easily from broadleaf deciduous forests. Old white pines photograph nearly as dark as red pine or spruce. Similarly, in southern France, MOLINIER *et al.* (1951) were unable to distinguish a forest of beech (*Fagus silvatica*) from a forest of oak (*Quercus pubescentis*) on aerial photographs.

The texture of plant communities is an additional aid in identifying details. As it varies from fine to coarse or from smooth to rough, texture can be quite characteristic of certain vegetation types. But, like tone, it can vary within the same stand according to the relative location of the sun or the angle of its rays. Thus, a given community may have different tones of grey on slopes facing in different directions. A phytocenose may look dark on its eastern slope and light on its western slope. The proximity to the margin of the (vertical) photograph may have to be considered, too. The texture is brought about by the character of the surface of the vegetation, the typical forms of tree crowns, etc. In this manner, broad-crowned oaks (coarse texture) are readily distinguished from the narrower beeches (fine texture) and pastures have a rougher texture than the smooth lawns. The dense or open forest canopies are also reflected in the texture, the more open canopy having the coarser texture.

It must be stated emphatically that it is not feasible to make generalizations beyond rather narrow regional limits. The phenological sequence is not the same everywhere, nor is the rate of change uniform over large areas. In mountainous areas, special care must be taken in identifying plant communities during spring and autumn because those at lower elevations foliate earlier in the spring and defoliate later in the fall than similar communities at higher altitudes. Even slight altitudinal differences can retard or accelerate the ontogenetic phases of the various members of a plant community. In such cases, therefore, where a given vegetation type covers the sides of a mountain range, it may be quite uniform in the landscape and yet on the photograph seem to consist of two or even three types rather than one, if the photograph was taken in the spring or fall.

A vertical aerial photograph shows only the uppermost layer of the vegetation whereas the lower layers remain concealed. This is all the more true, the denser the uppermost layer is. If the closed canopy is part of a plant community the structure of which is well known, the lower synusias can be expected to exist in concordance with the phytocenological nature of the plant community. Such knowledge must be very sure and be based on much experience. In all instances, careful ground inspection is imperative. In any case, it is important to check the structure of the vegetation frequently wherever a dense canopy prevails. Although winter photographs of deciduous forests permit the mapper to look through the canopy, he may not see much. The herbaceous synusia is not visible in the winter, and when no snow is on the ground it is even difficult to see the lower layers of the woody vegetation and to distinguish between trees, shrubs, and dwarf shrubs. If, on the other hand, deep snow covers the ground, it may very well bury all lower synusias and conceal them.

There is no way to formulate one method of photo-interpretation that can answer all needs. The specific character of each landscape, the particular requirements of given purposes, and last but not least, the available means necessitate a choice. As a general rule, information on the greatest possible number of the various landscape features should be gathered and synthesized into an integrated landscape mosaic.

It is imperative to check in the field a series of carefully chosen sections of the vegetation because these will be the key to the generalized interpretation of the whole set of photographs. Photo-interpretation is thus assured of accuracy because field inspection has proved the nature of the inspected item. This knowledge is then employed to establish the identity of items of the same character elsewhere. Proper photo-interpretation requires such a key, which includes appropriate information on the totality of the landscape features: surface relief, light contrasts and variations, boundaries, size relations, and, in short, every correlation between elements of the landscape and those observable on the photograph. Such a key is limited in its applicability both regionally and seasonally. Before exploiting the photographs, it is therefore important to check very carefully to what extent the key is valid.

The vegetation mapper will find it useful to study a variety of keys to acquaint himself with some of the possibilities. REY (1957a) prepared such a key for France, and RITCHIE (1958) presented one for an area in the southern spruce forest zone of Manitoba. The latter is here reproduced in part to illustrate the ways of correlating phytocenoses with their tone, texture, and stereoscopic appearance on aerial photographs (Table 4).

The most successful use of aerial photographs requires, first of all, a careful study of the area involved. Such a study should be based on the literature as well as on the aerial photographs. For such a study, it is particularly useful to have photographs taken in all seasons. The chief task of this preparatory work is to establish the areas and items that must be inspected in the field. These should include characteristic examples of all types of vegetation and site. It is also of fundamental importance that a correlation between vegetation and site be established whenever possible. Detailed information on such correlations will permit the mapper in some instances to identify vegetation types on the basis of his knowledge of site characteristics; in other cases he can deduce the site qualities from the vegetation types. Usually, it is not feasible to identify the exact character of a plant community on an aerial photograph, especially in a forest with a relatively smooth, unbroken canopy; all lower synusias remain concealed here. But changes in the vegetation are indicated by changes in topography (hence in exposure, slope, soil profile, etc.) because it can be assumed that any appreciable change in the environmental conditions will result in a change in the plant cover. Where the relief is bold, important conclusions with regard to the vegetation can be drawn readily, as for instance the broad flood plains of the rivers in eastern Kansas, the steep bluffs along the margins of these flood plains, and the rolling uplands on the interfluves.

The practical steps the mapper must take during the first preliminary phase of his work in the laboratory are:

1. Outline on the aerial photograph all units of vegetation that differ from one another physiognomically. This permits the mapper to distinguish forests, even certain forest types, fields, meadows and pastures, orchards, etc.

   If the mapper has only one or two sets of aerial photographs at his disposal, he is well advised to cover the photograph in use with a transparent plastic material or acetate, attached with masking tape. He must number the plastic cover with the number of the photograph, and

Table 4. Key to Aerial Photographs of the Southern Spruce Forest Zone of Manitoba *

Vegetation Type	Tone	Texture	Stereoscopic Appearance
Closed black spruce forest	Darkest tones, dark grey to black	Even stippling	Individual trees visible: tall and slender
Closed mixed spruce-birch forest	Even dark grey with light spots (birches)	Diffuse matrix, coarse stippling	Medium-size trees: scattered individual crowns of white birch
Open pine forest (seral)	Even light grey	Very fine, almost diffuse stippling	Small trees, diffuse outlines
Open pine forest with spruce	Even light grey with patches of dark grey	Fine stippling with small areas of coarse stippling	As for above but with groups of individuals of black spruce apparent
Closed pine forest on sand	Medium grey	Faintly stippled	Flat crown surface in which individuals are not conspicuous
Open pine forest on outcrop	Light grey on white	Finely stippled darker patches on smooth, lighter background	Individual trees with diffuse outlines: structure and relief of bedrock often visible
Mature birchwood	Medium grey with light spots	Smooth surface with fluffy appearance	Undulating crown surface of merging trees
Muskeg	Light grey	Diffuse background with coarse stippling	Small trees: light, flat background
Open bog	Lighter grey	Smooth surface	Surface without features, except in rare cases of strängmoor
Aquatic vegetation	White grey on black of open water	Smooth surface	Featureless: margins and islands often reniform
Mixed white spruce-poplar forest	Dark grey	Coarse stippling	Tallest trees: spires of spruce and crowns of poplar clearly visible

* From RITCHIE (1958).

then draw all outlines, etc., on it rather than directly on the photograph itself.

2. The mapper definitely identifies whatever he can recognize clearly and beyond doubt. This may include such items as cornfields, vineyards, truck farms, etc.

3. He tentatively establishes the structure of the observed vegetation types, especially their height and density. He also determines environmental features like slope and exposure.

The result of this laboratory work is the basis for the next phase, the field work. Some items are definitely recognized, others only tentatively so. Their outline and location can already be shown on a topographic map.

This preliminary work is followed by the field study. All vegetation types are carefully and systematically analyzed, using the aerial photographs to locate them rapidly and to establish or confirm their boundaries. This field work serves also to collect information for the key. It is important not to overlook details, including the characteristic sequence of contact and substitute communities, especially if they cover only small areas which are difficult to identify on the photographs; such communities may be important indicators. Once the field work has been completed it should be possible to identify correctly every item on the aerial photographs. The purpose of this field work has been accomplished when, for all plant communities of the area, their photographic appearance has been established (i.e., how they look on the photographs) as well as their site relations (i.e., on what sort of site they occur). A good key permits the mapper to correctly interpret his photographs. However, the interpretation of aerial photographs must not be confused with the study of plant communities, for the two are by no means equivalent.

The next step, back in the office or laboratory, is to extend the now available information from the inspected units to the entire area and on this basis draw the vegetation map directly from the photographs.

A major purpose of photo-interpretation is to gain an insight into the vegetation, and through it into the landscape. Such an insight permits the mapper to recognize in the vegetation the relation of the individual parts to the whole. This, in turn, permits the synthesis of the landscape: the mapper can observe the broad site relations, and also the broad and simple features of the natural landscape, in spite of the great modifications and subdivisions of the cultural vegetation, if he knows which of the very unlike substitute communities in a variegated landscape belong together through their site relations.

Without doubt, aerial photography offers the vegetation mapper great advantages. However, sources of error exist, too, and must be recognized. Assuming that the photographs are of adequate quality and scale, it is important to test in the field the observations made on the photographs. Such field tests must be made just as often as possible, especially if the vegetation has not been examined with great care prior to mapping it. Where large-scale maps are to reveal the plant communities in detail, it is necessary to inspect every stand individually because even the best photographs cannot be expected to disclose the finer features of the herbaceous ground cover.

McCONNELL and GARVIN (1956) mapped the vegetation of the state of Massachusetts on the basis of aerial photographs at a scale of 1:20,000. Later the information was transferred to topographic maps of the United States Geological Survey at 1:31,680, or 2 inches to the mile. Their interest was focused on wildlife research and management and, hence, on the actual vegetation. In forested areas, they distinguished units with more than 80 per cent needleleaf evergreen forests by the letter "S" and broadleaf deciduous with an "H," and combinations of these by "SH" if the former occupied more than 50 per cent, "HS" if the latter predominated. They established five height classes, up to (1) 20, (2) 40, (3) 60, (4) 80, and (5) 100 feet, each. A sixth class indicates uneven heights, with three or more height classes represented. Finally, three density classes (crown cover) up to (A) 50, (B) 80, and (C) 100 per cent coverage completed the forest classification. Thus a formula of "H4B" means that at least 80 per cent of the forest consists of broadleaf deciduous trees, and that it has an average height of 60–80 feet and covers 51–80 per cent of the ground.

Other distinguishable items include (1) open land, partly reclaimed by forest; (2) continuous, intensively cultivated farmland; (3) intensively cultivated farmland interspersed with stone walls, hedgerows, small forested areas, patches of abandoned land, or wet land; (4) abandoned fields reverting to forests; (5) productive orchards; (6) abandoned orchards (exceptionally good wildlife habitat!); (7–11) five types of freshwater areas (meadows, marshes, etc.); (12) coastal saline areas. Interestingly enough, the authors could establish the various freshwater marshes, etc., on the aerial photographs but failed to distinguish the five coastal saline types of vegetation recognized by the Fish and Wildlife Service classification of wet land. The five coastal saline types therefore had to be merged into one type.

Sometimes such units can be enriched by introducing structural or floristic elements or both, but this may not be feasible uniformly throughout the state.

The result reflects therefore the information which could be used to establish cover types, i.e., units of actual vegetation applicable to the state of Massachusetts as a whole. Predictably, the usefulness of the maps extended far beyond the wildlife research and management circles who initiated their preparation.

The vegetation mapper must always remain aware of the important fact that the key to the vegetation types may be a source of serious errors even though it was prepared with great care because it can fail badly to take local circumstances into account.

FOSBERG (1958) believes that the legitimate purpose of aerial photographs is to make preliminary vegetation sketch maps, outlining areas and revealing similarities and differences between types, and that this is even more true in the tropics than in other regions. This statement can be expanded by observing that vegetation maps based on aerial photographs and adequate ground inspection form the safest and soundest foundation of vegetation studies anywhere on the globe. An author desiring to study the vegetation of any given area will obtain particularly satisfactory results if he prepares a detailed vegetation map as a first step and bases his map on aerial photographs. He will then base his investigations on the map and on the observations he made in preparing it. To prepare a vegetation map after the study has been completed is to deprive oneself of the most enlightening study method yet devised.

9

Patterns, Colors, and Symbols

The method of presenting vegetation and its units and divisions is an important feature of the vegetation map because the clarity and legibility of the map depend on it. The primary purpose for using black-and-white patterns or color is, of course, to distinguish between areas of different types of vegetation.

Letters and Numbers

In the case of black-and-white patterns, there are three basic approaches, each of which permits a considerable number of variations. The first method employs letters, numbers, and combinations of these. Letters can be used in the form of capitals and lower case letters, italics, etc. Numbers can be shown as Roman or Arabic numerals, and the combinations of all these make for a vast variety. The possibilities are further enlarged by arranging the letters and numbers as straight sequences, fractions, or in some other form. The place of a number in such a fraction can then be given a definite meaning as well. This is illustrated (Figure 17) by the method developed by A. E. WIESLANDER (1949, 1955).

The method of using letters or numbers to distinguish different types of vegetation permits the production of vegetation maps at a low cost. The black color is used for everything: vegetation boundaries, symbols, grid, frame, title, legend, etc., and hence only one plate is required for printing.

The chief disadvantage of the method is that it fails to show at a glance the distribution of the various vegetation types. True, it is easy enough to establish the character of the vegetation at any given point. But in order to become aware of the distribution of any particular vegetation type, it is necessary to read all the symbols on the map. The reader is obliged to color by hand those types that are important to him, or indeed all of them, and that is time-consuming.

Shading and Patterns

Another method to distinguish different types of vegetation is by using different shades of grey. These may range from black to white and as they, too, require only one printing plate, the cost is not high. The shades of grey simulate different colors and can be very effective. The areal distribution of vegetation types is quite clear. However, the number of possibilities is relatively small because the various shades of grey must differ enough to allow a real contrast between them. Otherwise it is very difficult to read the map, and misinterpretations are made easily. JENKS and KNOS (1961) have studied this problem in detail. Contrasts result from varying the features of the patterns, especially darkness, texture (coarseness), and the design of pattern units (Figure 5).

A map can be made more meaningful by using the shades of grey in a given sequence. Rather than at random, they can be arranged in the legend in such a manner that an advance from dark to light coincides with a progression in one or more vegetational features, e.g., density, xericity, etc. It is then possible to see at a glance how such features are distributed, and this aspect makes the various shades of grey more valuable.

Finally, as a third possibility to show the vegetation only in black on white, there is the large variety of patterns. These consist of dots of various sizes, arranged regularly or irregularly, dashes thick and thin, fine lines and broad stripes running horizontally, vertically, diagonally, and in combinations of these. In addition, there are crosses, stars, triangles, squares, and a host of symbols of every description.

Unless the patterns are selected very judiciously, the map will be a bewildering jumble and the character of the vegetation cannot be determined readily. If at all possible, here, too, there should be a sequence from dark to light, meaningful in terms of some aspects of the vegetation, but such a sequence is difficult to achieve when many types of symbols are used.

Another method may be mentioned parenthetically. This is to print the names of the vegetation types directly on the map, as was done by LOUIS (1939) on his map of Turkey; he uses no patterns of any kind and neither colors nor symbols. At first sight, this method looks interesting enough, but it is not very practical and has rarely been adopted.

Color

A new world is opened up by the introduction of color. It is as if a composer of piano sonatas had suddenly discovered the dazzling world of symphonies. Colors occur in great variety, are readily distinguishable, and

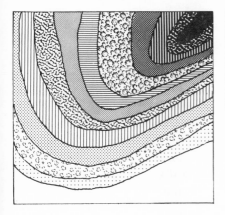 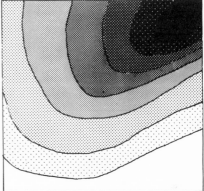

(a) The contrast between the features of the patterns, especially in darkness, texture, and design, aids the reader in distinguishing each pattern from every other one with ease.

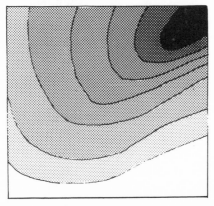

(b) The contrast between the features of the pattern is slight and it is difficult for the reader's eye to carry the correct pattern from the legend to the map.

Figure 5

can be applied flat or in patterns, in combinations, or as overprinted symbols. They can be mixed and superimposed. Often they can be made even more effective by simultaneous use of black or colored patterns and symbols and by judicious use of white (GAUSSEN, 1945b).

Just as there are various possibilities of applying black-and-white patterns, there are also several approaches to the use of color. By far the most common use of color is simply to select arbitrarily a variety of contrasting colors in order to facilitate the distinction of one vegetation type from the next (DRUDE, 1905; WANGERIN, 1915; RÜBEL, 1916; WAGNER, 1948). This is a rather primitive method but also the simplest. Indeed, it is not easy to raise the use of color to a higher level, and SCHARFETTER (1932, p. 157) repeats RÜBEL's (1916) advice urging prospective authors to follow the early leaders in using their color scale, possibly with slight modifications, rather than introducing new scales, even though these colors were selected arbitrarily, not to say accidentally. Their continued use implies no more than a "tradition" which lacks a scientific foundation. RÜBEL (1916) proposed eleven colors for the vegetation of Switzerland. Of these, five are for meadows and bogs, three for needleleaf forests, and one each for deciduous forests, dwarf shrubs, and cultivated land. This scheme was not generally adopted because of its obvious limitations.

EMBERGER and MOLINIER (1955), on the Carte des groupements végétaux de la France, tried to give their color selections a stronger foundation by basing them on a recommendation by the 6th International Botanical Congress (Amsterdam, 1935), to the effect that floristically related plant communities are shown in related colors. But they circumnavigate this reef by stating that such must not be done at the expense of common sense. Thereby, they are once again free to use colors as they see fit. EMBERGER and MOLINIER use the classification of vegetation by BRAUN-BLANQUET exclusively. Hence they assign one color to each order that appears on the map, and the various alliances are shown in different hues of the color of that order to which they belong. Smaller units, such as associations, are shown by the color of their respective alliances with the initials of the association overprinted in black, for example, "Q.i." for Quercetum ilicis and "Q.p." for Quercetum pubescentis. Where an alliance is represented by a single association, the overprinted letter symbols are omitted. Within this arrangement, the darkest colors are assigned to alliances of the smallest areal extent. This permits the reader to see these items quickly and clearly even though they occupy only a small area. But at times the authors will also be guided by the dynamics of the vegetation and give the darkest colors to those communities that are closest to the climax. A Quercetum ilicis climax is therefore shown by a darker green than a Quercetum cocciferae, a seral phase.

In a vague way, the colors are assigned to the alliances according to the degree of xericity of their sites, but this idea is not applied rigidly and experimentation continues. Broadly speaking, the use of colors is as follows: blue and purple for more or less hydrophilous (grassland) communities and aquatic associations; red, orange, and yellow for xeric communities; and green for forests.

Transitions between two alliances are shown with alternating bars of the colors of the respective alliances; these bars are relatively broad. In a mosaic-like irregular distribution, the color of the most extensive alliance is used as a base and the less extensive alliance is shown in its own color in overprinted circles. Pioneer communities are shown by narrow vertical bars. Regressive communities (e.g., due to erosion) are indicated by narrow horizontal bars.

More recently, EMBERGER (1961) showed that the Service de la carte des groupements végétaux in Montpellier has changed its approach to the use of color. The influence of GAUSSEN in nearby Toulouse resulted in adopting color schemes based on ecological rather than floristic criteria.

Thus, vegetation units on biotopes with similar environmental conditions receive similar colors. This offers the advantage that ecological relations and affinities become readily evident, and the vegetation map thereby becomes more useful. This approach to the use of color permits a high degree of accuracy in interpreting the vegetation if the scale is very large and, hence, the area involved is correspondingly small.

The large scales used in Montpellier (1:5,000 to 1:20,000) lend themselves well to such exact analyses. However, as the scale shrinks this accuracy fades. Obviously, a given color cannot show the degree of xericity on a vegetation map of the United States in the same manner as on a vegetation map of a single Kansas county. At the same time, the reader must always be aware of the fact that a yellow hue in Oregon does not signify the same xericity as in Texas, even though the vegetation maps of Oregon and Texas may be done at the same scale. The meaning of colors changes when ecological conditions of one region differ from those of another.

SCHMID feels free to select his colors at random, but being artistically inclined, he is careful first to establish color harmonies, so as to avoid any clashing colors. As a result, his map of Switzerland (SCHMID, 1948) is restful to the eye and easy to read.

Sometimes a given color system is best limited to a given range of map scales. Beyond this range, the system may be less successful because the change in detail alters the problems of presentation. If, for example, such a system is found to be well suited to scales from 1:200,000 to 1:1,000,000, as for instance the system proposed by GAUSSEN (1949, 1953), then it cannot be expected to do as well on the map of the Elbe Valley at 1:5,000 (WALTHER, 1957) because the entire map would have but a single color.

Colors come in a variety of tints. For instance, red occurs in carmine, rose, pink, lake, vermilion, and others, and these tints, in turn, can be varied by using them flat, ruled, stippled, or in some other fashion. In this manner it is possible to correlate colors with vegetation features by varying character. For example, various tints of green may be employed for deciduous forests according to what species dominate the forest (KÜCHLER, 1956a).

RÜBEL (1916) suggested that colors be selected in such a manner that they correspond to the actual colors of the vegetation. This same idea was much later tried again by BURKE and SHELTON (1953). But such an approach is rarely feasible because it ignores the seasonal color changes of the vegetation as well as a large number of details.

LÜDI (1921) introduced an interesting idea by correlating colors with succession. Pioneer stages are shown in shades of grey, seral communities in shades of dull green, and only the various climax types have their own different and uncoordinated colors. Anthropogenic vegetations, as illustrated by certain types of meadows, are shown on the map in a very vivid green, thereby indicating that they are neither seral nor climax communities and basically different from natural phases of succession. Ideas such as LÜDI's can be developed to meet a great variety of needs (cf. Chapter 17).

KUHNHOLTZ-LORDAT, in his historical approach to vegetation mapping at very large scales, has devised his own color scheme, although he was strongly influenced by the work of GAUSSEN, who works at much smaller scales (MARRES, 1954). A local color scheme relating the various phytocenoses to their respective substrata was developed by DUVIGNEAUD (1961). Applied only on maps at 1:50,000 and in a limited region, the number of phytocenoses is relatively restricted, yet the author was able to adapt GAUSSEN's ecological ideas to his area with a considerable degree of success.

It is always best to select light colors. They are usually more pleasing, make a map more legible, and are especially useful in connection with overprinted symbols. The latter are difficult to recognize if they are printed on a dark color.

Color-Number Combinations

If the number of colors on a map is large, it becomes difficult to distinguish between them, especially when the eye must go back and forth between the legend and the map. In such a case, it is best to number the legend items and repeat these numbers in the respective areas on the map. Any doubt about the color can then quickly be dispelled by referring to the number. Such numbers are not symbols in the strict sense, but they compete with the symbols for space and attention. KÜCHLER (1953c) presented a vegetation map of the United States on which he used colors for the physiognomy of the vegetation, and black overprinted number symbols to indicate the dominant genera. In this manner the physiognomic and floristic aspects of all vegetation types were kept strictly separated and could everywhere be identified with ease. In a later publication, KÜCHLER (1964) again combines various unrelated colors with numbers. However, this time, he is noticeably influenced by GAUSSEN. While insisting on a free choice, he admits that Gaussenian ideas have affected his selection of colors. On this, his second map of the United States, the colors have therefore technically no other purpose than to assist the reader in distinguishing one vegetation type from the next. Supposedly, it is incidental that there are parallels between KÜCHLER's choice of colors and GAUSSEN's system. The influence of the French master is nevertheless striking.

Similar principles have been adopted by Soviet vegetation mappers on their small-scale maps (LAVRENKO and SOCHAVA, 1956, and LAVRENKO and RODIN, 1957).

Gaussen's Use of Color

The most advanced and refined method of selecting colors yet devised is that by GAUSSEN. His first masterpiece was his map of France in four sheets at 1:1,000,000 (GAUSSEN, 1945b); the delicacy of the colors and the manner of their arrangement make it a joy to behold this map, especially if the four sheets are mounted together. But GAUSSEN is probably known best (and rightly so) for his map series at 1:200,000 of France and some areas overseas. The originality of this cartographic method consists in giving ecological values to the colors: blue represents moisture, black implies shade, etc. By superposition of well-chosen colors it becomes possible to present on paper a certain picture of the complexity of the ecological factors. When two factors have analogous physiological effects they are shown by similar colors. If the preponderance of one ecological factor becomes manifest in a much stronger color, the strength of the other colors (those representing other factors) may be decreased correspondingly.

GAUSSEN (1949, 1953, 1958, 1961b) has given detailed instructions on the use of colors. By employing colors for physiologically effective environmental factors, he establishes a series of what might be termed "plant climates" with implied natural vegetation. The color shows the more permanent aspect of the habitat, and the physiognomic character of the vegetation is shown by the manner in which a color is applied: flat for forest, ruled for heath and other shrub, stippled for grassland, etc. The colors, therefore, have a triple function: they set off one type of vegetation from another; they indicate climatic conditions; and they show the physiognomy of the actual vegetation. Similar colors imply similar climatic conditions. The dominants are shown as letter symbols in black where the background color is light and in white where the background is dark.

In transitions between two or more vegetation types, the colors of each type are given. The colors are arranged in alternating vertical bars, and the relative width of each such bar indicates the degree of dominance of one vegetation type over another.

GAUSSEN leaves all cultivated areas white, and on this white background, the messicol vegetation is shown in the form of symbols. These are usually letter symbols but not always. Letters are here used to great advantage, especially as they are the initials of the represented items. Their size and shape imply statistical values, and their color reveals the ecological affinities and ranges of the crops.

GAUSSEN therefore employs colors for multiple purposes, i.e., for the natural vegetation and its substitute communities, for physiognomy and floristic dominants, the cultivated crops and their ecological optima. GAUSSEN's imagination and genius for employing and organizing colors have never been matched, and authors of vegetation maps are urged to study GAUSSEN's instructions and his maps at 1:200,000 and 1:1,000,000 with the greatest care before embarking on their own color scheme.

Molinier's Use of Color

A novel approach to the use of color was occasioned by the work of ROGER MOLINIER (1960, 1961, 1963) and his collaborators. MOLINIER is not only a phytocenologist in the usual sense of this term; he is also a marine biocenologist who maps the biotic communities on the ocean floor. In view of the fact that many animals of the shallow seas and continental shelves are sessile in character, it follows that the mapper must concern himself with biocenoses, i.e., communities of both plants and animals, rather than limit his mapping work to phytocenoses. On land, where color schemes may be related to the xericity of the sites of the phyto-cenoses, it is usual to relate this feature to the colors of the spectrum so that red and orange are used for the most drought-resistant communities and blue and purple for those that constantly require large amounts of water. This approach is, of course, meaningless in a marine environment and, as a result, MOLINIER replaced the water factor with the light factor. The intensity of light declines with growing depth and this declining intensity is related in the color scale to a movement from red toward blue and purple, the latter corresponding to the smallest available amounts of light in the greatest depths below sea level. But MOLINIER found that sea level is not a satisfactory boundary and that it does not serve well to dif-ferentiate between unlike communities. He, therefore, divided the spec-trum into two sections and reserved the range from red to green for ter-restrial phytocenoses and the section from green to purple for marine biocenoses of growing depth. His map of the Cap Corse is the classical example of this approach.

Choosing Appropriate Color Schemes

The significance of colors and their standardization or lack of it was well illustrated at the exhibition of vegetation maps held in connection with the International Botanical Congress at Montreal, Canada, in 1959. KÜCHLER (1960a) made the following observations:

On many maps, the colors have no purpose other than to distinguish one vegetation type from the next, as on the maps of the Congo, e.g., the fascinating vegetation map of Kwango (DEVRED, 1955). Sometimes a certain reasoning can be detected in the selection and use of the colors, as for example on the three vegetation maps of southeastern Mount Desert Island, Maine (KÜCHLER, 1956a), but here, too, the choice was essentially arbitrary. In contrast to this, the maps by GAUSSEN of France reveal a carefully developed method of selecting colors so as to show more: the selection and application of colors inform the reader on the ecology and physiognomy of the vegetation. Thus these vegetation maps were greatly enriched.

The following examples will illustrate some of the contrasts in the use of colors on the exhibited vegetation maps.

1. The maps of the Soviet Union (LAVRENKO and SOCHAVA, 1956) and of the Labrador Peninsula (HARE, 1959) both show the vegetation of the Far North with tundra and types with sparse plant growth amidst deserts of rock and gravel. On the Russian map, blue colors have been chosen for these vegetation types, wheras on the map of Labrador the analogous types are shown in red and yellow.

2. The tropical rain forest is done in blue on the vegetation map of Africa (KEAY, 1959); thus it has the same color as parts of the arctic tundra on the Soviet maps! HUECK (1960) presents the tropical rain forest of Venezuela in green whereas the color scheme of GAUSSEN requires it to be in purple.

A discussion of the choice of colors makes it quite clear that methods like that of GAUSSEN offer great advantages on maps at medium scales, even though it may be necessary to adjust them to different regions. In contrast to this are the vegetation maps at large scales, where an analogous choice of colors is no longer feasible. Under the influence of local conditions and circumstances it becomes inevitable that the choice of colors and their use must differ more or less from the world-wide systems.

In general, it has so far not been feasible to develop a color scheme for vegetation maps that can be applied in all regions and at all scales. Indeed, such a scheme is not feasible because some maps show only vegetation whereas on others it may be linked to a host of unrelated features. On the next page follows a listing of vegetation maps on which their authors have related plant communities to one or more environmental factors, or on which they have limited the map content strictly to vegetation. They also illustrate some of the difficulties in devising a universally acceptable color scheme.

DAVIS (1943), southern Florida: vegetation and geology
GAUSSEN (1948), Perpignan: vegetation and climate
HUECK (1960), Venezuela: vegetation only (physiognomic)
KÜCHLER (1964), U.S.A.:   vegetation only (physiognomic and
                                          floristic)
TRAPNELL (1948), Northern Rhodesia: vegetation and soils
TÜXEN (1956a), Baltrum: vegetation only (floristic)
WIESLANDER (1934), Ramona, Calif.:   vegetation, fire, and economics

Insistence on one color scheme that must be applied to all vegetation maps
is therefore futile and, in fact, quite undesirable. There is, after all, only
one spectrum, and it must be applied to all the maps listed above and to
all others. It is therefore quite inevitable that a given color will have different implications on different maps. This was demonstrated years ago at
the Bundesstelle für Vegetationskartierung in Germany (TÜXEN, 1963, p.
114).

It is best that authors remain free to use colors as they wish. The Toulouse Colloquium (GAUSSEN, 1961) urges them, no matter what plan they
may wish to follow, to devise a method which is logical with regard to the
distribution of colors as well as their intensities. The Toulouse Colloquium also recommended (Resolution No. 10) that on maps at medium
and small scales the height and density of the vegetation be correlated
with the colors. Accordingly, the colors should be darker, the taller and
denser the phytocenoses are, and lighter, the lower and more open they
are. Colored symbols on a white background are considered specially
effective for all forms of messicol vegetation.

Whatever an author of vegetation maps may think of these recommendations, the following observations seem to hold true anywhere and for
all types of vegetation maps: A systematic and well-reasoned approach to
the use of colors is most desirable, and as far as is feasible, an author
should keep his colors light. He should feel encouraged to enrich his colored maps with symbols but use them sparingly. Beyond this, he should
permit himself plenty of time to experiment with colors and color
schemes; he will find this both revealing and rewarding.

The geologists have solved the color problem for their maps by using a
one-dimensional system as implied in the time sequence of the geological
formations. Such an approach is not possible in vegetation mapping because phytocenoses cannot be arranged in a one-dimensional system.

Use of Symbols

There have been several references to the use of symbols. As the name
implies, these signs of different character symbolize what can be shown by
other means only in a less satisfactory way if at all. Symbols may indicate
individual taxa or entire phytocenoses. What a symbol represents usually

covers such a small area that it is not feasible to portray its exact outline. Often these areas are so small that they should be suppressed altogether. Whether a feature is shown by a symbol or in some other fashion is thus a question of scale. A symbol, of course, covers a certain area on the map, but it also implies that its true area stands in no relation to that on the map. It is therefore "off-scale" and cannot serve as a basis for measurements.

The overprinting of black symbols on black-and-white patterns should be avoided as the reader finds it difficult to read and hence to use such a map. On a colored map, symbols may be black or in color. Black symbols are difficult to see on dark colors, and colored symbols are not easily distinguished from surrounding colors if the color contrast is weak. The author must therefore be very careful with the selection and placement of his symbols.

GAUSSEN (1936), RÜBEL (1916), TROCHAIN (1961), and others have introduced black symbols of given shapes, and assigned one each to the most common species of their regions (Figure 6). Symbols of this kind are also used extensively on the Soviet vegetation maps by LAVRENKO and SOCHAVA (1956) and others. This idea would be even more useful if the phytocenological authorities had agreed on what symbol to adopt for which species, but such a general agreement has not been reached so far. A map on which the vegetation is shown by symbols only is difficult to read. If, on the other hand, the vegetation is shown in color, a judicious use of black symbols can greatly enrich the map without lowering its legibility. WIESLANDER (1937), on his colored vegetation maps of California, uses black letter symbols for species. He thus shows the dominant species of every plant community, using letter combinations of capitals and lower case letters and thin lines above or below the letters to cope with the wealth of species. Colored symbols have been employed with great success by GAUSSEN (1948) but they are expensive. KÜCHLER (1956a) and TROLL (1939) have also employed colored symbols in order to portray the geographical distribution of some life forms or taxa more graphically.

The spacing of symbols can be done in two ways. It may be irregular, possibly implying that the position of a symbol on the map corresponds to the actual location in the field. Where numerous stands of a plant community permeate an extensive vegetation type, it is clearer and simpler to have the symbols spaced evenly throughout the area involved. In neither case may the symbols be so crowded as to affect the legibility of the map adversely.

Symbols can be given statistical values by varying their character, size, and density (number per unit area). The CANADIAN FOREST SERVICE (1948) and GAUSSEN (1948) have offered good examples of this method (Table 5).

Symbols may represent taxa which occur sparsely while colors show

GYMNOSPERMS

Abies	cephalonica		Picea	excelsa	
	pectinata			pungens	
	Pinsapo				
			Pinus	Cembra	
Arbres de parc (conifères)				Halepensis	
				Lar. austriaca	
Biota	orientalis			Lar. corsica	
Callitris	quadrivalvis			L. mauretan	
				L. Salzmanni	
Cedrus	atlantica			maritima	
	Libani			mesogeensis	
Cunningh	sinensis			Mughus	
				Pumilio	
Cupressus	arizonica			pinea	
	Lambertiana			silvestris	
	sempervirens			uncinata	
Ephedra	distachya			insignis	
	nebrodensis			rigida	
				Strobus	
Juniperus	communis		Pins de reboisement		
	nana				
	Oxycedrus		Pseudotsuga	Douglasii	
	phoenicea			glauca	
	Sabina				
	thurifera		Taxodium	distichum	
Larix	europaea		Taxus	baccata	
	leptolepis		Wellingtonia	gigantea	

Figure 6. Examples of Gaussen's symbols for various species.

Table 5. Informational Use of Colors and Symbols on
Canadian Forestry Maps

Shown in Color	Shown as Overprinted Symbols	
Softwood above 30 feet	*Crown cover:*	*Height:*
Hardwood above 30 feet	A: 10– 30%	1: up to 30 feet
Mixed above 30 feet	B: 30– 50%	2: 30 to 50 feet
Softwood below 30 feet	C: 50– 70%	3: 50 to 70 feet
Hardwood below 30 feet	D: 70–100%	4: 70 to 100 feet
Mixed below 30 feet		

these same taxa when they form the bulk of the vegetation. For instance, a spruce forest may be shown by a green color, but in addition, the legend can show spruce by a symbol. If, then, an area is covered with a spruce forest, it appears on the map in green. If, on the other hand, a beech forest has a significant admixture of spruce, then the beech forest is shown by its own color with spruce symbols overprinted on it. Of course, the use of symbols is by no means limited to taxa; symbols may just as well be employed to indicate the occurrence of plant communities, especially those which cover small areas but are scattered through a larger formation at a relatively high frequency.

To assure the legibility of the map, care must be taken to use symbols sparingly so as not to overload the map or to overshadow the colors on which they are printed. A cluttered map is difficult to read and its usefulness is correspondingly impaired. But a vegetation map can be greatly enriched by symbols, especially when these are well selected and sparingly used. A good example for a judicious use of symbols is the map of Central Asia (LAVRENKO and RODIN, 1956).

In a very real sense, patterns and colors determine the character of the vegetation map. In a way, they "make" the map. On a colored map, the colors are the most obvious feature of the map. With such prominence, colors should be used for the most prominent items to be portrayed. Patterns and symbols are secondary and should therefore be employed to designate items of secondary importance.

When an author must decide on a color scheme for a new vegetation map, he will find it wise to study first the use of patterns, colors, and symbols on other vegetation maps. He will thus become aware of a great variety of possibilities in applying them. But not every vegetation map is a model. The author can therefore learn from past mistakes in judgment and execution, too, and so, perhaps, avoid these on his own map.

10

Boundaries and Transitions

The chief task of a vegetation map is to show the areal distribution of different types of vegetation. This implies that unlike types will be contiguous and, on the map, separated by a boundary. The author of vegetation maps must therefore concern himself with the problem of boundaries.

A boundary separates two different types of vegetation. It is not enough to observe one type in the field and draw its boundary. The accuracy of the map is much greater, if the character of the surrounding communities has also been determined before the boundaries between the types are established.

When the vegetation mapper observes the vegetation, his task is to establish mappable vegetation units which must fit the purposes of his map. His endeavor to identify the vegetation units inevitably leads to a search for their boundaries, and sometimes these are not easy to find. This may be due to the fact that a boundary is actually rather vague. It may also depend on the observer's point of view concerning vegetation types. For instance, the Wisconsin school of thought under the leadership of JOHN CURTIS developed the idea of the continuum, which implies in many instances a denial of the existence of vegetational boundaries. At the other extreme stands TÜXEN, who draws boundaries with remarkable precision, based at times on the presence or absence of a single species. Where the area of occurrence of such a species ends there ends the vegetation type, too (see below).

The mapper's power of observation must be keen if he is not to misinterpret what he sees. An example will illustrate this. If a vegetation mapper works in high altitudes he will recognize timberline as one of the most important vegetation boundaries of his area. The location of timberline can easily be determined and often it is a very clear line, especially when viewed from a distance, as for instance, from one mountain to the next across a valley.

If the mapper asks himself (as he should) why the timberline is where he observes it, he may discover that he cannot necessarily show it on his map in the place where he found it in the field. The alpine meadows above the forests are often fine pastures; the forests below them are rarely as fine. Hence it has been the tendency of local herders to extend the alpine meadows downward at the expense of the forest. If the vegetation mapper plans a map of the natural vegetation and places the forest boundary where he observed it, then his natural forest vegetation will be more restricted than it should be, as the alpine meadows will be overextended.

The location of timberline can have other causes and need not be due to climate or to man. For instance, the forests on the eastern slopes of the Sierra Nevada in California along the Owens River Valley have two sharp boundaries: a climatic timberline forms the upper limit and another timberline terminates the forests against the desert below. However, it is not the lack of precipitation that enforces an end to tree growth. The steep and rocky slopes of that impressive mountain wall have been eroded through thousands of years and the debris in the form of coarse, loose rock and gravel has piled up at the foot of the mountains, slowly climbing higher as the millennia pass. This gravel has little ability to retain water from rain or melting snow and trees therefore find it impossible to get established on it. There is, therefore, a sharp forest boundary coincident with the boundary of the loosely accumulated coarse gravel. The vegetation boundary is hence neither climatic nor cultural but owes its existence to the abrupt change in the quality of the ground. This timberline is therefore a natural timberline. At this point, the vegetation boundary cannot be used to illustrate the effect of climate on vegetation as in the case of the upper (alpine) timberline; instead, it clearly indicates the boundary between two unlike physiographic features of the landscape.

Boundary Lines — Types and Advantages

The technical problems of vegetation boundaries consist above all in having to decide how the boundaries are to be shown on the map. One way is to draw lines separating one vegetation type from another. The lines should always be quite thin so as not to affect the quality of the map and detract the reader's attention from more significant features; the space occupied by thick boundary lines may be more than is justifiable, especially on small-scale maps. Lines may be continuous for the major vegetation types and dashed or dotted for their divisions and subdivisions. Sometimes continuous lines are used where vegetational boundaries are well established while dashed or dotted lines imply that the location of the boundary is uncertain. In this manner, HUECK (1960) showed the reliability of his vegetation map of Venezuela by establishing three categories of boundaries: continuous lines for accurate boundaries, and dashed and dotted lines for fairly accurate and inaccurate boundaries, respectively. In order to render boundary lines unobtrusive they can be printed in grey.

Boundary lines have the advantage of making a map clear and of permitting precision to a very considerable degree. But some authors object to the sharp contrasts between vegetation types produced by continuous lines as being unrealistic; therefore they omit boundary lines altogether. The contrast between different colors or patterns is considered adequate to offset one vegetation type from another whereas the sharp lines are felt to exaggerate the differences. GAUSSEN's (1945b) map of France or SEIBERT's (1954) map of Schlitz are good examples of maps without boundary lines. The absence of sharp contrasts is pleasing, indeed.

There are, however, other aspects to the problem of having boundary lines. One such aspect is that lines help to distinguish between similar though unlike colors or to offset similar black-and-white patterns from one another. A further aspect is the fact that the lines are a great aid in assuring better registration when printing a map with different colors. This is important because poor registration makes it difficult to read the map and distracts from more significant features.

Locating Boundaries

A boundary is a line between two vegetation types. It is not always easy to locate such a line in the field, and where good topographic maps or soil maps are available, these may be consulted to advantage. In this manner, a line which at first may have seemed rather arbitrary is given more justification.

If a large-scale vegetation map is to be prepared, it is best to obtain aerial photographs of the area. These will aid in locating the boundaries accurately and rapidly; the amount of time, energy, and funds saved thereby is very great and the map is much more reliable.

Theoretically, a boundary line on a vegetation map corresponds to a boundary in the field. But in practice, such a boundary may or may not exist. SCHARFETTER (1932, pp. 108–111) quotes BECK-MANNAGETTA, CAJANDER, DU RIETZ, FRIES, GLEASON, OSVALD, SCHARFETTER, TENGVALL, and WARMING as authors who feel that boundaries, as a rule, are sharp and clear. They admit exceptions in the form of transitions, but it is felt that these only confirm the rule. KÜCHLER (1955a) observed boundaries between plant communities that were remarkably sharp and clear: A wagon road led through a relatively undisturbed forest in the state of Maine. The turning wagon wheels and the action of the horses resulted in a herbaceous plant community that covered the road but never once penetrated into the surrounding forest. Indeed, the road community and the herbaceous community on the forest floor had not a single species in common.

The species listed in column I, below, occurred exclusively on the road, i.e., in or between the ruts. The species in column II grew in the surrounding forest—not one of them occurred on the road.

Column I	Column II
Agrostis alba	*Clintonia borealis*
Leontodon autumnalis	*Cornus canadensis*
Lycopus americanus	*Gaultheria procumbens*
Oxalis corniculata	*Maianthemum canadense*
Plantago major	*Mitchella repens*
Poa sp.	*Osmunda claytoniana*
Prunella vulgaris	*Pteridium aquilinum* var.
Ranunculus acris	*latiusculum*
Veronica officinalis	*Vaccinium angustifolium*
Viola blanda	

Perhaps the most detailed method of establishing sharp boundaries is given by TÜXEN (1954c), whose work is based on the tenets of phytosociology *sensu* BRAUN-BLANQUET. He says: "Sites merge unobtrusively and gradually because neither the individual ecological factors nor their unlimited combinations change abruptly. However, phytocenoses do change at definite points quantitatively because their components are (generally indivisible) species. Floristic variations imply therefore a change by at least one species. For this reason, too, a plant community can be defined and its extent can be established much more accurately than the site on which it depends. These one-species variations gain in significance the poorer the floristic composition of the vegetation is, or in other words, the more extreme certain ecological factors are (e.g., Salicornietum, Puccinellietum, etc.). Floristically rich communities on balanced heterogeneous sites usually differ from each other by several or many species. Abrupt and considerable site variations imply strong vegetational differences whereas small changes in site qualities result in slight floristic variations which, however, remain abrupt as long as one species disappears from the community or is added to it. Still more delicate changes in the character of the environmental complex find a fluid expression: the numbers and frequencies of the individual specimens of the species within the community fluctuate gradually and smoothly between various degrees of intensity."

There is no doubt that sharp vegetation boundaries are very common, due to more or less abrupt changes in the topography, the soil, the geology, the climate, or the water economy of the substratum.

In contrast to these observations are those to the effect that sharp boundaries are rare, that transitions are usually more or less broad, that, indeed, the vegetation of a region may consist more of transitions than of clearly identifiable vegetation types. The most extreme view was perhaps held by Curtis, who believed that vegetation changes continuously, that boundaries are largely absent and, therefore, cannot be observed and recorded. Even Curtis, however, agreed that vegetation can change quite abruptly (Curtis and McIntosh, 1951; Curtis, 1959).

Transition Zones

In sifting the evidence, it becomes clear that boundaries exist indeed but are not universal. On the vegetation map existing boundaries can be shown without much difficulty. Where it is desirable to show sharp boundaries when, in fact, they are blurred, the author must decide whether a transition zone should be shown on the map. The transition should certainly be shown if it is very wide, considering the scale of the map. Where it is narrow, it may, in some instances, be ignored. This implies that a vegetation type appears to be more uniform on a map than it is in fact because at its margins it may be merging gradually with the neighboring type.

Where a boundary is not clear because of gradual transitions, it can be shown as broken lines, zigzag lines, or by an interpenetration of two contiguous vegetation types (Figure 7a, b). Some transitions are so gradual that there may, in fact, be no place where a boundary line is justified. It is then necessary to decide arbitrarily how much of an admixture may be tolerated in an established type and to draw the boundary accordingly. Even if the place for the boundary in a transition zone has been selected very judiciously, field inspection may reveal little or no difference on the two sides of the boundary. An interpenetration, including its width, can be shown by alternating bars or arrow-like extensions. The degree of dominance of each of two vegetation types in a transition can be shown by the relative width of the color bars. In a transition zone, two vegetation types A and B merge; type A gradually gives way to type B. Therefore, in crossing the zone, the mapper usually finds at first type A more prominent; hence the color bars representing it are wide compared with those of type B. But sooner or later the situation is reversed and type A remains but is poorly represented; its color bars are therefore shown distinctly narrower than those of type B before they vanish altogether.

Where symbols are used, the more prominent vegetation type is shown by its color whereas the competing type is shown in the form of symbols overprinted on the color. Near the opposite end of the transition zone, the case may be reversed: the second type is now shown in its color with the symbol of the first type overprinted on it.

In case of an invasion, the use of arrows can be quite effective. The arrows are shown in the color of the invading community, overprinted on the invaded one. The shape of the arrows is related to the degree of suc-

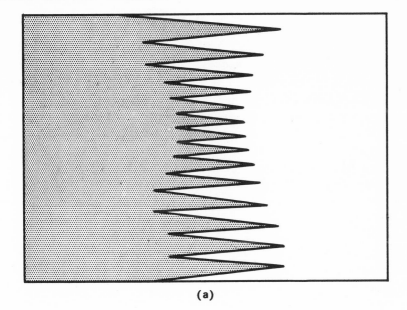

(a)

(b)

Figure 7

cess of the invasion, thus: broad arrows imply a massive invasion, slender arrows an invasion of modest success at least up to the time of mapping, and the length of the arrows shows the depth of penetration. The arrows can also be shown in grey or black. In that case, the mapper is advised to experiment amply so as to find just the right size and number of arrows, else the black arrows can easily become too prominent.

Ultimately, the use and manipulation of boundaries and transitions are left to each author. However, it is well to be acquainted with the existing possibilities and their variations in order to assure the most appropriate and the most effective choice, and thereby keep the quality of the vegetation map at its highest possible level.

11

Organization of Content

The organization of the map content is the orderly arrangement of the various aspects of the vegetation to be shown on the map. A vegetation map cannot portray all aspects of plant life in the landscape; therefore an author must select one feature, or several, of the vegetation, e.g., certain physiognomic aspects or perhaps the dominant species. The author will present the selected features throughout the map, preferably to the exclusion of all others.

The vegetation mapper organizes the map content by beginning with a survey. This establishes just what sort of items are to be shown on the map. He makes a complete list of all items and then proceeds to group them meaningfully.

For instance, if the natural vegetation is to be portrayed, the mapper can establish a number of physiognomic groups, such as deciduous forests, evergreen forests, various types of grasslands, shrub communities, etc. Each group consists of one or more communities that are described floristically. By reviewing his list of items critically, the mapper quickly discovers which groups he can establish, and into which of these he must place every single item.

Depending on the purpose of the map, the same material may be organized in different manners. For instance, ecological factors may be the controlling features, and therefore the major groups are established with this in mind. However, where environmental features are to be included but are considered secondary in importance to other features, they are relegated to the subdivisions of the major groups. It is, for instance, possible to establish a few major groups, each described as a forest type, a grassland type, etc., and within these groups arrange the items ecologically, requiring more or less heat, water, etc., as the case may be. But in other circumstances, the major groups are distinguished on the basis of some ecological factor, e.g., water. In such cases the major groups may range from lake and river vegetation via swamp vegetation and communities periodically flooded to those with a permanently high water table, a medium-high and, finally, a low water table, or one subject to great seasonal fluctuations. The different communities of the region are then placed in the appropriate ecological group and the vegetation of the entire area has been presented in an orderly fashion, and according to criteria established *a priori*. Thus it is possible to show major features of the vegetation in a manner that permits the reader at once to grasp the significance of each group and, within the group, of each community.

Alternative Approaches

DANSEREAU (1961) illustrates five different approaches to mapping vegetation (Figures 8A–8E). On each of these maps, all phytocenoses are expressed and shown according to one method. If, for instance, the mapper wants to show the vegetation floristically and as members of some formation, he will want to consult Figures 8A and 8C. His solution might be to show the formations in six different colors and overprint thirty types of symbols in the appropriate places to show the floristic features. As a result, his map content is strictly organized: every phytocenose is shown both floristically and in its proper formation, which was the goal. But his map says nothing about dynamics, ecological controls, or other aspects. To introduce any one of these would have added irrelevant material that might have reduced the legibility of the map or detracted in some other way. The mapper can also combine parts A and E, or C and E, or select some other combination. But if he decides to combine three approaches, he must experiment patiently in order to obtain a clear and unequivocal map.

On maps at very small scales, the number of features basic to the organization should be kept small, preferably not more than two or three. But on large-scale maps, an extraordinary variety of detail can be shown if the map content is well organized.

A strict organization of the map content should result in a map on which the reader can see at once not only that there are different types of vegetation but also which of these are related and which are not. This can best be accomplished by a judicious use of colors. Thus, several related communities, perhaps all within a given group, are shown by various shades and hues of the same color, whereas a very different and quite unrelated group will be shown correspondingly in a different color. If a vegetation mapper wishes to show both the natural and the cultural vegetation on one map, the most effective solution is to show each of the various phytocenoses of the potential natural vegetation with its own color. Usually there are several types of actual vegetation for each type of potential natural phytocenose. The different types of actual vegetation are then

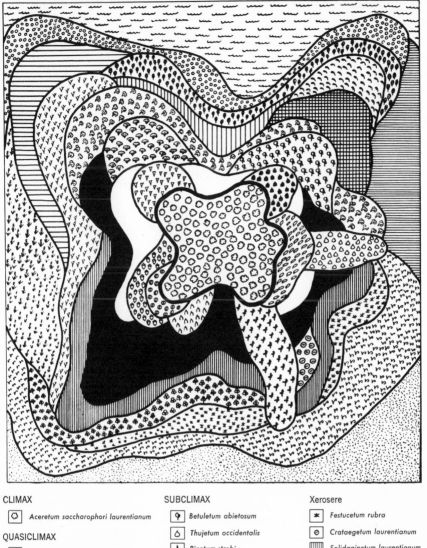

CLIMAX

⬡ *Aceretum saccharophori laurentianum*

QUASICLIMAX

▮ *Aceretum saccharophori betulosum*

ρ *Aceretum saccharophori tsugosum*

Υ *Aceretum saccharophori ulmosum*

θ *Aceretum saccharophori quercosum*

⊘ *Aceretum saccharophori caryosum*

∧ *Aceretum saccharophori nigroides*

SERCLIMAX

φ *Acereto−ulmetum laurentianum*

ᖰ *Alnetum rugosae*

SUBCLIMAX

φ *Betuletum abietosum*

△ *Thujetum occidentalis*

✦ *Pinetum strobi*

■ *Betuletum populifoliae*

☐ *Aceretum rubri*

CONSOLIDATION

Hydrosere

▤ *Calamagrostetum canadensis*

Υ *Spiraeetum latifoliae*

▥ *Salicetum riparium*

θ *Myricetum galeae*

↷ *Chamaedaphnetum calyculatae*

▦ *Piceetum ericaceum*

Xerosere

✱ *Festucetum rubra*

⊘ *Crataegetum laurentianum*

▥ *Solidaginetum laurentianum*

PIONEER STAGES

Hydrosere

〜 *Nupharetum variegati*

⋰ *Scirpetum elatum*

▤ *Caricetum rostratae*

↓ *Agrostetum canadense*

Xerosere

⋱ *Oenotheretum dumetorum*

Υ⌐ *Danthonietum spicatae*

φ *Trifolietum repentis*

Figure 8A. The thirty most characteristic plant associations of the landscape of the Montreal Plain assembled in a model that shows their actual contacts. (After Dansereau, 1961.)

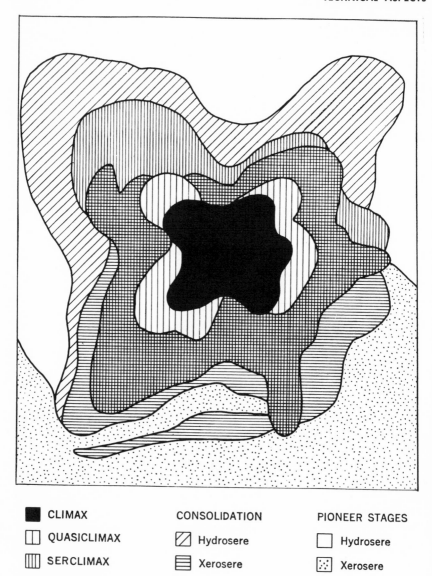

CLIMAX	CONSOLIDATION	PIONEER STAGES
QUASICLIMAX	Hydrosere	Hydrosere
SERCLIMAX	Xerosere	Xerosere
SUBCLIMAX		

Figure 8B. The associations of Figure 8A classified according to their dynamic position. (After Dansereau, 1961.)

shown in the form of symbols or line patterns overprinted on the potential natural vegetation. This method permits the mapper to show both natural and cultural vegetation together. It further reveals which types of cultural vegetation are tied to particular natural phytocenoses, and with

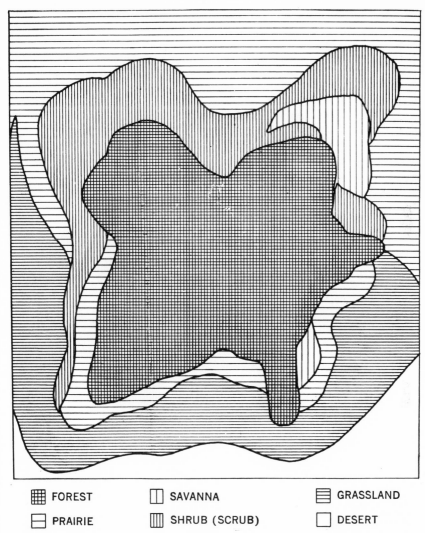

Figure 8C. The associations of Figure 8A classified according to the type of formation to which they belong. (After Dansereau, 1961.)

what degree of consistency this is so. The natural vegetation is actual rather than potential where a color has no overprint.

In order to prepare a vegetation map, the mapper should consider all the means at his disposal to portray the vegetation in such a manner that the map will best serve its purpose. Although the ways in which he can present the vegetation on the map are limited, they are nevertheless so numerous, especially if used in combination, that he must make his selection with great care. A variety of mapping methods is discussed elsewhere

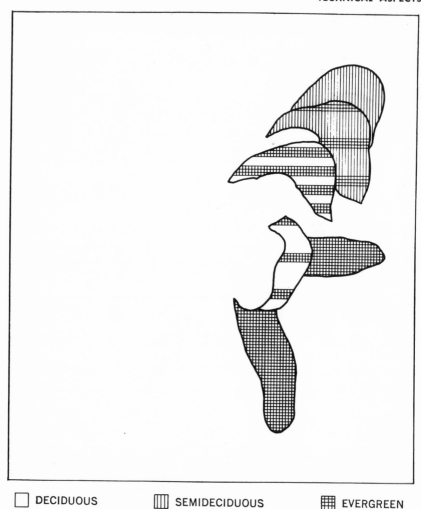

DECIDUOUS   SEMIDECIDUOUS   EVERGREEN

Figure 8D. The associations of Figure 8A classified according to their periodicity. (After Dansereau, 1961.)

in this book, but all methods rest on certain basic features of the vegetation, and it is these that must be considered, and the extent of their use weighed judiciously, before the actual mapping can begin.

Basic Vegetation Features

There are six such basic features or groups of features but the mapper will be quick to realize that each of these features is more or less complex, that parts of one may be combined with parts of another, and that therefore his means of presenting the vegetation must be flexible. This flexibil-

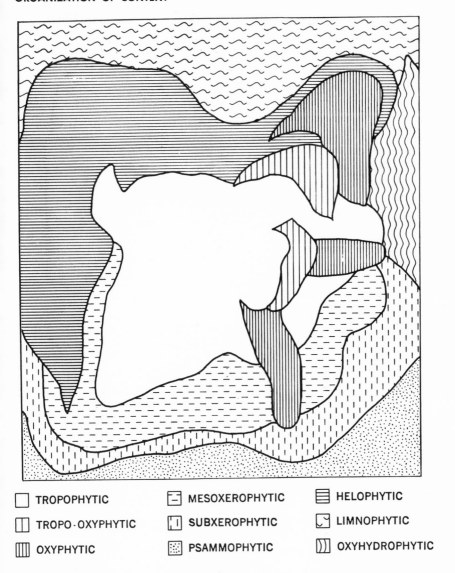

☐	TROPOPHYTIC	⊡	MESOXEROPHYTIC	⊟	HELOPHYTIC
▯	TROPO·OXYPHYTIC	▯	SUBXEROPHYTIC	⌣	LIMNOPHYTIC
▥	OXYPHYTIC	▦	PSAMMOPHYTIC	))	OXYHYDROPHYTIC

Figure 8E. The associations of Figure 8A classified according to the dominant ecological control. (After Dansereau, 1961.)

ity permits him to adapt his map to any one purpose or to certain groups of purposes. The degree to which the mapper succeeds in serving his purpose depends to a considerable degree on his organizational skill.

The first of the basic approaches to a description of the vegetation is to use its physiognomy and structure. The physiognomic approach can range from the broadest descriptions—geographical terms such as heath, meadow, savanna, etc.—to the most detailed structural analysis of height, density, layering, and life forms (KÜCHLER, 1953b; 1956a, map I).

The second basic feature, the floristic composition, is in part a matter of detail (scale), and to a considerable degree a matter of judgment. One approach lists the dominant species, and this may be contrasted with the community approach. Species may also be grouped according to their areal affinities or in some other manner. The mapper must be familiar with the existing possibilities. To insist on one method because he has always used it or because he has not thoroughly acquainted himself with others implies a limitation that can only be detrimental.

The third basic approach to mapping the vegetation is to present it as the natural vegetation, be this actual or potential. This is usually described physiognomically or floristically, or both, which shows that sometimes the various approaches are not mutually exclusive and may be complementary to one another. For many purposes, a map of the natural vegetation is particularly valuable, and the most recent methods permit the construction of such a map for certain areas with a reasonable accuracy. This accuracy, however, depends somewhat on the regions, on the experience of the mapper, and on the time and information at his disposal. In the light of these arguments, the mapper must decide whether under given circumstances he can prepare a map of the natural vegetation with such a degree of accuracy that his effort will be worthwhile, and the result of his endeavor will meet all requirements.

The fourth basic means to show vegetation is to present the cultural vegetation types or substitute communities, i.e., the actual vegetation. These may be considered the derivatives and counterparts of the natural vegetation. They can be shown in a great variety of ways and may include statistical values. The purpose of the map is here the determining factor, as usual. Maps of the substitute communities are usually made for "practical" people, such as silviculturists, range managers, planners, etc. However, this should not detract from the fact that maps of the cultural vegetation can also be valuable for purely academic purposes, especially as a basis for research (e.g., GAUSSEN, 1930.)

The fifth basic means to show vegetation on a map is to employ the phytocenoses as expressions of the environment. Some vegetation mappers object to this approach because it includes features that are not vegetation. However, these "ecological" vegetation maps have been found useful and popular. It is, of course, not possible to combine vegetation with all environmental factors, and the mapper is forced to be selective. He usually has two choices. One is to introduce on his map those environmental features that are of particular significance for a given type of vegetation. In the case of marshes the dominant environmental feature is the high water table, in the case of deserts it is lack of rainfall, on alpine meadows it is the short growing season, and so on. Such maps are often highly descriptive. But it must not be overlooked that many environments are not so overwhelmingly dominated by a single factor. References to the environment are then usually omitted. To ignore the environment when elsewhere it was stressed may leave the reader wondering. But the omission at least implies that the site qualities are relatively balanced in their effects on the plant communities.

The other choice for the vegetation mapper lies in selecting one particular environmental feature and relating all plant communities to it. This method is particularly useful with regard to various aspects of water, be that precipitation, drainage (Figure 9), depth and fluctuation of the water table, duration of snow cover (in mountains), or others. Although such maps are limited in their uses, they can be very valuable.

The sixth and last feature of the vegetation the mapper must consider is its dynamism. It is, of course, much simpler and less time-consuming to ignore the dynamic qualities of vegetation altogether and to map only what can actually be observed in the field at the time of mapping. This is the usual procedure in many instances and can be entirely adequate and satisfactory. There are, however, instances where information on the dynamic aspects of vegetation is desirable, even necessary. It is not difficult to organize the vegetation on the basis of its dynamism because all plant communities are either climax communities, or members of a sere evolving toward a climax. Assignment of a plant community to its proper sere, and possibly to its place in the sere, is the chief problem. Although the problems are not numerous, they are not therefore solved easily. Mapping the successional aspects of vegetation is discussed in Chapter 17.

The six complex approaches to showing vegetation on a map permit a very complete treatment of the subject. But it is not feasible to show all features of vegetation and it is important that the right selection be made. The information must be available and it must serve the purpose of the map. How the features are combined on the map is left to the imagination of the mapper. Sometimes it happens that he finds it difficult to organize his material so as to get it all on the map. In that case he may want to consider printing part of his material on transparent paper which can be overlaid on the map.

Consistency

Organization implies consistency. A consistent organization of the map content places all parts of the map on the same basis and permits comparisons, both within the scope of the map and on maps of other areas with a homologous vegetation, and even with maps showing climate, topography, soils, or geology.

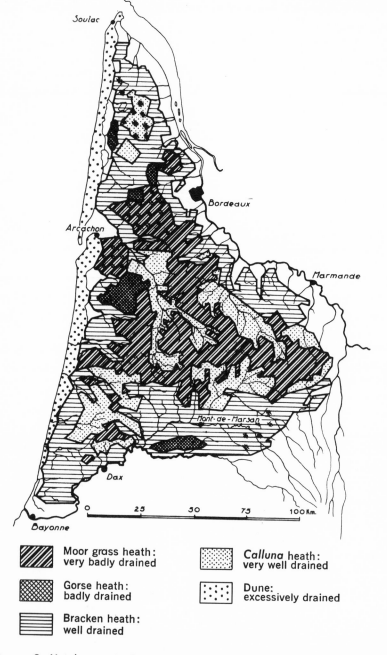

Figure 9. Heath types in Gascogne, France. (After Emberger, Gaussen, and Rey, 1955.)

Once the mapper has selected an approach to mapping and decided on the features of the vegetation he wants to portray on the map, he must then express his observations accordingly. If the dominant species are to be mentioned, they must be mentioned in every plant community on the map. It is not appropriate to list the dominants for some communities and then elsewhere on the map include items like meadow, deciduous forests, chaparral, etc. Similarly, if the structure of the vegetation is to be shown on the map, it must be shown throughout the area covered by the map. Only then can one part of the map, or one community, be compared usefully with other parts or communities so that the similarities and contrasts really become clearly evident.

Sometimes it is desirable to show items which clearly differ in character from all others on the map. For instance, on his well-organized map of Perpignan, GAUSSEN shows a number of "botanical curiosities." Items of this kind should be shown in such a manner that the reader is immediately aware of their exceptional character. In the legend these items can be placed in a group by themselves, preferably at the end, and on the map they should appear as a boldly different overprint. In any case, the number of such exceptional items should be kept to a minimum.

It may not be possible or even desirable to be entirely consistent at all times, but in general it is true that greater consistency implies a greater usefulness of the vegetation map.

Some authors may find these remarks superfluous because they take consistency for granted. Examples of maps which are entirely consistent are those by GAUSSEN (1948), KÜCHLER (1953c), SCHMID (1948), TÜXEN (1956a), or WIESLANDER's blue-line series of California (e.g., CUSHMAN and LUSK, 1949). On these maps, consistency implies that all parts of a given map are comparable. If a certain aspect of the vegetation is not shown in a section of the map, then the reader knows that it has not been shown because it is absent, and not because, although present, another aspect was shown instead, for whatever reason. In other words, all vegetational features to be considered appear on the map wherever they occur.

There are numerous vegetation maps on which a consistent organization of the map content is lacking, and the character of the map is thereby changed completely. If the material is not organized with any degree of consistency, different parts of the map are not comparable and the interpretation of the map may lead to erroneous conclusions. Two examples will suffice to illustrate this point.

1. The map of the United States (SHANTZ and ZON, 1923) is not consistent in that the vegetation is shown sometimes by species, at other times by genera; elsewhere on the same map the vegetation is shown by

life forms, regional affinities, or according to ecological controls. This approach can be very descriptive but makes a comparison of any one part of the map with another impossible.

2. On the maps of the southern states (U.S. FOREST SERVICE, 1934) a striking emphasis is placed on certain aspects of the vegetation whereas other aspects are neglected or ignored. Among the legend items, conifers (mostly pines) are very prominent: nine different species are listed individually. Broadleaf trees often cover a larger area but are collectively referred to as hardwoods, usually divided into bottomland hardwoods and upland or mountain hardwoods. Only occasionally is a genus (e.g., oak) mentioned, rarely a species. One can also find such combinations as "oak-hardwoods," as if oaks were not hardwoods. Hardwood forests with 20 per cent or more pine are called pine forests. All non-forested areas are grouped into one category only, regardless of the character of the vegetation. This inconsistency so undermined the value of the maps that a modification has been introduced on the more recent editions.

Complexity

It has been said above that all vegetational features to be considered must appear on the map wherever they occur. This leads to the problem of complexity.

The permissible degree of complexity of vegetation maps depends only in part on the scale and very considerably on the ability of the author to organize his material. In addition to skill, the organization requires an appropriate terminology and a clear grasp of the purpose of the map. If these prerequisites are not met, irrelevant material will needlessly complicate the map. The various prerequisites for good organization are easily underrated or ignored and the value of the map thereby depreciated unnecessarily. The need for thought and experience can hardly be overemphasized, and authors should always limit the scope of their offerings to such an extent that whatever they show is readily seen and appreciated by the reader of the map.

The degree of complexity can vary enormously on maps of similar scale; this is best illustrated by two examples.

1. The Distribution of Forests in the Upper Peninsula of Michigan (1:250,000; U.S. FOREST SERVICE, 1941) is a very simple map. The forests are shown in the following manner:

    1. Northern hardwoods, saw timber
    2. Northern hardwoods, young growth
    3. Mixed hardwoods and softwoods

4. Pine
5. Conifer swamps
6. Aspen brush
7. Agricultural land

In the legend a number of dominant tree genera follow each forest type parenthetically. No variations in the floristic composition within these groups are shown. Seven different flat colors appear on the map, each one representing a type. As the description of the forest types is limited to the mention of a few genera, there exists no particular problem in showing each type on the map. All one has to do in mapping the vegetation is to name the forests according to one of the established categories. Greater simplicity can hardly be expected of a vegetation map at this scale.

2. The second example, showing the highest degree of complexity, is the Carte de la végétation de la France (1:200,000), feuille Perpignan (GAUSSEN, 1948). The following information appears on this map: the natural vegetation is shown in forty-one categories; floristic distinctions are made both by genera and by species; life forms from trees to dwarf shrubs appear in nine different height classes, in addition to herbaceous and aquatic vegetation. All these are grouped into series of dynamic character with facies as subdivisions; several related series are combined into zones (étages) which are climatic in character. The cultural vegetation (land use) is shown in forty-two categories ranging from different types of afforestation to truck farms and individual crops. In every canton, land use is shown in four major types, each of which is indicated according to the percentage of the area it occupies; there are five percentage classes. Nine kinds of fruit trees are shown in groups of 1,000, 10,000, and 100,-000 each; ten other crops appear, in five percentage classes, and the ecological affinities are given for both orchard and other crops. Vineyards are indicated separately by symbols representing 10 hectares each. Finally, there are sixteen individual "botanical curiosities and significant sites." In addition, the nature of the environment is shown, based above all on temperature and precipitation.

It is obvious that such a bewildering amount of information cannot be shown on one map of this scale without rendering the map completely illegible, unless it is subjected to the strictest organization. Thus the natural vegetation is shown in variously screened colors and overprints whereas the cultural vegetation is shown by symbols which have statistical values, and each of which has a significant size, shape, and color. To this may be added the number of symbols per unit area. Even then, it required the keenest imagination and skill to keep the map on a level of usefulness. That we have in the Perpignan map proof that this can be done so well is, of course, gratifying and propitious. Yet, we must understand that to reach such heights of achievement is the exception rather than the rule, even as not every painter can be a Rembrandt. On the other hand, the way has now been shown, and it may be followed by less imaginative minds, too.

There are, of course, other vegetation maps which reveal a very carefully planned organization of the map content. Models among these are the maps emanating from the Bundesstelle für Vegetationskartierung in Germany, and the map of Leonberg by ELLENBERG and ZELLER (1951). The latter is related to GAUSSEN's approach insofar as here, too, the vegetation and some site qualities are shown in conjunction. The color system is not the same, as it was devised for the area around Leonberg rather than for a world-wide application. Nevertheless, there are notable parallels. Also like GAUSSEN, the authors recognized the need for clarity and that the presentation must be spatial (three-dimensional). As colors are the most obvious means of presentation, they must express the most important features. For ELLENBERG and ZELLER this means differences in site qualities. Their scale (1:50,000) is much larger than GAUSSEN's on his map of France (1:200,000), and the emphasis rests, therefore, on the substratum rather than on the climate.

The colors are arranged according to the water economy and other qualities of the soil. Particular features of local significance, such as slope and exposure, effects of the wind, etc., are shown by overprinted symbols.

The large scale is also reflected in the approach to climate. Unlike GAUSSEN's meteorological data, it is phenological information that is the basis of the climatic zones. This ties vegetation, climate, and soils together most effectively, and the vegetation map becomes a strong expression of the local scene.

All types of information on this map are arranged in tabular form, where each unit of a table has its letter symbol; a number of such symbols can be combined into formulas which succinctly express a complex set of features. Thus the map content is strictly organized, permitting the authors to organize its exploitation just as efficiently and, indeed, most effectively. This organization of both the map content and the method of its exploitation is the main reason for the map's success in agricultural circles.

Minimal Area

A particular organizational point relates to the minimal area. Before the actual mapping begins, the minimal area that a plant community may occupy in the field can be calculated. All phytocenoses that do not attain the minimal areal extent are omitted from the map. But the size of an area occupied by a plant community is not necessarily proportional to the significance of the community. If an author wishes to show a plant community that is smaller than minimum size, he can go one of two ways. First, he can exaggerate the size of the area, i.e., he can show it larger than it really is. This is quite as justifiable as the more usual suppression of small areas. Secondly, if the area is much too small and an enlargement would give quite a misleading impression, then the vegetational feature is shown in the form of some symbol which is overprinted at the appropriate spot on the color of the surrounding community. For instance, rows of trees along highways are usually too narrow to be shown on a vegetation map; they are best presented in the form of lines of small dots or some pattern of this kind. Where noxious plants are to be shown, their location can be indicated by small red crosses that contrast sharply with the surrounding vegetation colors, warning the reader against danger. Enlargement or symbolization of very small areas should be kept to the very minimum in order to keep the map legible.

The problem of the minimal area is also involved in another feature of the vegetation. This is the consistent repetition of features, each of which is too small to be shown and therefore should be omitted on the map. For instance, on the foothills of the Rocky Mountains west of Denver there is a well-developed pattern of two vegetation types, one of forest and one of scrub. The forests are spread over the cooler and hence moister north-facing slopes, whereas the scrub clothes the south-facing slopes, exposed to a scorching sun for many months. This pattern is repeated for miles with monotonous regularity. Whenever the map scale is too small to show each community individually, such a catena arrangement can be expressed on the map as a single unit, and the corresponding legend item is so stated as to leave no doubt about the dual character of the vegetation in the mind of the reader.

This solution applies also to formations, of which the over-all character is quite uniform but which are permeated with phytocenoses of a very different nature, like the cedar bogs and similar wet spots in the forests of northern New England, or scattered rock ledges with their lichen communities, etc. Depending on the scale of the map, such items appear only in the legend, elaborating the description of the chief formation. If the scale is too small even for this, they are ignored altogether.

All these features show that to some degree the organization of the map material is a function of the map scale. This is not the case where slight, possibly very slight, differences occur between two communities with regard to their physiognomy or their floristic composition. The latter, for instance, may be a difference of a single species. It is then a matter of judgment on the part of the mapper, who must know to what extent such a species is essential in the description of the community. If it is a key species, present in only one of two otherwise similar communities, then the two communities should be shown as separate units. But if the species is known to possess wide tolerances, able to occur in a great variety of environmental conditions, then the two communities are mapped as one, and the presence or absence of this species is ignored.

What has been said of consistent organization applies to all vegetation maps. The need for consistent organization increases with the number of vegetational features to be shown simultaneously. And as a corollary: the most skillful and consistent organization permits the greatest degree of complexity.

12

Terminology, Legends, and Texts

A clear and unequivocal terminology is imperative on vegetation maps. Many examples can be cited where authors have disregarded this basic rule, apparently without concern for the reader, who is left baffled by the obscurity of the terms. MANGENOT (1956) discussed the analysis and mapping of tropical rainforests and urged that the results of our researches be presented in a generally comprehensible manner. Similar pleas have been made again and again (cf. KÜCHLER 1947a, 1950, 1954b).

A rigorous organization requires a set of terms each of which produces the desired picture in the mind of the reader. Strictness in terminology is even more necessary than in organization because a poorly organized map makes reading difficult whereas poorly chosen terms may prevent any appreciation of the information which the author wishes to convey to his readers.

The terms must conform to the purpose of the map. To illustrate: on a vegetation map which is to show the floristic associations of a given area, all terms should be floristic names. To introduce occasional ecological or physiognomic terms instead of association names only weakens the organization of the map. Such procedure undermines the unity of the map and leads to confusion because it requires a change in thought as one passes from one item to the next and in most cases this is not practical.

Making Terminology Meaningful

Usually an author is very familiar with the area on his map and, as a result, he may be inclined to use terms that are based on local features which he knows so well that to him they become self-evident. He easily forgets that the reader lacks this intimate acquaintance, is not familiar with the local terminology, and is therefore unable to interpret the mean-

ing of the map. For example, on the map of Arkansas (ARKANSAS STATE
GAME AND FISH COMMISSION, 1948) there appears the term "Crowley's
Ridge Vegetation." One can gather from this term that there is a topographic feature named Crowley's Ridge, and that it bears a vegetation distinct from the surrounding types. But the reader has no means to discover
what sort of vegetation is growing on Crowley's Ridge. It may be a forest
or perhaps a grassland, it may be one plant community or several. Unless
the reader happens to be familiar with Crowley's Ridge (most people are
not), this term is so obscure as to be useless. The map itself is thus useless throughout the area of Crowley's Ridge, and if more such terms are
used on one map, the corresponding amount of the time, effort, and money
spent on it have been wasted.

Vegetation is usually so complex that only a few characteristics can be
mapped directly. For this reason, many authors establish categories with
given names, and these names are then expected to act as symbols and
imply the sum total of all features of such a vegetation category. For
instance, the name "Caricetum curvulae" indicates only that there is a vegetation type in which *Carex curvula* may be assumed to be prominent.
The name reveals neither the physiognomy of the community nor its structure, neither its floristic composition nor the qualities of the site on which
it occurs. But to a phytocenologist acquainted with BRAUN-BLANQUET's
method of classifying vegetation and familiar with the vegetation of the
Alps, this name implies a certain combination of species that form a community, and in addition, it indicates a series of environmental features.

This is not necessarily the most desirable way to describe vegetation,
because most of the implications are lost to most readers. A different kind
of problem was described by AUBRÉVILLE (1961). The large evergreen and
semi-deciduous forest type which stretches from Guinea to the Congo
Basin is called Uapacetalia by one author in Ivory Coast, Lophiretalia by
another, and Strombosio-Parinatea with a subdivision of Piptadenia-
Celtideltalia by a third author in the Congo. However, *Strombosia,
Parinari, Piptadenia,* and *Celtis* are just as characteristic of this forest type
in Ivory Coast as *Lophira* and *Uapaca* in the Congo Basin. These names
do not, therefore, correspond to the floristic composition of this forest
type. They can give the wrong impression, namely, that the species mentioned are particularly frequent, constant, or abundant in these forests,
which is not so at all. Their distribution is irregular and discontinuous
like that of the other species and to name the forest by yet another species
would in no way improve the matter.

Where maps with this kind of terminology are prepared for some practical application, they must therefore be accompanied by a lengthy statement so that the reader may obtain the full benefit from his map. On the
other hand, it is quite feasible to describe on a map, by other methods, the

most significant features of the vegetation, and, if desired, of the environment as well. What is significant is left to the discretion of the author, who is guided by the purpose of his map.

TÜXEN (1956a), one of the most prominent members of the BRAUN-BLANQUET school of thought, has sought to overcome the terminological difficulties of his map readers by describing the vegetation in nontechnical terms. On his exemplary map of Baltrum he presents items such as grasslands of silver grass, dune scrub, crowberry heaths, salt meadows, etc., each of which is followed by the technical (Latin) name of the community in parentheses. In this manner, the map is rendered useful to a wider public and hence more valuable, solving an important problem without sacrificing anything. TÜXEN's success is based solely on his manipulation of the terminology used in the legend; it did not require a modification of the map content.

The author who sets out to draw a vegetation map must critically analyze every term he proposes to use in order to discover whether it fulfills the basic rule of being clear and unequivocal *to his readers.* Wherever there is any doubt, he should discard the term and replace it by one which leaves no doubt in the mind of anyone. To be ambiguous is unscientific. The more a reader can be in doubt about the meaning of a term, the weaker is the map as a whole. Nor is it useful to select an esoteric phraseology. Here as elsewhere simplicity is a virtue, and the more readily a term produces the correct picture in the mind of the reader the more valuable is the term. Cryptic terms, on the other hand, are often useless or can lead to misinterpretation.

This attention to the quality of the terms must not be limited to the legend items. It must be trained on all terms used anywhere on the map, including the title. If, for instance, a map is entitled Vegetation Map of Jefferson County then the logical conclusion is that it portrays the vegetation. If, however, the effects of climate, soil, water, topography, or other environmental features are introduced, then the map ceases to be a vegetation map *sensu stricto.* As the author does not want to mislead his readers, he should state in the title what he really attempts to show. If the title does not lend itself to an adequate description, a subtitle can be used to elaborate the title and thus lead the reader in the right direction. As a result of FOSBERG's (1961a) observations, Resolution No. 3 of the International Colloquium on Vegetation Mapping recommends that vegetation maps be based strictly on features of plant communities. These are to be distinguished in their title from maps which include or are based on ecological facts or ecosystems, describing both vegetation and environment. For example, the Vegetation Map of Tunis (GAUSSEN and VERNET, 1958) might be entitled more adequately Vegetation Map of Tunis with Colors of Ecological Values.

The terms must also be as true as possible. Who, indeed, would choose terms that are untrue? But no map can be quite true unless its scale approaches 1:1, which is obviously absurd. The truthfulness of a map then becomes a function of the scale: the smaller the scale, the greater the generalization, i.e., the greater the departure from the truth. Boundaries become less meaningful as the scale shrinks, the areal content emphasizes, more and more, one feature at the expense of all others and, in the end, the departure from the truth on small world maps is so great that the maps can give, at best, no more than broad hints.

A map of the province of Ontario may show muskegs scattered through the forests of that region. On a small-scale map this is permissible in a variety of cases. But if these types of the vegetation are to be shown at a large scale, then the term "muskeg" becomes ambiguous to the extent of being meaningless, because both floristic composition and the life forms may vary greatly from one muskeg to the next. Ambiguity and obscurity are the greatest enemies of good vegetation maps and must be avoided at all cost.

It happens often that authors use the names of taxa to characterize vegetation types. This is, of course, perfectly legitimate and often the most useful method. The quality of the map is, however, influenced by the manner in which these names are used.

The clearest and therefore the best way is to use both the local names and the scientific names, as for instance "tall grass prairie of big bluestem (*Andropogon gerardi*) and Indian grass (*Sorghastrum nutans*)." Such a statement is descriptive, explicit, and clear. Where it is not feasible to employ such lengthy terms, the author will omit part of the information. In so doing, he must be careful to remain consistent. Throughout his legend, the plants should be named uniformly, either in the vernacular or in scientific terms. If the latter, all names should be uniformly on the same level, i.e., all names should be specific or else all names should be generic. It is not good practice to mention only the genus here, give the species there, use the vernacular elsewhere, and perhaps no plant names at all in a fourth instance.

There are many descriptive terms for vegetation types that are independent of taxonomy, for example, "tundra." This term belongs to the vegetation of the Far North, on the poleward side of the arctic timberline. It originated in Russia but is now accepted and employed for analogous phytocenoses in Siberia, Alaska, Canada, etc. This extension of the use of the term "tundra" is logical and practical.

The matter becomes more problematical when this same term is applied to high-altitude vegetation in regions like Colorado or Utah. Different conditions prevail in these more southerly latitudes, and significant differences may exist between the vegetation of Utah summits and that of the plains around Great Bear Lake. The use of the term "tundra" should therefore be avoided for high-altitude vegetation in the middle latitudes, or else additional details must be given to avoid ambiguity or misinterpretation.

Constructing Legends

The legend is the key to the map. It gives the map its meaning, reveals the number and variety of vegetation types and their mutual relationships (if any). It is always an integral part of the map and therefore requires much thought and care. The mapper will find it useful to study a large variety of legends; this will assist him in devising the best possible legend for his own map. The legends, of course, present the map content. It has already been pointed out that the legend should reveal how the map content is organized and that it must consist of terms which are clear and unequivocal to the reader. There is, in addition, the possibility of manipulating the legend items in such a manner that the author can thereby affect the organization, the use of colors, the length of the legend, etc. Two examples will illustrate some possibilities.

In a landscape to be mapped there occurs a grassland type of vegetation, pure stands of junipers, and grassland sections over which junipers are thinly scattered. There are here three types of vegetation and they may be shown as such (Figure 10a). It is also possible to select two pat-

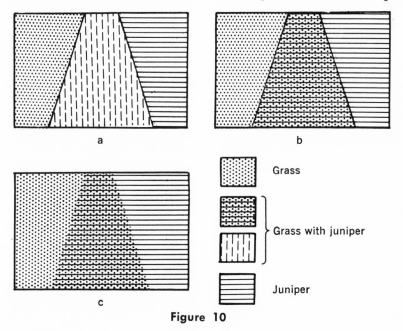

a

b

Grass

Grass with juniper

Juniper

c

Figure 10

terns that may be combined. In that case, one pattern is used for the grassland, one for the junipers, and where the junipers occur in the grassland, one pattern is superimposed over the other (Figure 10b). In this instance, it would be quite feasible to omit all boundaries and thereby produce an effect of a more gradual change from one type to the next (Figure 10c).

If the junipers occur not only as a pure stand and in the grassland but also in other types of vegetation, e.g., sagebrush, it may be better to add a symbol for juniper to the legend. The juniper is then shown by its pattern where it occurs as pure stands and as a symbol where it grows in a matrix of grass or sage.

It is also possible to show the junipers only as a symbol, even where they form pure stands. In this last case, there are only three basic types and hence patterns: (1) grasslands, (2) sagebrush, and (3) juniper. But in fact, there are five types, and the additional two are (4) grassland with junipers and (5) sagebrush with junipers. However, the last two types do not require separate patterns. The most logical arrangement of these items in the legend would be as follows:

1. Junipers
2. Grassland
3. Grassland with junipers
4. Sagebrush
5. Sagebrush with junipers

If the mapper prefers to show the close relationship between the grasslands with and without junipers, etc., his arrangement of the legend should be rather as follows:

1. Junipers
2. Grassland
   a. Same with junipers
3. Sagebrush
   a. Same with junipers

Correspondingly, the mapper can separate all types on his maps by boundaries. Or else, he can omit those between items 2 and 2a and between 3 and 3a. The latter way will be the most pleasing and also appear most "natural" and hence convincing.

The term "grassland" is physiognomic whereas "junipers" is floristic. To be consistent, the grassland should be described floristically, too, and the genera of the grasses should be given, for example, "wheatgrass and needlegrass" or else "grassland of *Agropyron* and *Stipa*."

If junipers, grass and sagebrush occur together, it may be that they represent a transition. If this is the case and the author wishes to further refine his map, he can divide the transition according to dominance: grass with sagebrush and sagebrush with grass, etc. In such a case, the map legend should read as follows:

1. *Juniperus* woods
   1a. Same, with *Agropyron* and *Stipa*
   1b. Same, with *Artemisia*
   1c. Same, with *Agropyron, Stipa,* and *Artemisia*
2. *Agropyron-Stipa* grassland.
   2a. Same, with *Juniperus*
   2b. Same, with *Artemisia*
   2c. Same, with *Juniperus and Artemisia*
3. *Artemisia* shrubs (sagebrush)
   3a. Same, with *Agropyron* and *Stipa*
   3b. Same, with *Juniperus*
   3c. Same, with *Agropyron, Stipa,* and *Juniperus*

In such a detailed legend, it is best to have one color each and also one symbol each for numbers 1, 2, and 3. Item 2b will then be printed in the color of No. 2 with the symbol of No. 3 overprinted. In this manner, items like 1a and 2a cannot be confused. The difference between 1a and 2a is clear: 1a represents a forest, perhaps rather open, with some grass between the trees. The over-all impression of this type is that of a forest. In item 2a, on the other hand, the trees are scattered in a matrix of grass. It is the latter which dominates the landscape and the junipers seem supplementary.

The author must establish criteria to determine the degree of density or coverage of each of the basic items (grass, juniper, sagebrush); only then can he hope to assign the various combinations to their appropriate legend category.

If his mapped area shows all these entities, his legend will correspond to the complete table. But it may well be that some items do not occur in the mapped area. In such a case, the author will find it wise to set up such a table anyway, on a separate sheet of paper. This will assure him of a logical and clear arrangement of the possibilities. From these he can select the items that occur in his area and present them in their proper sequence.

In an altogether different instance, profound changes like burning or clear-cutting a forest can result in mapping problems. No such problems exists if the potential natural vegetation is to be shown, unless severe soil erosion must be anticipated, and hence an altered substratum. Otherwise, the vegetation will promptly return, perhaps at first in the form of herbaceous communities, surrounding and engulfing the stumps of the departed trees. These stumps have their own significance, affecting the soil, the fungal population, etc., and may therefore be of interest to the mapper.

It is not necessary to have a separate color, pattern, or symbol for the stumps. All that is needed is to mention them as part of the community in which they occur. If, for instance, this is a herbaceous community of *Epilobium*, etc., the mapper will elaborate his legend item by saying "*Epilobium* community on recently logged spruce forest sites." The stumps are then implied. If this seems inadequate, a symbol may be added, such as a fine black stippling, to be overprinted on the logged sections. The U.S. FOREST SERVICE published maps showing "old burns" and "recent burns." This procedure is unsatisfactory insofar as it says nothing about what was burned nor what existed at the time of mapping. Such legend items constitute a severe but unnecessary reduction in the value of the map.

Supplemental Texts

It is well known that the vegetation of an area can consist of phytocenoses which are so complex in their structure and composition that it is difficult, if not impossible, to express them concisely. Many authors resort then to the method of coining a conveniently brief term and elaborating on the details in a text which accompanies the map or which, at times, is printed on an enlarged margin of the map.

Occasionally, a map consists of a number of more or less independent sheets, like the vegetation map of France (1:200,000) or the vegetation map of Central Asia (1:1,000,000). In such a case, the terminology of all sheets must be coordinated so that, in a sense, the entire series has but one legend. However, this does not prevent the mapper of a given sheet from presenting all justifiable details even though they may not occur on any other sheet of the series. The main consideration remains that the map must be in harmony with its purpose and must be designed so as best to serve the reader.

As a general rule, a good map is independent of a text. This does not mean that a text cannot greatly elaborate and supplement the information of the map. It does mean, however, that even without such a text and with no more than a well-chosen legend, a good map is a complete unit, capable of conveying the information which the author wishes to convey.

Sometimes it is desirable to have a text which brings in additional information, as it is not always possible to place all vegetational features on a map, although they can easily be described in a text. We have then a vegetation map, complete in itself, and supplemented by a text. An excellent example of this approach was given by LAVRENKO and SOCHAVA (1956) or by GAUSSEN and VERNET (1958). At times, however, authors have put the cart before the horse: a complete text is written first, describing the vegetation. Then, a vegetation map is attached, almost as a sort of afterthought, if at all. This procedure is dangerous. If somebody wishes to describe the vegetation of an area and also have a map, let him prepare the map first. This is the best procedure because the cartographic representation of the vegetation forces the author to resort to an exact and comprehensive observation. The map then becomes an excellent guide to the formation and organization of the ideas on which the textual description of the vegetation rests.

It has already been pointed out that a good vegetation map is strictly organized and uses clear and unambiguous terminology. It is difficult to do this unless the author spends a good deal of thought on just these items; if he succeeds, his map is likely to be good.

But if he writes his text first, the situation is different because this pointed clarity of the map may then be absent. A beautiful and eloquent description may be highly readable, and each individual aspect, thus described, can be visualized by the reader. But the usual subjective approach emphasizes one aspect here, another one there, and if this information is then, after completing the description, placed on a map, the author can show only what he has already put into words. He has thus limited himself and his map will be weak in its terminology because he uses the terms of his subjective and possibly inconsistent descriptions rather than purely objective ones. Of course, this need not be so, and after a good description, no matter how subjective, it is still possible to prepare a good map. But most authors are by then so steeped in the text's approach that a new and independent terminology is impossible for most of them, largely because it simply does not occur to them. It is easy enough for a mind to get into a groove, but it is difficult to get from there into another one.

One might ask here, parenthetically, whether observations that are embodied in a description must needs be subjective. If the author plans primarily a description and later decides to attach a vegetation map, then his activity is influenced by what he sees subjectively. For instance, in describing the physiognomy of the vegetation, he may be impressed by the unusual height of the trees in a given area. He will certainly mention this in his description. Elsewhere, not being equally impressed, he will not mention the height of the trees at all, even though local differences in the height of trees may be more significant. A good example is the vegetation map of Tanganyika (GILLMAN, 1949) with an excellent descriptive text. Nevertheless, the result is not a map of superior quality because GILLMAN stresses here the density of vegetation, there the height, in a third place other features, so that the chances of analyzing the vegetation of Tanganyika on the basis of this map are reduced, and different parts of it cannot be compared.

If, on the other hand, an experienced author of good vegetation maps plans to describe the vegetation of an area, he will draw his map first and will express his data in a manner which embodies all necessary prerequisites for a good map. In other words, he is sufficiently aware of his needs for a vegetation map that his original observation will be both objective and comprehensive to the extent of expressing every feature in terms that can be accepted on the map. If he collects more information than he can place on the map, he will have to select those items which can conveniently be shown; this becomes a matter of organization. But the subjectivity which creeps in so easily can be avoided more readily. Even though, in his text, the author should assemble his data in the form of a poetic essay with a style and beauty all its own, his map will yet be one of a high quality in a scientific sense.

Some authors realize that a vegetation map should be a unit, complete in itself. But they are also aware of the fact that the value of the map would be increased if the legend information on the map could be supplemented by a text. In order to permit the map to be independent of any book or article and yet supply desirable additional information, they place a well-chosen, concentrated text directly on the map, i.e., on an enlarged margin. GAUSSEN (1948), BRAUN-BLANQUET (1947), and WIESLANDER (1937) may be cited as examples; that their maps have gained through the addition of the marginal texts is beyond doubt.

GAUSSEN on his map of France at 1:200,000 brings a fourfold elaboration for each major legend item: (1) the habitat conditions, (2) the natural vegetation (climax), (3) the evolution of the vegetation, and (4) the land use. This sort of text is enlightening not only because of the information it contains. It also illustrates GAUSSEN's outlook: though technically a botanist, he is a geographer at heart, and the colors on his vegetation maps refer in reality to climatic regions.

GAUSSEN then further elaborates his material by adding six inset maps of the same area at 1:1,250,000; these show (1) climax vegetation, (2) soils, (3) land use, (4) agriculture, (5) climate (precipitation and temperature), and (6) agricultural hazards.

BRAUN-BLANQUET (1947) groups his plant communities at 1:20,000 into alliances of one or more associations each. For each of these, he reports on the soil, lists the more important species, and hints at the possible land use.

He adds two inset maps (about 1:78,000) of (1) the natural vegetation (climax), here showing only two associations and "aquatic vegetation," and (2) soils (6 soil types).

GAUSSEN is therefore more elaborate than BRAUN-BLANQUET in spite of his smaller scale. It might be argued that BRAUN-BLANQUET does not require such elaborations because the very nature of his associations implies certain environmental features. But this is not a strong argument because, if taken at face value, it would make the entire supplementary text unnecessary.

WIESLANDER's (1937) major legend items are physiognomic. For each vegetation type he lists the most prominent species and comments on the height of the formation, fire hazard (extremely important in California), effects on runoff, economic aspects, and other features. He has no inset maps. But WIESLANDER then adds a cross section or profile to illustrate the relation of the vegetation to altitude and exposure.

Other authors use profiles to show the relation between the various vegetation types and the underlying geological strata. Cross sections can therefore be valuable additions to the indispensable legend on a vegetation map.

Once an author has decided to have a text on his map margins, he can organize his material in such a manner that the text and the map become an integrated unit, each one supplementing the other.

13

Reduction and Other Technicalities

Reduction

It is always best to prepare the manuscript of a vegetation map at a scale appreciably larger than that planned for the final, printed version. Drafting is easier, and changes and corrections can be made more readily without affecting other parts of the map. Eventually, however, the map must be reduced, and it is most important that this reduction be kept in mind during the preparation of the manuscript. Patterns, symbols, and words on the manuscript map must be so large that they remain plainly legible after their reduction. The proper choice of the lettering size, etc., implies therefore that the author knows in advance the approximate scale of the printed map.

Many a manuscript looked most pleasing to its author but turned into a disappointment when the reduced version was printed. The names may be difficult to read without a magnifying glass if they are legible at all. Line and dot patterns may be ruined similarly. "Theoretically, reproduction of shading patterns should not affect the value of the tones, even at reduced scale. Many cartographers, however, have experienced failures where patterns have either 'dropped-out' or 'closed-up' in the reproduction process. This is a vexing problem since a pattern may be used satisfactorily at one reduction or with one printing technique and give poor results with another. The problem becomes especially acute when dot style patterns of fine texture are used" (JENKS and KNOS, 1961). The reduction may therefore lower the utility of the vegetation map or even destroy it altogether. Obviously, the author must calculate the probable degree of reduction before he starts his manuscript and then select his patterns and his lettering accordingly.

Some authors find it convenient to draw their manuscript maps with inks of different colors. They must remember that the usual photographic reduction not only eliminates color differences but affects the colors unevenly. For instance, red in the original turns black on a photograph, whereas blue appears very pale and, indeed, may vanish altogether. The mapper can use this reaction of the colors to his advantage. For example, he may obtain a base map of his area on which such items as county lines, etc., are printed in pale blue. These blue lines will guide the mapper while drafting and thus assure a greater accuracy of his map. But when his manuscript is photographically reduced, these blue lines will disappear and only the vegetation types remain.

Some mappers keep map and legend independent of one another during the drafting stage. This is entirely legitimate and indeed an advantage because one may be in the way while the other is being done. But it is important that the reduction for printing applies equally to the map and the legend so that all patterns and symbols in the body of the map and in the legend are of the same size. If this is ignored, the symbols may be appreciably larger in the legend than on the map and the result can be confusing and make the reading of the map more difficult (cf. ZOHARY, 1947).

Proofreading

To err is human—even the most careful mapper cannot avoid making mistakes. All vegetation maps must therefore be proofread. However, authors are warned that proofreading a vegetation map is very different from proofreading an article. It is more difficult and more tiring for the eyes and very time-consuming. Just because it is difficult and tiring, the proofreader himself is apt to make mistakes, i.e., he overlooks or fails to recognize the mistakes on the map. Therefore proofreading should be done at least twice, and preferably more often. It is always best to have the proofreading done by more than one person.

Whatever the mapper places on his map must be proofread. This excludes the items he did not place on his map. For instance, if the author uses a standard base map with grid, cities, rivers, etc., then there is no need to proofread these. On the other hand, if he places rivers, cities, or anything else on his vegetation map, he must proofread these, too.

Proofreading a vegetation map includes above all the proofreading of the vegetation types, and their boundaries. If the map was compiled from source maps or aerial photographs, the proofreading consists of comparing the new vegetation map with the source maps or the photographs. This is done most efficiently by cutting a rectangular hole into a white sheet of paper. The paper may be standard letter size (8½ by 11 inches)

and the hole should approximate 3 by 4 inches. Sometimes it is convenient to adjust the hole to the grid. For instance, on a map at 1:1,000,000,
the hole may correspond to one degree of latitude and longitude. This
should be considered the maximum size for the hole because a larger size
reduces its effectiveness.

The white sheet of paper with the hole is placed on the manuscript map.
This focuses the eye on the part of the map that can be seen through the
hole whereas the remainder of the map is excluded. The paper is laid on
the manuscript map so that the northwest corner of the map is seen
through the hole; the left and upper edges of the hole should coincide
with the western and northern margins of the map in the northwestern
corner. The author then compares the vegetation features and everything
else that must be proofread within the hole with the corresponding part
of the source maps or aerial photographs. The paper may not be shifted
until everything within the hole is completely proofread. The author
then moves the paper eastward (to the right) just enough so that the left
margin of the hole comes to rest where the right margin was before. The
latitude is not changed. The new area is now proofread just as carefully,
and when this is completed, the paper is shifted eastward again. In this
manner, the author works his way methodically across the map from the
left margin to the right one. When he has arrived at the right margin of
the manuscript map he has finished only a strip across the northern part
of the map.

The white paper is now shifted back to the left margin of the manuscript map. This time the hole is placed below the original starting position so that the upper edge of the hole comes to lie where the lower edge
used to be at the beginning. From here, the author proceeds eastward
again in the same manner until he arrives at the right margin. Then he
proceeds to the third strip, still farther south, and so on until the entire
map is done.

If the author must interrupt his work, he should note on a paper the
exact latitude and longitude of the position of the hole. He can then
return to this position on resuming his work without having to fear dupli-
cation or omissions.

Everything must be proofread: the colors, the patterns, the symbols, the
boundaries and their location, the title, the scale, the legend, etc. If the
legend items are numbered and the numbers are repeated on the map, then
the numbers must be proofread, too. The author must check whether the
number on the map portrays the correct item and is properly placed on
the map, i.e., into the area of the correct type.

If a variety of features must be proofread, it is sometimes more efficient
to proofread just one at a time through the entire map, and then proofread the whole map again with regard to another feature.

When the proofreader finds a mistake, he records it. This is better and less time-consuming than to correct every mistake as soon as it is discovered. There are two ways of recording mistakes. If the map is small and simple, the proofreader will draw a straight line from where the mistake is located to the margin. At the margin end of the line he records the distance to the mistake and its character, as, for instance: "*14 cm*, change number to 28"; "*4 inches*, blue missing"; "*10 cm*, remove triangular symbol"; etc.

Another way of recording mistakes is useful on larger and more complex maps. It is done on a separate sheet of paper, not on the margin of the map. On the separate sheet, the location of the mistake is indicated by latitude and longitude; the character of the mistake is described as above.

Proofreading means moving one's eyes from the hole to the source and back to the hole, back and forth, back and forth, dozens of times, hundreds of times. This is the tiring feature. The efficiency of the proofreader usually does not last long. As soon as he observes that his eyes are tired, he should rest them for ten or fifteen minutes. Even so, many proofreaders find that their concentration suffers after two or three hours. It is a waste of time and effort to proofread a map when tired.

The reader will appreciate now why proofreading vegetation maps is so time-consuming. This should not induce him to rush the job. Hurry is fatal. In planning his mapping project, the author must therefore allow ample time for proofreading every individual step at least twice. Proofreading is not likely to be overdone.

Necessary Information

When the manuscript is completed and entirely proofread, it is ready for the printer. But a completed manuscript may have different forms and the author must be aware of this because the printer depends entirely on the manuscript as it is submitted to him.

The manuscript is not complete when all vegetation patterns have been applied correctly. There must be a title which reveals what the author intends to show and what the reader may hope to find. It is most important that the title be explicit. If the author wants to show the potential natural vegetation or the dynamic features of the vegetation or its structure or its relations to some ecological factor, then the title should say more than "Vegetation Map" and include a reference to the particular character of the map. For instance, a title may read "Potential Natural Vegetation of Humboldt County" or "The Structure of the Vegetation in the Humboldt Reserve."

The map must also have a grid showing latitude and longitude, and where feasible, the projection should be given, too. There is no absolute need for these where the area involved is very small, such as a bog, but they should be given if at all possible. A grid does become necessary as soon as the mapped area exceeds 2 kilometers in diameter. Accurate data on latitude and longitude can be gleaned from topographic maps as published by the U.S. Geological Survey. The grid lines may indicate minutes or degrees and their spacing must conform to the needs of the map.

The map must have a frame. Such a frame is most effective when it consists of two lines, a thin inner line and a heavy outer line. The numbers which indicate the degrees of latitude and longitude may conveniently be placed between such two lines of the frame.

The map *must* have a scale. This is more essential than some authors seem to realize, for there are vegetation maps without a scale of any kind and such maps are much less useful than they might have been. It is always best to have both a fractional scale and also a linear scale. The first type readily permits comparisons with other maps and the second allows the reader direct measurements on the map. To have only one of these may be adequate, but there is no problem involved in having both and therefore both should be given. The author must take care to give on his manuscript the scale that the final printed version is to have, and not the scale of the manuscript. This applies only to the fractional scale. A linear scale is reduced with the manuscript, hence the proportions do not change. But the fractional scale of the printed map must be known in advance and placed on the manuscript even though the scale of the manuscript is quite different, i.e., larger.

The name of the author or authors must be given on the map. Brevity is best; there is no need to say more than "by John Smith" if that covers it. Sometimes it is desirable to list individually the names of the persons who did the field work, the compilation, the drafting, etc., if the author did not handle these matters himself. But the author's name should stand out boldly among the others as the one who is essentially responsible for the map content and its organization. The map is not the place to reveal the reason for making the map. For instance, the map may have been prepared as a part of a thesis in partial fulfillment of the requirements for the degree of Doctor of Philosophy. If it is necessary to state this, then it should be done in a paper that may accompany the map but not on the face of the map itself.

The map should also show the year or years during which the map was prepared. Considering the dynamic character of the vegetation, this can be a crucial item and should not be omitted. The year when the field work was done may not coincide with the year of publication; the latter is a useful thing to know, especially for bibliographical reasons; both may well appear on the map together. From a scientific point of view, the year of the field work is the more significant. On the other hand, only the year of publication should be shown if the map is compiled from source maps and is not based on field work. This is the case with most maps of very small scale.

Layout

Title, author, scale, etc., and the legend must be arranged and distributed on the map so as to serve their purpose best. This is referred to as the layout of the map. Printing costs are high and therefore the layout should be such as to avoid a waste of space. A waste of space on the map implies larger printing plates and this raises the cost substantially and unnecessarily. On the other hand, the various items should not be squeezed together too tightly, as this will spoil the appearance of the map. If an author is at all uncertain about his layout, he will find it most useful to observe the work of others. The layout is a technicality and has nothing to do with the map content. The author may therefore consult not only other vegetation maps but also geological maps, soils maps, and others. Their problems are the same.

The layout includes the map itself, the title and possibly a subtitle, fractional and linear scales, the projection of the map, year of preparation and of publication, authorship, and complete legend. If the map is part of a journal article, appropriate bibliographic data may be added.

The mapper should make a complete list of items to be shown and then experiment with their distribution and with the sizes of the letters, which may be different in each line. If one or more inset maps are used, their location on the main map, and their own layout and letter sizes, must be considered separately. Letters printed on gummed transparent material may be purchased in a wide variety of sizes.

The mapper should not hesitate to reject his layout if he is not entirely satisfied, and improve it. This may take a great deal more time than an inexperienced mapper may anticipate but undue hurry at this stage must not be permitted. Vegetation mappers will find patience a virtue of singular value.

If the map is to be printed in black-and-white, the vegetation types will best be distinguished by a variety of dot and line patterns. The author can place such patterns on his manuscript map by using Zipatone, Craftone, or similar materials which may be obtained commercially. There is a vast variety of such patterns available. The patterns are printed on transparent material which is easily cut. The author need only lay it on his manuscript and cut out the areas of the different types of vegetation. He places it in the exact position wanted and presses it down. It will then stick to the paper of the manuscript map.

Printing in Color

The matter is more delicate if the map is to be printed in color. The author should consult the printer on available colors and discuss the matter with him. A great deal of research has recently been done on color printing (LACLAVÈRE and DEJEUMONT, 1961) and the author will find it worth his while to acquaint himself with the latest developments in this field. The author must know exactly which color is to be applied to what type of vegetation. He must also know the form in which it is to be applied, i.e., as a flat color, in the form of lines, dots, or some other pattern.

A good printer usually has some kind of a color chart which the author may study. There are three basic colors, red, yellow and blue, and of course, black. The latter is used for title, frame, grid, etc. The three basic colors can be combined in a variety of ways and thus greatly enlarge the number of available colors. The printer's inks may be transparent or opaque. Two colors will combine only if the inks are transparent. If large dots are printed with blue ink on a yellow background, the dots will be green. If the author wants blue dots on yellow, then the blue dots must be printed with opaque ink. This means two different printing plates for blue and the author must be sure to discuss with the printer the cost of printing, its relation to the number of color plates, the need for more than four plates, etc.

Most printers can identify their colors by a number. This is a great aid to the author. All legend items can be numbered and these same numbers can be entered on the map in the appropriate areas. For example, if an area on the map bears the number "8," then this refers to legend item 8. Wherever legend item 8 occurs on the map, the 8 should appear written plainly. Every area on the map, regardless of size, must have a number that relates it to a legend item. Once this is done, the author can make a list of his legend numbers and after each number give the printer's number of the color that is to be used. This will be a simple and clear guide for the printer and will greatly aid in proofreading the color proof.

When all the details have been worked out, the printer can make an accurate estimate of the cost of printing the map. Authors should insist on a color proof. If they find on such a proof that some colors are wrong or too bright or too dark or are unsatisfactory for any reason, then a different ink can be selected for the final printing. A color proof must also be proofread with regard to the accuracy of the color selection and application for every vegetation type on the map and in the color boxes of the legend.

Choice of Paper

The cost of printing will vary according to the quality of the paper. The printer will have samples and the author should be guided in his choice by the use of the map. If the map will be used much, possibly even in the field, the paper should be relatively heavy and sturdy. If the map serves only to illustrate an article in a journal, the paper may be lighter. It also makes a difference whether the map on publication is to be folded or rolled. It is always desirable to have strong paper for maps because they tear easily when much used. But heavy paper does not fold easily and the author must compromise accordingly.

A minor cost feature is the width of the margin of the map. The margin is the strip of paper which surrounds the frame. There again the author must use his judgment: too wide a margin is wasteful and too narrow a margin spoils the appearance of the map. The author can find adequate guidance by studying other maps that correspond to his in size.

Number of Copies

Finally, the author will want to obtain an adequate number of free copies of the map for his own use and for distribution among his colleagues. Most authors do not publish colored vegetation maps very often. But a colored vegetation map is an impressive piece of work and an adequate number should be kept on hand because requests for reprints have a tendency to arrive for long periods after publication.

IV
MAPPING METHODS

14

General Considerations

We believe with GAMS (1918, p. 369) that we obtain the most accurate portrayal of plant communities by mapping them. This can be done by a variety of methods, each of which has its own peculiar merits and imperfections. It happens occasionally that an inspired author develops a new method of mapping vegetation. In the course of many years, and heeding the advice and criticism of his colleagues, he gradually improves his method until it reaches a high degree of perfection. The author is then convinced that his method is superior to all others. Frequently, he also believes that his method can be employed everywhere with the same degree of success and produce equally good results. It is now well established that such authors are carried away by their enthusiasm.

There is no single method of mapping vegetation that will do justice to all the divers purposes for which vegetation maps are now prepared, and it was quite inevitable that different methods should evolve in order to serve the whole gamut of purposes in widely different regions (KÜCHLER, 1960a). For instance, maps like those of Malaysia by VAN STEENIS (1958) and of the Pasterze in Austria by FRIEDEL (1956) are not only quite unlike but required quite different methods. In a region like Malaysia, the vegetation is known only in its broader aspects, and not even that in some parts of the country. In Austria, on the other hand, a great deal of skill and talent has been focused for decades on a vegetation already well known and understood in its details. The two maps could hardly have been prepared by the same method and still be meaningful. Of course, these are maps of widely differing types of vegetation and scale. But even within a given area, one mapping method can never do what two or more methods can achieve in presenting the character of the vegetation. SCHARFETTER (1932, p. 162) even went so far as to say that nothing will advance vegetation mapping as much as the portrayal of the vegetation of a given area according to different points of view. This is not only scientifically sound but has been shown to have considerable practical value as well (cf. Chapter 5 and KÜCHLER, 1956a).

The methods of mapping vary according to the classification of vegetation. Some of these classifications are better adapted to very large scales, as illustrated by the map of the Brabantse Biesbosch (ZONNEVELD, 1960) whereas others fit smaller scales much better as illustrated by HUECK's map of Venezuela (1960).

The need for different methods is therefore well established, and it is useful to discuss several such methods. Some of these are widely used; others are not but nevertheless rest on some interesting idea. A cross section of such methods will permit the vegetation mapper to choose whatever is best adapted to his purpose. It will also allow him to make comparisons and perhaps to modify one or more methods through simplifications, amplifications, or combinations, thus serving his particular needs even better.

The purpose of a vegetation map determines the content and character of the map and these, in turn, determine the method to be used in preparing the map. When the purpose of the map is clearly established and the desired content and character of the map have been determined, then, and only then, can the mapper select an appropriate mapping method. For instance: a vegetation map is to serve as a basis for the establishment of site classes. As the site class is equivalent to the biotope, a vegetation map will be useful only if it shows the plant communities as completely as possible. The purpose of the map therefore demands that the scale be large and that both structure and floristic characteristics be shown in combination, directly or implied. A physiognomic classification like RÜBEL's (1930) is therefore inadequate, because it ignores the flora. On the other hand, methods like those developed by ELLENBERG and ZELLER (1951), GAUSSEN (1948), or KÜCHLER (1955a) permit a satisfactory combination of the necessary details.

Basically, there are two types of methods: mapping by field observation and mapping by compilation. The latter is fully treated in Chapter 18; the following material deals therefore only with mapping methods based on observations in the field.

Planning the Field Work

Before the mapper begins to map, he must plan and organize his work. This is the only way in which to complete the work without waste of time and funds and to assure the highest quality. Such planning includes first of all a knowledge of the relevant literature. This will acquaint the mapper with the various approaches used in the past, the types of vegetation, and their interpretation.

A study of the literature includes a study of maps. If large-scale vegetation maps of the area have been prepared before, they should be scrutinized with great care. The author may, for instance, discover some old large-scale maps prepared by early surveyors or by railroad companies, and he is likely to find one or more maps of small scale. He should not scorn any of these; rather should he collect them, treasure them, and use them to understand and appreciate the character of the vegetation. If there are no large-scale maps, there may nevertheless be a variety of small-scale maps which will reveal general relations and affinities of the phytocenoses.

It is also useful to study all available topographic, geological, climatic, and soil maps. They help the mapper appreciate the problems in interpreting the real vegetation and he will understand better which environmental features are dominant.

Finally, the mapper should become thoroughly familiar with the flora of the region. He should be able to identify the species on sight, including grasses when they are not in bloom. If the mapper does not know the flora adequately, he must obtain the assistance of a professional taxonomist (systematist).

Having made these preparations, the mapper will review and sift the information as it relates to the purpose of his map. He will then know in what types of categories the vegetation is to be expressed.

The inductive approach to vegetation mapping is particularly recommended. Whatever method the mapper selects, he must avoid premature generalizations and must not project into his observations concepts that he or others evolved elsewhere and at other times. The field work should always begin with establishing the vegetational units as they occur in that area at the time of mapping. In other words, the mapper should always map first what he observes: the actual vegetation. This basic mapping must not be complicated by the introduction of ideas on affinities, dynamism, etc. Every one of these may be important but must be considered separately after the vegetation is mapped in its present state. Only experienced mappers who are thoroughly acquainted with the character and history of the vegetation of their area may successfully combine the two phases of (1) mapping the actual vegetation and (2) interpreting it. However, the mapper must always be equipped with a notebook in which he records observations on dynamic and other features of the vegetation. Such a record will be of great value later, when the time has come to interpret his map.

As the mapper walks through the area to be mapped and carefully observes and distinguishes the types of vegetation, he concentrates exclusively on what he sees before him. The resulting freedom from preconceived notions will permit him to test the validity and usefulness of existing concepts and points of view. This is particularly relevant to maps of large scale, because they force the mapper to observe in great detail and very accurately.

By definition, vegetation consists of mappable units. It is therefore the first task of the mapper to establish such units. Under optimum conditions, these are homogeneous with regard to structure, floristic composition, and site qualities, but such optima are not frequent. Indeed, the very concept of homogeneity is not entirely clear; recent discussions (GOUNOT, 1956; AUGARDE, 1957) do not reveal any general agreement on the subject. As a first step, it may therefore be wise to single out all types of vegetation that can be clearly identified in one manner or another. What lies between these can be established more readily as further types, transitions, subtypes or variations, etc.

Of course, the eventual vegetation map is to be useful and, even during the preliminary inspection, the mapper must therefore endeavor constantly to see the vegetation and all its units as a feature of the landscape. In SÜKACHEV's terminology (1954, 1960), the mapper should observe and record biogeocenoses and not only phytocenoses. In mountainous terrain, the three-dimensional character of the distribution of vegetation types must also find expression on the map. In part, the landscape determines the character of the vegetation, and in part the character of the landscape can be deduced from the vegetation, for the interrelations between the two are most intimate. If the vegetation changes, something else must have changed in the landscape. Just what it is that has changed must then be discovered by careful investigation. Such a comprehensive approach to mapping vegetation will help the reader of the map to interpret the vegetation as an integral part of the landscape; it results in the most meaningful vegetation maps and permits their fullest exploitation.

It is desirable to map an area as quickly as possible and also in the greatest possible detail. Therefore some preliminary considerations are necessary. According to the size of the area, the available time, and the state of knowledge on the vegetation to be mapped, four types of mapping may be distinguished:

1. Exploratory
2. Reconnaissance
3. Extensive
4. Intensive

Exploratory Mapping

This type of mapping applies to areas where the vegetation is not well known, if at all. Often it is difficult or impossible to identify the species, as in large areas in the tropics where the vegetation has not been studied adequately. Many people in non-tropical countries picture the tropical vegetation as a bewildering jungle with thousands of species arranged without order or patterns over vast areas. It seems hopeless to map such an area for lack of distinct vegetation types and it is simpler to refer to the vegetation of the whole area with some general term like "tropical rainforest." One may realize that within the tropical rainforest different types do exist, but they merge imperceptibly and cannot be identified.

There are indeed cases to exemplify such difficult conditions but in many regions these examples are the exception rather than the rule. Many of the less dense forests, especially in regions where the rainfall is less extreme, are simpler and can be described and classified without the seemingly insurmountable difficulties presented by some rainforests of tropical lowlands. Where the forests give way to still more open communities like the Brazilian campo cerrado or some of the African savannas, the possibilities of identifying particular vegetation types improve still further.

One way to overcome some of the obstacles to mapping an unknown vegetation is not to think in fixed terms, or in the terms of any one particular classification of vegetation (KÜCHLER, 1960b). It happens often that one classification will succeed where another fails, and frequently it is possible to combine certain features of one classification with those of another. Men like CHAMPION (1936), BURTT-DAVY (1938), RICHARDS, TANSLEY, and WATT (1939), BEARD (1944), and others have prepared very useful ways to classify the physiognomy and structure of tropical vegetation down to the finest detail. This includes the height and density of every individual synusia, the character, amount, and location of epiphytes and lianas, and even the size and character of the leaves and tree trunks. It may not be necessary to always use all characteristics listed in such classifications, but wherever any one of them can contribute to a better and more accurate description of vegetation types, it should be used. This is particularly important where such a feature permits a mapper to distinguish one vegetation type from another. The mapper can go one of two ways and should make it clear which one he selects: (1) He may prefer to mention only those features which contribute directly to the characterization of the community. This means that while the community has many other features, these contribute nothing to set it apart from the neighboring communities. (2) Or else he carefully prepares a list of all features he deems significant, and then consistently describes all of them in every stand throughout the area. The features may at times be of very little significance but the uniformity of analysis is useful later on, when the mapper, working in his laboratory, compares his data on the various units of vegetation. On the other hand, the second way is distinctly more time-consuming than the first, and this may make a difference to the mapper.

Therefore, while the resources to analyze the physiognomy and structure of the vegetation permit the mapper to indicate any differences that may distinguish two types from each other, the use of physiognomic data is not at all the only means at hand. The vegetational analysis can be greatly enriched and refined by floristic information. Of course, this is the very approach which in the tropics is so forbidding that it forced the evolution of advanced physiognomic classifications. But even though the number of species may seem overwhelming, there are yet certain floristic groups which differ so much from the rest that they can be treated as separate items, useful in identifying vegetation types. Such groups include especially the palms, bamboos, tree ferns, cacti, and others. Among these, however, the number of species is often relatively small in any one vegetation type. This can help materially in refining the details established physiognomically.

In addition to the physiognomic and structural analysis, supplemented and refined by floristic data, a third type of information can give additional help in establishing individual plant communities. This consists of a large variety of environmental features which affect or even control the extent and distribution of certain vegetation types. The task of the vegetation mapper is therefore to recognize the various biotopes of the landscape. Both the physiognomic and the floristic features of the vegetation react usually to changes in the environment, especially where such changes are relatively abrupt. A few examples may illustrate this. Phytocenoses on river flood plains which are periodically inundated can often be distinguished from those on low terraces rarely flooded and from those on still higher land, always out of reach of even the highest floods. Or compare the flood plains of rivers with the steeper sides of the valleys, and possibly with less steep uplands: each is likely to have its own peculiar type of vegetation. The sequence of salt water, brackish water, and fresh water displayed along the seashore reveals a zonation of the vegetation, and even the beach alone can possess two, three, or more striplike vegetation zones, based on the amount of spray blown by the wind from the waves to the shore. Changes in the substratum are often reflected in the vegetation with remarkable clarity, and limestone, sandstone, granite, lava, sand, and organic accumulations all produce their characteristic plant communities. Varying degrees of exposure to drying or rainbearing winds can result in noticeable differences in the vegetation of mountainous regions as can many other microclimatic features.

Such physiognomic, floristic, and ecological features permit the mapper to identify a host of plant communities even if he should be mapping the vegetation of an area with which he is quite unfamiliar. It is therefore entirely feasible to map an unexplored vegetation and thereby lay the foundation for future research. The example offered by Wyatt-Smith (1962) illustrates this case excellently.

Another way of exploratory mapping was demonstrated by HUECK, who had the task of mapping the vegetation of Venezuela, an area larger than Texas and Oklahoma combined or about as large as France, West Germany, Switzerland, the Netherlands, Belgium, and Luxemburg put together. HUECK flew back and forth across the country, mapping the vegetation from the air. He marked the start and direction of a given flight on graph paper and then noted the character of the vegetation at regular intervals and, in addition, at all clearly identifiable points in the landscape. Sometimes he was equipped with base maps but often there were none. Even those available proved so unreliable that occasionally galeria forests had to be moved for miles in order to accompany their rivers! Yet HUECK was able to produce a remarkably fine physiognomic vegetation map of Venezuela (HUECK, 1960) which can now serve as a guide for more detailed studies.

A vegetation mapper must be thoroughly acquainted with all possible approaches to the description of the vegetation. He can then use a wide variety of resources and distinguish units of vegetation that might well have been overlooked. The chief purpose of such a broad approach is to permit the actual mapping of vegetation, especially where highly organized systems cannot readily be applied. What is important here is to have the vegetation mapped at all. Once different types are shown on a map, the more important ones can be singled out for further study.

Reconnaissance Mapping

Reconnaissance vegetation mapping is in a sense the same as exploratory mapping, but the term is commonly employed in regions where the vegetation is already better known than in unexplored regions. Usually there is no great difficulty in identifying the component species and aerial photographs are used frequently, although by no means always. Whereas exploratory vegetation mapping usually serves the purpose of discovering the general nature of the vegetation or of the biogeocenoses, reconnaissance mapping is mostly a preliminary step to more intensive mapping. It fits best into large parts of the United States and Canada, the Soviet Union, much of Africa, Australia, Argentina, etc. Smaller areas permit greater detail but the chief function of reconnaissance mapping remains the same: to give a general impression of the vegetation as a prelude to work at larger scales.

Reconnaissance maps imply the availability of some kind of base map on which the field observations can be entered. If the area to be mapped is very large, the base map must be of relatively small scale. But the danger of misjudging an appropriate scale for the base map is quite real. For instance, TANSLEY and CHIPP (1926, p. 36) state that "except in totally unexplored regions, some sort of survey map will usually exist, and if it does not, it is clear that a topographical survey must be made either before or concurrently with the recording of vegetation. A map on the scale of 1:100,000 or thereabouts can be used as a field map for reconnaissance work (though this is on the small side) but the largest scale map obtainable (up to, say, 1:25,000) should be used." For Englishmen whose country has been completely mapped at very large scales, it may be difficult to appreciate that even in a country like the United States, technologically among the most advanced nations on earth, there are large areas for which maps at 1:100,000 or larger do not exist, even several decades after TANSLEY and CHIPP made their statement. This is, of course, even more true of many other countries.

Fortunately, map sheets at 1:1,000,000 are now available for practically all parts of the world. When, during the process of mapping, a 1:1,000,-000 sheet is found unreliable in some of its features, detailed notes on the errors should be taken during the field work so as to permit the eventual vegetation map to be more accurate than the original base map. Even for very large areas and for general surveys, the scale of 1:1,000,000 should be the smallest scale to be considered for base maps. In the great majority of cases, the areas to be mapped at any one time are small enough to justify base maps of scales larger than 1:1,000,000.

In the old days, explorers mapped the vegetation along their routes of travel through unknown lands. But their days have passed. With the availability of modern base maps and possibly of aerial photographs, such "route maps" have slipped into history and can now be justified only in rare cases. The need today is for maps that show areas rather than lines and while in the days of the early explorers this was not feasible, modern technology has reached a level where that need can be satisfied. As a matter of fact, line surveys are still used but they are placed so closely together that they enable the mapper to use such lines as a basis for a vegetation map of the entire area. In a sense, the lines become part of a grid. When the lines of such a grid are spaced closely the vegetation of the entire area will be included.

Where modern topographical maps exist, the observed vegetation can be shown directly on the map. The use of color crayons is advisable, but care must be taken that every color and every symbol is explained on the margin or the back of the map. In countries where communications are good, as in the United States and in western Europe, much reconnaissance work can be done with the help of an automobile, but the mapper should not be the driver of the car. The journey may lead for many miles in one direction but a return journey should be planned on roads parallel to the outward trip, so as to cover different though perhaps similar terrain. Several such round-trip journeys will cover a large area in a relatively short time. Whenever the mapper is in doubt about the dominant species he should stop and ascertain them or collect samples, mindful to number them so that he can later, i.e., upon identification, properly relate the species to the areas where he collected them. If at all possible, the identification of the species should be done upon return from the day's drive or, at the latest, immediately after the end of the trip if this lasted more than a day. On such trips, the mapper must also be careful to map only the vegetation in the proximity of the highway and confine his observations of more distant terrain to the notebook. If he nevertheless wants to record his observations directly on the base map, he should distinguish between vegetation clearly seen near the road and distant types for which he can vouch with less assurance. In a sense, this is the modern version of the ancient route maps but there is an important difference: on the modern reconnaissance map the spaces between the routes can easily be filled in with the help of cross journeys and aerial photographs. Remembering that he is confining himself to reconnaissance work, the mapper should avoid spending much time on investigations of soil or geology. Such matters are better left to more intensive work. In mountainous terrain it is often possible, with the help of powerful binoculars, to recognize vegetation types of one mountain side from another one across a valley. This saves much time as progress in mountains is often slow. The general accessibility of the landscape in the United States leaves the recognition of the species as the major problem. If the mapper works in an area where he does not know the flora well, he will find it less expensive to hire a taxonomist who is well acquainted with the local flora than to do without one.

In many parts of the world the landscape is less accessible than in the United States or in western Europe. One must therefore rely on other means of locomotion. Trains, busses, horseback, and flying are all possibilities, but the latter is useful only if the plane remains at low altitudes. A helicopter can come close to being ideal. Trains and busses have the disadvantage that they do not stop when this may be desirable and travel on foot is very slow and seriously retards progress.

The actual mapping in the field is affected by a variety of features. The time available to the mapper is a consideration only when it is severely limited. In that case, experience will soon teach the mapper how much territory he must cover every day in order to complete his task. However, while the mapper will want to complete his field work in the shortest period possible, his objective should not be record speed but high quality. Unforeseen delays are almost inevitable and it is better to return from the field with a good map of part of the area rather than a poor map of the whole area.

Usually the mapper can estimate in advance the size and scale of the planned vegetation map in its published form. This enables him to calculate the minimum size of an area he can show. However, remembering that he is engaged in reconnaissance work, he will find it more practical to record only areas which are appreciably larger than the minimum area. This will speed up his work considerably and keep his map from being cluttered. The scale of his base map should be two to four times as large as that of the printed map-to-be, ranging from 1:100,000 to 1:500,000 or less. This will permit the publication of his final version at scales anywhere between 1:200,000 and 1:2,000,000.

A reconnaissance map will give its reader a good though broadly generalized view of the vegetation of a region. It can reveal clearly where problem areas exist or are likely to arise, thus guiding the reader in his planning of detailed mapping. One reason why even a reconnaissance map should always be of the highest possible quality is the very fact that the sections to be mapped in detail may not be contiguous and can therefore be related to one another only on the reconnaissance map. The latter is the only link between all parts of the map or between all types of vegetation in the mapped area.

GAUSSEN and VERNET (1958) called their vegetation map of Tunisia the Tunis-Sfax sheet of the International Vegetation Map at 1:1,000,000; it is essentially a reconnaissance map. The implication of the title is that the vegetation of the world is to be mapped at this scale. Such a development should receive every possible encouragement. The International Map of the World at 1:1,000,000 can serve as a uniform base, and progress could be rapid if every vegetation mapper mapped the vegetation on the sheets that cover his country or at least the sheet with the area in which he lives.

Extensive Mapping

There is no clear boundary between reconnaissance and extensive mapping, nor is there one between extensive and intensive mapping. From exploratory to intensive mapping there is, therefore, a gradual change, and one should not insist on placing a map in any one category. As extensive and intensive mapping merge imperceptibly, the differences become a matter of degree: intensive mapping is mapping at a high degree of intensity and extensive mapping implies a lower degree of intensity.

Terms like "intensive" and "extensive" are therefore relative, depending primarily on scale and map content. For a mapper who always works at scales of 1:5,000 or larger, a scale of 1:25,000 will seem extensive. But this same scale will imply intensive mapping to one who usually maps at 1:250,000 or 1:1,000,000. Another distinction can be made on the basis of the map content. In the case of extensive mapping, the different types of vegetational landscapes occupy the center of attention whereas the result of intensive mapping reveals the individual vegetational features of a given landscape, resulting from the microclimate and other similar details. The vegetation map of the Nanga Parbat (TROLL, 1939) is intensive at a scale of 1:50,000. Similarly, the Pflanzenstandortskarte (1:50,000) by ELLENBERG and ZELLER (1951) is intensive. On both maps the correlations between vegetation and environment are shown in a detail that permits an intimate insight into the character of the vegetation and of the sites on which it evolved. Larger scales would not appreciably alter the character of these maps or the methods of their production, in spite of the possibility of showing more detail.

GAUSSEN on his map series of France at 1:200,000 also establishes relations between the vegetation and the environment, especially the climate. But at this scale, a regional survey has replaced the details on the other maps and the work has become extensive. Instead of analyzing individual phytocenoses, the broader vegetation types are shown and thus the character of these maps is different, too. Indeed, the difference between intensive and extensive mapping may be based on the individual plant community as the criterion. The mapping may be thought of as intensive if the individual plant community is a matter of major concern; if this is not so, then the mapping may be considered extensive.

It is usually the purpose of the map which dictates the mapping method. If the mapper bases his choice of an appropriate mapping method on the character of the vegetation, he should begin by focusing his attention on the most complex part of the area. Once he has satisfied himself that the method of his choice can be relied upon to produce the desired results where the vegetation is least homogeneous, he will find no serious difficulty in the remainder of his area. If, on the other hand, he begins in the simplest section, the procedure is reversed and he may find himself confronted with a series of increasing difficulties, leading to continual revisions of his method. It may also imply that the mapper will have to retrace his steps and review the work already done in order to keep it in harmony with the sections done last.

In portraying the vegetation on the base map, the physiognomy is recorded first. A method of analyzing the physiognomy and structure of the vegetation is described in Chapter 15; it is adapted to mapping at any degree of intensity. In extensive mapping, it is not necessary to show every individual synusia; the mapper will prefer to limit himself to the uppermost stratum of the vegetation or to those two strata which seem to him the most significant. Likewise, the dominant species should be listed in every established type but there is no need for detailed floristic analyses. However, the mapper may find it worthwhile to mention the dominant species of each synusia he includes in his physiognomic description. It will be useful to view the recorded plant communities in their landscape setting and to link them broadly, where possible, to altitude, exposure, rock, water, etc. This is largely a matter of appropriately formulating the legend items, as has been discussed in Chapter 12.

Aerial photographs are most desirable in extensive mapping. In fact, this is perhaps the degree of intensity in mapping vegetation where aerial photographs are most useful. They give an amount of detail that fits extensive mapping very well and frequently suffice for the preparation of the map.

Intensive Mapping

Intensive vegetation mapping is, just as in the case of extensive methods, a generalization of the facts, although the mapper attempts to reduce the degree of generalization to a minimum. Every plant community is mapped individually as far as the scale will permit. The mapper now records every detail of the structure and all species instead of the dominant or most abundant ones only. Intensive mapping usually implies a small area, but this may require the same amount of time as a much larger area mapped extensively. It is now possible to reach an unprecedented degree of accuracy in intensive mapping, based on an advanced technology which results in superior base maps of any desired scale, and on high-quality aerial photographs which permit the precise mapping of the vegetational boundaries. The mapper, however, must not permit himself to be seduced by beautiful photographs. Granted that scale and quality can now approach the ideal, the photographs do not give adequate information on all features of the vegetation. In forests, the upper synusia often covers or blurs the lower synusias to the degree that a careful study of every individual stand remains indispensable. In grassland communities, aerial photographs frequently fail to show the details the vegetation mapper wants to record. On the other hand, the aerial photograph is the ideal means for mapping the outlines and boundaries of the communities. The quality of large-scale vegetation maps can now be assured as far as the tools are concerned.

During the past decades, the mapping methods have been greatly improved, too. However, much discussion continues on which method is the best, the most reliable, the fastest, the cheapest, and so on. Some authors, believing they are objective and scientific, use statistical methods; but a lot of numbers is not science, and some statistical methods lead to poor results. Objectivity is, of course, desirable, but it is not always attainable; there are instances when subjectivity seems preferable, as for instance in the choice of sample plots. Such a choice must always be left to the mapper, and his good judgment and experience are often better guides in selecting a sample plot than some statistical method.

From the mapper's point of view, the important first step is the recognition of mappable vegetation units. How he determines such units may vary from one occasion to the next. When his work is intensive, it should always include the most detailed description feasible of (1) the physiognomy and structure of every individual phytocenose, and (2) the floristic composition and characteristics. The vegetation is then adequately described as it is at the time of observation. In his notebook, the mapper should collect further information on the vegetation, such as dynamic features, land use, etc.

The recognition of plant communities is based on experience that a given combination of life forms and taxa will grow in an area where given environmental conditions prevail. Such an area may be large or small; but the assumption is always that, if its character is relatively uniform, the plant community will also be relatively uniform. Where environmental conditions are quite unfavorable to plant growth, as in deserts, on salt pans, in high latitudes and in other extreme conditions, the vegetation may indeed be remarkably uniform with regard to both physiognomy and floristic composition. But as living conditions improve, it becomes increasingly difficult to speak of real uniformity. The vegetation is then perhaps "relatively" uniform, i.e., it is uniform in its broader features and its minor local variations may be ignored under given circumstances. What constitutes minor local variations depends on purpose and scale of the vegetation map. For instance, FRIEDEL (1956) mapped the Pasterze area in Austria at a scale of 1:5,000 and showed much fine detail. But a large amount of this detail would have been suppressed, i.e., incorporated in broader units, if the scale had been 1:20,000, which is the standard scale of the Carte des groupements végétaux de la France, of the Carte de la végétation de la Belgique, and others. All these, however, are considered intensive mapping. On the other hand, FRIEDEL's Pasterze map might have been different, had it been published at a scale of 1:1,000, although it may be argued that a larger scale would not have changed FRIEDEL's map because the extreme environmental conditions above the alpine timberline result in a rather simple vegetation which can be shown in all its details at 1:5,000; a larger scale would therefore mean nothing but an enlargement of the map without leading to a more refined content.

Phytocenoses are not usually uniform. The distribution of life forms and species within the community is irregular and often leads to more or less distinct subdivisions without boundaries. Such a random distribution makes it necessary to establish an abstract phytocenose, i.e., one that incorporates the various characteristics observed in the field, even though they may not all occur on the same sample plot. It is this abstraction that is then recorded on the map. During the field work, the mapper may very well map individual stands, give each one its own name, and treat them as individual units even though they are essentially alike. The abstraction is best made in the laboratory when the nature of all mapped communities can be compared.

The mapper should always move about on foot in his area to acquaint himself thoroughly with the general features of the landscape and its vegetation prior to beginning his mapping activity. This aids the mapper materially in recognizing what vegetation types are most characteristic in his area and on what sites they find their optimal living conditions. The first observation in the field is directed toward the physiognomy and the structure of the vegetation. It happens often that two communities differ in both physiognomy and floristic composition so that the more readily observed physiognomic units imply floristic units as well. For instance, a landscape may be covered with a needleleaf evergreen forest of spruce (*Picea rubens*) which, in places, is enriched with birch (*Betula papyrifera*) and in other parts with birch and fir (*Abies balsamea*). A closer look reveals no undergrowth in some parts, a few widely scattered forbs like bunch berry (*Cornus canadensis*) in others, and in a third section bracken (*Pteridium aquilinum* var. *latiusculum*) and dwarf shrubs like blueberries (*Vaccinium angustifolium*) seem rather common. These distinctions are physiognomic; they are also floristic. Frequently, a physiognomic unit consists of two or more floristic divisions. This means that several floristically distinct communities are physiognomically alike. The opposite happens, too, on rare occasions.

Physiognomic and structural features on one hand and floristic characteristics on the other are the basic criteria in recognizing a plant community. They allow a detailed analysis and also comparisons between the different communities. The mapper in the field, wishing to establish units that he can record on his map, must therefore base his observations on these criteria. They have the great advantage that they are common to all types of vegetation anywhere in the world.

In intensive vegetation mapping, an analysis of the site is necessary, too, for at large scales the vegetation should not only be described but also interpreted. An interpretation, however, is not feasible without an analysis of the sites. Mapping vegetation, strictly speaking, means showing the vegetation on a map. But the value of such a map, especially if it is done at a large scale, is greatly increased if the various types of vegetation are shown in their relation to the landscape. Certain landscape features exercise a controlling influence on the vegetation pattern and a vegetation map is more useful to its reader if he can see the relations between the vegetation and the environmental characteristics that are responsible for its distribution in his area.

Topography, slope, and exposure are noted with relative ease and should never be ignored. Where geological maps are available, they should be consulted; and even without them, the mapper will often be in a position to distinguish the general geological character of the landscape. Many mappers ignore the geology of their area, thereby weakening their maps unnecessarily. This is not to say that the geological features should be shown on a vegetation map. In fact, they should definitely not be shown. But the map is greatly enriched if, in its legend, vegetation types on limestone can be distinguished from vegetation types on granite, etc.

A major feature of the environment is the soil, which is in part the result of the vegetation and in part derived from local bedrock. In some areas, wind, water, and ice deposit loess, silt, and till; the soils are then independent of the local bedrock, at least if these deposits are so thick that the roots of the vegetation do not reach through them. Soil maps are most valuable tools for the vegetation mapper and he should obtain them if at all possible. Where no soil maps are available, the necessary soil samples can be obtained with a soil augur. However, it is better to dig a pit, about one meter square and with walls smoothed out carefully. This permits very close observation of the soil and its profile, but field data must be supplemented with laboratory tests. Soil observations and analyses require special training and the mapper will find it most useful to get such training or else enlist the cooperation of a professional pedologist.

Another feature of the environment which can have a decisive effect on the distribution pattern of the plant communities is water. Frequently there are distinct contrasts between the windward and the leeward sides of mountains, as for instance in trade wind regions or in the Sierra Nevada of California. The amount of available water is sometimes a matter of altitude so that increasing elevation means more water. The mountain ranges in the arid west of the United States supply good examples and SHREVE (1914, 1915) has made excellent studies of these phenomena. The available soil water is also of major significance. In the vegetation-water relations it is not only the precipitation falling on the ground that is important but also the water-holding capacity of the soil, the depth of the water table and its fluctuations, the rate of flow of underground water, and its chemical nature. In the Flint Hills of Kansas, horizontal geological strata outcrop on the slopes and the differences in their water-holding capacity are faithfully reflected in the different plant communities on each outcrop. Some of these water relations can be observed only by specialists and are not of immediate concern to the vegetation mapper. But he should consult with such a specialist whenever he wishes to both map and interpret the vegetation and finds the distribution pattern of the plant communities baffling.

Methods of describing the physiognomy and structure are discussed in Chapter 15; the reader is referred to these for further information.

The detailed floristic analysis of plant communities records far more than the dominant species to which the mapper confines himself when mapping extensively. The detailed floristic analysis is not simply a more intensive version of the extensive approach. Besides recording all species, it is now important to indicate the role they play in the community. This is one reason why it is always preferable to precede the floristic analysis with a structural analysis. The observed species are then studied in each individual synusia separately and so recorded.

Floristic analyses usually rely on sampling techniques and therefore do not include the entire community. Every floristic analysis is only an approximation, but this can be entirely adequate and remarkably accurate. Many methods of sampling and analyzing the floristic composition have been used successfully, but for reasons of speed and accuracy the use of the transect method and the quadrat method with tables have become particularly widespread.

The Transect Method

The transect method has certain advantages which recommend it highly. Line transects are distinguished from belt transects and both may be used profitably. The line transect is the simplest and the fastest method to analyze a plant community and therefore particularly useful where time is an important element in the mapper's budget. The mapper simply runs a long measuring tape (preferably a metal tape) along a straight line through the community, and on his base map or in his notebook he draws the line to scale. He then observes the species that touch or shade the line and the distances between them, and records these on his map or in his notebook on both sides of the line just as they occur in the field. If the vegetation is homogeneous, the line transect will produce results quite as reliable as those of the quadrats and in less time. Instead of a series of sample plots, the mapper may prefer a few line transects and thus progress rapidly. The disadvantage of a line transect is that it is one-dimensional, which makes it sometimes more difficult to record the structure of the vegetation and to establish subdivisions of the community. The mapper will find little difficulty, however, in recording the structure of the vegetation in his notebook in such a manner that the notes can be correlated with points along the line. For instance, points at given intervals can be numbered and the structure described at each point. Or else the structure at a given initial point is described in the notebook and assumed to remain essentially unchanged for some distance. At the point where the structure changes, a new entry is made in the notebook.

The line transect is frequently replaced by the belt transect, which combines some of the advantages of the line transect with those of the quadrats. In a belt transect, the mapper also runs a measuring tape through the vegetation but records the communities on narrow strips of even width on both sides of his line. Belt transects are therefore like quadrats except that one dimension is much longer than the other. The strips are narrower than the quadrats or else a belt transect would be no more than a number of quadrats put end to end. It is usual to observe the vegetation the full length of the belt transect but where this is very long, it is entirely feasible to record the vegetation only at regular intervals, say every other 20 meters, and still obtain satisfactory results. In tropical forests where progress is difficult, the belt transect offers great advantages over other methods (CAIN and CASTRO, 1959). A straight line is cut through the forest to allow the mapper to proceed, and from this line he can investigate the narrow strips on both sides with relative ease because the strips in such a case need not be wider than 5 meters. This gives the mapper a better chance to progress rapidly and with satisfactory results than any other method of intensive mapping. Belt transects should be arranged in straight and parallel lines but where there is a distinct zonation of the vegetation, as at the sea shore or from rivers across their flood plains to surrounding uplands, the belt lines should be more or less at right angles to the vegetation zones. The width of the strips must be uniform throughout but the decision as to the actual width depends, of course, on the character of the vegetation. In the Kansas prairie, for instance, 10 centimeters on either side of the line are adequate. The belt transects are recorded on the base map if it is of sufficiently large scale; otherwise it is recorded in the notebook where a drawing supplements the notes. Needless to say, the mapper must be careful to find the exact location and direction of the transect on the base map in order to assure the proper relation of the vegetation to the topography and other features of the landscape.

When the mapper returns from his field work, he prepares a new copy of his map based on the transects. This clean sheet shows the physiognomy and structure of the actual vegetation, as well as the floristic composition of the plant communities. He makes a legend for his map and then studies each legend item in the light of the notes he collected in his notebook. This will permit the mapper to enrich his map greatly, for the notes will enable him to relate the individual phytocenoses to one another, to various features of the landscape, to dynamic aspects, and to land use. By properly wording and grouping his legend categories, the mapper describes and interprets the vegetation he has portrayed on his map. For further details on proper arranging and wording, the reader is referred to Chapters 11 and 12.

The Quadrat Method

The quadrat method differs from the transect method in that the sample areas are not long lines or belts that give a profile-like portrayal of the vegetation. It is based rather on individual sample areas that are scattered through the vegetation type at random or in a systematic fashion.

The term "quadrat" is German and means square. This implies that the sample areas are squares. The advantage of a square is that its area can be determined easily, accurately, and rapidly. It is therefore a simple matter to relate the number of species or the number of specimens of a given species to a unit area. However, it is not at all necessary that a sample plot must have a square shape. It may also be triangular, circular, or of any other shape, regular or irregular in outline. One advantage of a square of given size is that it greatly simplifies the process of establishing a number of sample plots of uniform size.

The size of a sample plot should be adjusted to the phytocenoses. It depends on the physiognomy and structure of the plant community, and also on its floristic homogeneity. A simple dense and uniform stand of meadow grasses may require no more than one square meter (1 m^2). Even plots of only one quarter that size have been found adequate. A stand of widely spaced desert shrubs obviously requires a larger sample plot, and a forest plot with many tree species may range from a minimum of 25 meters to as much as 100 meters measured along one side of the square. In the case of forests with an herbaceous ground cover, it is entirely admissible to limit the observations in the large plot to the trees and then use a number of smaller and more manageable meter squares for the herbaceous synusia. Cain (1932) suggests the following minimum quadrat sizes:

1. For the soil layer, small cryptogamic synusias, etc.: 0.01 or 0.1 m^2, depending on the complexity of the synusia.
2. For herbaceous layers: 1.0 or 2.0 m^2
3. For rank herbs and low shrubs: 4 m^2
4. For tall shrubs and low trees: 16 m^2
5. For the superior arborescent synusia of tall trees: 100.0 m^2

Obviously. these dimensions do not apply everywhere. For instance, a sample plot of size 5 may vanish almost within a single tree if employed in Sequoia National Park. Cain's table is a valuable guide but the mapper must decide for himself what modifications, if any, are needed for his particular circumstances.

Within a sample plot, every species is recorded by name and coverage. The latter represents the area covered by a species if it were projected vertically downward to the ground. Coverage is always estimated and expressed in percentages of the total area of the sample plot.

The number of sample plots in a given stand cannot be predetermined because it depends entirely on the size of the stand. A small stand implies few quadrats, and a large stand, many. Stands may be so small that the entire unit is used as a quadrat. If a stand is extensive, the number of

sample plots may reach 100 or more. Most phytocenoses are so extensive
or occur in so many stands that a large number of sample plots is feasible.
A floristic analysis requires a large number of sample plots in order to be
reliable. A single quadrat is entirely inadequate.

A large number of quadrats permits a high degree of accuracy in determining the frequency of species. Frequency is the consistency or regularity with which a species is distributed throughout the area of the phytocenose. It is equal to the number of quadrats in which the species is
present compared with the total number of quadrats observed within the
community. This proportion can be expressed as a percentage, but need
not be.

The vegetation is analyzed in the field in order to establish mappable
units. Some authors study the vegetation of their area before they start
mapping it in order to make a "key" to all phytocenoses of their area.
Once such a key is available, the mapper expresses whatever he observes
in the terminology of the key. Such categories can be kept sufficiently
broad so as to avoid too many transitions. As the categories are abstractions, their components are never exactly alike anyway. The preparation
of the key should, of course, be complete but mappers may overlook one
or more units. When during the field work a phytocenose is observed
which is not contained in the key, the mapper should not "force" it into
an existing category but establish a new one. He should record this inci-
dent in his notebook and carefully check later to make quite sure that no
mistake has been made. It is essential that the mapper record the real
vegetation just as he observes it. This most adequately assures the recognition of local vegetation entities. The vegetation of the mapped area can
thus be portrayed in detail with all its own peculiar features. Affinities to
other areas are a different matter altogether and should be considered
later.

The Step-Point Method

The step-point method is used only in herbaceous vegetation. It was
employed successfully in the grasslands of California and the CALIFORNIA
FOREST AND RANGE EXPERIMENT STATION (1955b) has issued detailed instructions on how to analyze vegetation with it. The following paragraphs are based on these instructions.

The step-point method of sampling consists of recording one herbaceous plant at each of 20 points along each of 5 transects, and recording
the herbaceous density estimates for 10 square-foot quadrats, on a square
acre plot (refer to Figure 11 for sampling design).

In addition to his usual equipment, the mapper needs a sample pin,
⅛ inch in diameter, 8–12 inches in length, with a ¾-inch loop at one end

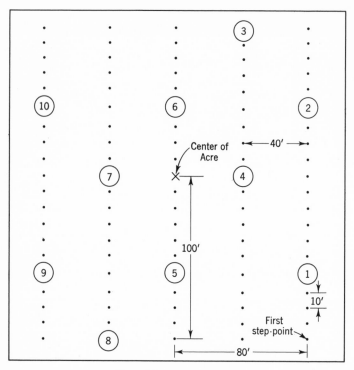

_·   Step-point

(1)   Square foot quadrat and step-point

Figure 11. Type of acre plot for sampling level I. (From California Forest and Range Experiment Station, 1955 b.)

and a sharpened point at the other. He also needs a square-foot frame which is collapsible and divided into four equal sections. Specially prepared forms or "grassland data sheets" facilitate a rapid recording of the observations. On these forms, annual grasses, perennial grasses, and forbs are distinguished and each of these three groups is divided into desirable and undesirable species.

The step-point is established by the mapper lowering a sampling pin to the ground, guided by a definite notch on the toe of his boot. The positions of these step-points are determined by the sampling design. At each step-point the mapper places his boot at a 30° angle to the ground to avoid disturbing the plants in the immediate vicinity and lowers the sampling pin perpendicularly to the boot until it either "hits" a herbaceous plant or the ground. The first herbaceous plant "hit" by the *point* or the *side of the point* of the pin is recorded on the grassland data sheet. If no herbaceous plant is "hit," the pin is pushed into the ground and the herbaceous plant nearest to the pin in a forward direction (180° arc) is recorded.

Herbaceous cover density is estimated using a square-foot frame subdivided by crossbars into four equal sections. At each square-foot quadrat point the mapper locates a density quadrat by aligning one of the subdivision crossbars of the frame with the notch on the toe of his boot. He then estimates the percentage of herbaceous cover in the area bounded by the frame (all herbaceous material, green or dry, of the current growing season is considered herbaceous cover).

The Curtis Transect

CURTIS and his collaborators in Wisconsin experimented much with various methods of sampling forests. They found the following technique to be relatively fast, simple, and statistically reliable.

First, a line of progress is selected along which to make a transect through the forest. Near the beginning of the line, one tree is selected and its surroundings divided into four equal quadrants. The species of the tree nearest to the center tree is determined in each quadrant. Trees must be over 10 centimeters (4 inches) in diameter at 1.5 meters (5 feet) above the ground in order to be considered. This observation reveals, therefore, the generic and specific names of five trees. The same observation is repeated along the transect, i.e., the line of progress determined earlier. Observations should be spaced evenly about 40 meters apart or approximately 40 observations per mile. Marginal areas of the forest should be avoided if disturbances may be confusing.

To speed up the work, it should be done by teams of two. The leader selects the center tree and the other four trees. His helper measures the distances of these four trees to the center tree to determine density. He also measures the circumference of all five trees to obtain the basal areas. The leader records names, distances, and circumferences.

Lower synusias are recorded with line transects between the center tree and the nearest observed tree in each of two opposite quadrants, for instance, the northeast and the southwest quadrants.

The reader is referred to the scholarly and comprehensive treatise *Manual of Vegetation Analysis*, by CAIN and CASTRO (1959), for further information on the theoretical and practical aspects of sampling phytocenoses.

Naming Phytocenoses

It is necessary to name the phytocenoses that have been established in an area or that are used in a key because these names will be employed in the legends of the vegetation maps. Such a name should describe the plant community so completely that a person unfamiliar with it can visualize it with a reasonable degree of accuracy. On many vegetation maps, such names could have been improved if their authors had given them more thought.

Once for instance, on an excursion, a vegetation mapper made the following experiment. He selected a phytocenose and then asked his unsuspecting colleagues individually to describe how they would map it. Every vegetation mapper consulted had a different answer, of which the two extremes may be given here. One colleague spoke vaguely of bog. When he was reminded that there are different kinds of bog, he concluded by dividing the plant community into a Callunetum and a Sphagnetum. Unfortunately, the Sphagnetum contained much more *Calluna* than the Callunetum. The trees were not mentioned at all. The other colleague described the vegetation well as follows: a boggy dwarfshrub heath of *Calluna* and *Sphagnum* with scattered *Pinus uncinata* (KÜCHLER, 1961, pp. 292–293).

15

Analyzing Physiognomy and Structure with Symbols

A system to describe and map the physiognomy and structure of vegetation with the help of symbols was introduced some time ago (Küchler, 1949, 1950, 1955a) and its application from the very largest map scales to the very smallest (Küchler, 1950, 1951b, 1953b) has been fruitful in clarifying trends and needs. These have been further elucidated by a number of publications such as the recent vegetation map of Australia (Cochrane, 1963) and through research sponsored by governmental and other agencies. The following paragraphs present a revised version of this system (Küchler, 1966).

The idea of using symbols is not new and was employed with particular success by Wladimir Köppen (1931). His classification of climates has been applied all over the world and, although the climate of any place is something very elusive, he has nevertheless succeeded in expressing its major aspects simply and clearly. As Köppen was much influenced by the distribution of vegetation when he formulated his system, it was not a very long step from his climatic classification to a classification of vegetation along similar lines. The Köppen classification describes the climate of any region with satisfactory detail. It does not state what weather may be expected there on any given day, even though the climate of a place is ultimately the sum total of individual weather conditions. Likewise, a physiognomic method can describe the physiognomy and structure of the vegetation of any region with satisfactory detail but it does not give the species of which this vegetation is composed.

For the vegetation mapper, a flexible physiognomic system of analyzing vegetation has five major advantages: (1) it can be used on maps of any scale; (2) it can be used on maps of any country or region; (3) it can be expressed in a clear and unequivocal terminology; (4) it can be employed readily because it does not require taxonomic knowledge; and (5) it forms an excellent basis for studies in comparative phytocenology. The latter point is one of great significance and, regrettably, ignored all too often. In the following paragraphs, such a flexible system to describe the physiognomy and structure of vegetation is outlined.

This physiognomic system resembles KÖPPEN's classification of climates insofar as it, too, relies on letter symbols and letter combinations (formulas) to designate the various types of vegetation. Some groups of letters consist of capital letters whereas others consist of lower case letters and numbers. The capitals are used to describe the basic character of a phytocenose and some special life forms; the small letters and numbers are added as appropriate; they serve to indicate structural details as the case may require. The capitals together with their associated small letters permit the mapper to present the vegetation with remarkable and often unexpected refinement (KÜCHLER, 1950, 1956b) because the number of letter combinations is very large. This leads to the great flexibility which is the basic prerequisite and, indeed, one of the major virtues of this system.

Each type is, of course, physiognomic in character. The use of bamboos seems to introduce a floristic element, but bamboos are used strictly as a life form, and no distinction is made between the numerous genera and species of bamboos.

Basic Woody Vegetation Categories

The entire plant kingdom is divided into two major sections: woody plants and herbaceous plants. Woody vegetation is seemingly more varied in its appearance than non-woody or herbaceous vegetation. In accordance with physiognomy as the guiding principle, the woody vegetation is shown on the basis of leaf characteristics, i.e., whether it is evergreen or deciduous, broadleaf, needleleaf, or without leaves. This at once establishes five categories, each one with its particular capital letter.

B: *broadleaf evergreen.* The plants have broad leaves in contrast to needles (see below) and are not bare or without green leaves at any season. Broadleaf evergreen plants include the *Mora excelsa* of the tropical rainforests in British Guiana, the mangrove (*Rizophora mangle*) of tropical tidal flats, the carob tree (*Ceratonia siliqua*) of the Mediterranean region, the Australian *Eucalyptus* tree, etc. Forests composed largely of broadleaf evergreen trees are common in the wet tropics, as in northern Borneo and along the Amazon River, in parts of Australia, in regions with a Mediterranean climate such as California, and elsewhere.

D: *broadleaf deciduous.* The plants have broad leaves as in the case of "B," but defoliate periodically so that they carry no green leaves during a part of the year. The time during which the trees are bare may vary greatly in length. Representatives are the tulip tree (*Liriodendron tulipifera*) in Tennessee, the paper birch (*Betula papyrifera*) in Quebec, the Kapok tree (*Bombax malabaricum*) in Indonesia, the baobab (*Adansonia grandidieri*) in the Sudan, and many others. Forests consisting mostly of broadleaf deciduous trees are well known in Kentucky, France, India, and elsewhere.

Deciduousness is a complex feature. How long must a tree be without green leaves to be deciduous? If a tree is bare only two weeks out of fifty-two, is it deciduous?

The opposite case occurs, too, especially in arid regions where plants may keep their leaves for very short periods only, doing without them most of the time. Or the leaves may be reduced, possibly to small scales, so that they technically still exist but become negligible. There is also the fact, common in the tropics, that different members of a given species do not lose their leaves simultaneously. In extreme cases, it may even be that an individual specimen loses its leaves on some branches at one time and on other branches at another time! The mapper must remember in all such cases that he maps plant communities and not individual life forms. He is therefore guided by the general appearance of phytocenoses in making his decisions (cf. Chapter 30).

Where the degree of deciduousness of a given forest varies with individual synusias, the mapper can describe each synusia separately and so attain a high degree of accuracy. For instance, the type of "seasonal evergreen forest" of the American tropics (BEARD, 1944) is entirely evergreen except the uppermost synusia of emergent trees which are up to 25 per cent deciduous.

E: *needleleaf evergreen.* The term "needleleaf" is here understood to apply to the typically needle-shaped leaves of such trees as the pitch pine (*Pinus rigida*), the hemlock (*Tsuga canadensis*), the true cedars like *Cedrus libani*, etc. It also applies to leaves that are more scale-like in appearance, such as the leaves of the arbor vitae (*Thuja occidentalis*). It includes all plants with needle-like leaves, even though these are not conifers, e.g., the chamise (*Adenostoma fasciculatum*) of the California chaparral and some Australian acacias like *Acacia verticillata*, and *A. asparagoides.* The most magnificent and varied forests of needleleaf evergreen trees occur in the western coastal region of the United States.

N: *needleleaf deciduous.* The term "needleleaf" is here used as in the case of "E," and the term "deciduous" has the same meaning as in "D." Some of the best-known examples of plants which shed their needles seasonally are the larch (e.g., *Larix laricina*) of northeastern North America and the bald cypress (*Taxodium distichum*) of the southeastern United States. Extensive forests of needleleaf deciduous trees (*Larix*) occur especially in eastern Siberia.

O: *leaves absent or nearly so.* Plants without leaves are termed "aphyllous";
they have their chlorophyll in their stems, branches, and twigs, which
are frequently succulent. The *Casuarina* formations of Australia and the
Euphorbia forest of Ethiopia are examples. Aphyllous plants are most
common in arid and semi-arid regions, and include such genera as
Ephedra, Tamarix, and many others. Technically, some of these plants
do have leaves, but they are either very short-lived or else they are
extremely small, often reduced to scales or thorns; in all these cases, the
leaves play a negligible role in photosynthesis as compared with the twigs
and branches.

The five major categories are therefore those of B, D, E, N, and O. As
the vegetation mapper is usually pressed for space on his map, frequently
occurring combinations may conveniently have their own symbol. To the
above symbols, therefore, two more are added, namely:

M: *mixed.* Unless a phytocenose consists of a pure stand, all plant communities
are mixed. However, the term is here employed in a much more restricted
way and limited exclusively to a mixture of needleleaf evergreen ("E")
and broadleaf deciduous ("D") plants. The combination of "E" and "D"
is very common but in order to use the "M," it is necessary that each of the
two components occupies at least 25 per cent of the area. Good examples
occur in Michigan, Georgia, Manchuria, etc. If either "D" or "E" does not
cover at least 25 per cent of the plant community's area, the two letters
are recorded separately.

S: *semi-deciduous.* This term applies to combinations of broadleaf evergreen
("B") and broadleaf deciduous ("D") plants in which each of these
occupies at least 25 per cent of the area. This type is particularly important
in tropical and subtropical countries because the "B"-forests of the humid
tropics merge very gradually with the "D"-forests of the drier regions.

Basic Herbaceous Vegetation Categories

The second basic group of categories is applied to the non-woody or
herbaceous vegetation. It happens frequently that herbaceous plants are
decidedly seasonal in character (KÜCHLER, 1954a). This is, of course,
more true of some types than of others, but in any event, herbaceous vegetation is always shown on a map as it appears in the landscape at the
time of its fullest development. As in the case of woody plants, the herbaceous categories are divided according to their appearance, their physiognomy. There are three categories.

G: *graminoids.* This term includes all herbaceous grasses. To these are added
all plants which are grasslike in appearance even though they are not
grasses in a taxonomical sense, such as sedges, reeds, cattails, and others.
The bamboos are also grasses but they are here excluded because they

are woody. Plants of the "G" category are illustrated by the little bluestem (*Andropogon scoparius*) of the North American prairie, sedges like *Mariscus jamaicensis* of the Florida Everglades, species of *Imperata* of the tropical savannas, and many others. Examples of vegetation types composed primarily of graminoid plants are the Argentine pampa, the Russian steppes, the North American prairie, the African savannas, etc.

H: *forbs.* The term "forb" is applied to the numerous broadleaf herbaceous plants, in contrast to the narrowleaf graminoids. They are usually of the flowering type, but "H" includes also all non-epiphytic ferns except tree ferns. "H" is a common synusia in many broadleaf deciduous forests, especially when these are not very dense and their soil is more or less permanently moist. It is also common in many arid and semi-arid regions where these forbs are referred to as "ephemerals" because their life cycle is very brief.

L: *lichens and mosses (bryoids).* This category includes all mosses and lichens which grow on the ground, whether soil or rock outcrops. Epiphytic lichens and mosses are here excluded. Lichens (e.g., *Cladonia* spp.) may cover large areas, especially in higher latitudes, as in the forest tundra and the tundra of North America and Eurasia. Mosses can be equally important, for instance the *Sphagnum* of the Irish blanket bogs that cover the landscape for miles. In moist climates of the middle and higher latitudes, mosses and lichens may form important elements of the lowest forest synusia.

Algae are here included if aquatic vegetation is to be mapped. Fungi and bacteria are not included in this system. They are physiognomically of no significance in the landscape and therefore need not be shown on a vegetation map.

Special Life Form Categories

The ten capital letters stand for broad categories, but the vegetation of the earth consists, obviously, of more than ten types. In order to refine the vegetational descriptions, a number of special categories is added, each of which has some very distinctive features. The features usually lend the physiognomy of the vegetation a new character and so lead to new physiognomic types. The special life forms are not mentioned on a map unless they appreciably affect the general appearance of the vegetation. Just when this is the case is left to the judgment of the mapper.

C: *climbers (lianas).* The term "climber" or "liana" is here used for all woody plants that climb trees and shrubs. Herbaceous climbers belong to "H." Lianas are most common in tropical rainforests (e.g., *Paullinia cupana*) but are frequent in many North American flood plain forests, too, like the fox grape (*Vitis vulpina*).

K: *stem succulents.* These striking life forms of great variety are concentrated in the more arid or semi-arid regions of the world. Where they grow in appreciable numbers the general physiognomy of the vegetation is profoundly affected. The barrel cacti (*Echinocactus grandis*) in some Mexican semi-arid regions are well-known examples.

T: *tuft plants*. These plants have in common that they consist of a trunk (often unbranched) which carries at its apex a tuft of leaves, as do most palms. A forest with many palms certainly presents a different picture from one without them. This is even more true where palms dominate the open tree synusia of savannas, as for instance the *Mauritia* savannas of northern South America or the *Areca* palm groves at Angkor in Cambodia. Climbing palms are listed with lianas. Tree ferns (e.g., *Alsophila camerunensis*) are exceedingly graceful tuft plants with slender stems and very feathery leaves, and where they occur in large numbers, every observer becomes acutely aware of them. But tuft plants can also be quite stocky, as when short trunks bear a rosette of simple leaves, e.g., *Espeletia hartwegiana* and *Senecio keniodendron* on the high volcanoes of equatorial regions. Some plants have tufts of long grasslike leaves, e.g., the Australian *Kingia australis*.

V: *bamboos*. Taxonomically speaking, bamboos are grasses; but because they are woody and because of their peculiar life forms they are given a separate letter. Bamboo groves usually consist of individual clumps of bamboo with tall graceful trunks and feathery twigs, e.g., *Gigantochloa maxima* in Java. Elsewhere, as in Chile, bamboos may form impenetrable thickets; thus the *Chusquea quila* represents a shrub synusia in temperate rainforests. The "V" also applies to woody canes.

X: *epiphytes*. Epiphytes are plants which grow upon other plants, as for instance mistletoe on apple trees in New England or Spanish moss on live oaks in Florida. Strictly speaking, epiphytes are not life forms. They range from mosses and lichens to ferns and many flowering plants. Obviously, they include a great variety of life forms. For the purposes of mapping vegetation, they are grouped together. While they are therefore not at all uniform in appearance, they do introduce a new physiognomic element into the life forms of their host plants, and it is this changed look of the latter that is here significant.

These five additional types, the special life form categories, help to further describe the ten basic types, and their presence or absence in a given plant community is often highly significant. They should therefore be shown wherever they attain any degree of prominence in the physiognomy of the vegetation.

The introduction of special life forms is subjective and perhaps not always entirely logical. However, in analyzing and mapping phytocenoses it is often necessary to proceed quite pragmatically. The special life forms listed above change the physiognomy of the vegetation appreciably. Yet without their own symbols, they would be submerged in other categories and the reader would remain unaware of their presence. Palms, for instance, would have to be included with other broadleaf evergreen trees such as live oaks; stem succulents like barrel cacti would merge with Mormon tea (*Ephedra*), both being aphyllous. To classify bamboos would be baffling as they, too, are evergreen. Should they perhaps be in one physiognomic class with mango trees and coconut palms?! Obviously, the special life forms have their place, and it is necessary to record them if important variations in the physiognomy of plant communities are not to be ignored.

Parenthetically, one of the finest collections of illustrations of tropical life forms may be found in *The Tropics* (AUBERT DE LA RÜE, BOURLIÈRE, and HARROY, 1957); it is difficult to match this superb book.

Leaf Characteristics

The life forms, identified by capital letters, may be further described by adding small (lower case) letters to reveal some particular leaf features. This is important because the physiognomy of the vegetation may be profoundly affected by the character of the leaves. Five categories are here introduced but some of these are employed more frequently than others.

k: *succulent.* Fleshy leaves are always striking in appearance, as for instance, some species of *Mesembrianthemum.* Due to their water-storing capacity, they usually occur on evergreen plants.

h: *hard;* w: *soft.* The degree of hardness of leaves is not usually significant to vegetation mappers; this is especially true of soft leaves. As a result, these letters are usually omitted. Hard leaves, however, may be important. They are also termed "sclerophyll" or "leatherlike" and are common in regions with a Mediterranean climate and in tropical regions. On medium- and small-scale maps, the letter "w" may be considered implied and need not be used in describing broadleaf vegetation. Sclerophyll broad leaves should be indicated ("Bh"). On large scale maps with "Bh," the letter "w" may be used where applicable in order to make the contrast with hard leaves clearer.

l: *large;* s: *small.* RAUNKIAER (1934) has presented a scale of six leaf size classes with quantitative values. While this scale is occasionally quoted in the literature (CAIN and CASTRO, 1959), it is not usually applied on vegetation maps. Nevertheless, the more extreme sizes of leaves noticeably affect the physiognomy of phytocenoses and they should be recorded. For instance, in the Mojave Desert, there are areas covered with almost pure stands of creosote bush (*Larrea divaricata*). The shrubs are up to 2 meters tall but their evergreen leaves are tiny, producing a remarkable physiognomic effect.

In general, leaves are considered to be of medium size if no reference is made in the record. Only the more extreme sizes are indicated. The question then arises as to the particular limits at which these extreme sizes begin. The sizes here proposed are as follows: large leaves ("l") cover at least 400 cm² and small leaves ("s") cover not more than 4 cm². Obviously, the size of most leaves remains unmentioned. However, large and small leaves as defined above should be recorded. Thus, the symbol for the creosote bush communities is "Bs."

When different species of one life form, e.g., "B" (broadleaf evergreen) have leaves of different sizes, the large ("l") or small ("s") leaves are recorded only if their respective species together cover more than 25 per cent of the area.

It is often difficult to appreciate the ecological significance of leaf sizes. However, when the latter become extreme, it is usually reasonable to conclude that an extreme ecological condition may also prevail. The interpretation of extreme leaf sizes is therefore often easier and more correct than the interpretation of less extreme leaf sizes. This is the reason for proposing here to ignore all leaf sizes except the more extreme ones.

RAUNKIAER has six leaf size classes; they may be used whenever details on leaf sizes are needed. However, it is usually adequate to limit the record to the extreme sizes. The limits here proposed fall well within the range of RAUNKIAER's scale: both leptophyll and nanophyll size classes are less than 4 cm², and the upper limit of macrophyll and the whole megaphyll classes is well above 400 cm². The class of small leaves ("s" < 4 cm²) includes therefore all of RAUNKIAER's leptophyll and nanophyll classes and the lower margin of the microphyll class. The large leaves ("l" > 400 cm²) include most of the macrophyll and all of the megaphyll classes. The unrecorded medium-sized leaves therefore include the upper part of the microphyll, all of the mesophyll, and the lower part of the macrophyll classes. It is as if, in the system here proposed, RAUNKIAER's mesophyll class had been extended beyond its margins into each of the adjoining size classes.

It is tedious and often difficult to determine the exact size of a leaf. However, CAIN and CASTRO (1959) have discovered a simple solution to the problem. They have shown that it is possible to obtain results of reasonable accuracy by taking two-thirds of the rectangle formed by the length and the width of the leaf. If, therefore, a leaf measures 40 cm in length and 28 cm in width, the area of the rectangle of length times width is $40 \times 28 = 1120$ cm². The area of the leaf is then approximately two-thirds of this area, or 746 cm². As this exceeds 400 cm², the minimum size of large leaves, the measured leaf is classified as large ("l").

Compound (pinnate, palmate, etc.) leaves are considered in their entirety when their sizes are to be determined. Some authors prefer to express the size of a compound leaf by referring only to an individual leaflet, and sometimes this is convenient. For instance, no problem arises in clearcut cases, as with the common locust tree (*Robinia pseudoacacia*). However, it is often difficult to establish a leaflet. The matter becomes quite problematical when leaves are pinnately divided, as for instance in the case of the compass plant (*Silphium laciniatum*) of the Kansas prairie. Indeed, some plants may have simple and compound leaves simultaneously, such as the Rocky Mountain maple (*Acer glabrum*) of the western United States, or the Japanese woodbine (*Parthenocissus tricuspidata*). Even the same compound leaf may have distinct leaflets in its lower parts and be only pinnately divided in the upper parts, as for example in the case of the poison hemlock (*Conium maculatum*). There are numerous transitions between simple and compound leaves and many problematical cases, especially in the tropics. The problem is solved simply by always considering the surface of the whole leaf and not of just one of its parts.

Structural Categories

The physiognomy and structure of the vegetation are dependent not only on deciduousness, the presence of forbs or palms, etc. It is essential to describe two other characteristics because of their profound effect. They are height and coverage. Both can be measured accurately. Usually, however, it will suffice to estimate rather than measure them. Applied to the individual synusias, they enable the mapper to describe the structure of the vegetation in remarkable detail, especially on maps of large scale. On small-scale maps the mapper can show only the uppermost synusia and describe it in general terms.

As in the case of KÖPPEN's classification of climates, here, too, it has been impossible to avoid the introduction of arbitrary delimitations. Whenever an arbitrary choice is made, it is open to criticism, but this is inevitable. It is not possible to satisfy everybody, but the numerical values here proposed should be acceptable to most vegetation mappers.

The height of the vegetation is measured from the ground upward to the "surface" or average height of the upper limits of a synusia. The mapper can ignore the fact that the height of some plants differs from the average; such a detail need not be important. In the tropics, however, many rainforests have a "surface," albeit a most irregular one, which is pierced by widely spaced trees which tower above the rest, for instance, the Brazilnut trees (*Bertholletia excelsa*). They form a very open synusia of their own and should not be ignored. The mapper must acquaint himself with the characteristics of the vegetation before mapping it. This will assist him materially in all cases where he must use his own judgment and decide arbitrarily whether or not to show a given feature and how to show it.

The height classes, here proposed, are as follows:

Class		Height
8	=	>35 m
7	=	20 –35 m
6	=	10 –20 m
5	=	5 –10 m
4	=	2 –5 m
3	=	0.5–2 m
2	=	0.1–0.5 m
1	=	<0.1 m

The height of woody vegetation does not usually present any problems. It can be measured or estimated without difficulty.

The reader may have noted that no specific distinction has been made between trees and shrubs. There are many examples where such a distinction is difficult or impossible to make. For instance, if the mapper is confronted with a dense stand of Douglas fir (*Pseudotsuga menziesii*) on a large recently burned-over area, and the young Douglas firs are barely 1 meter tall, does he record trees? Or perhaps shrubs? At what height does a plant change from a shrub into a tree? Some authors, e.g., ELLEN-BERG (1956), consider a height of 2 meters an acceptable dividing line but many shrubs grow much taller than 2 meters. On the other hand, DANSEREAU (1957), used 8 meters as a dividing line between trees and shrubs. As many trees are less than 8 meters tall, his proposal does not seem to offer an improvement over ELLENBERG. In some regions, especially in semi-arid areas (e.g., western Texas or much of the Gran Chaco in Paraguay), many square miles are covered with a vegetation that consists essentially of a transition between trees and shrubs. The palo verde (*Cercidium* spp.) in Arizona, the mesquite (*Prosopis* spp.) in Texas, and many others occur as shrubs, trees, and in every intermediate form. It is therefore often impractical to distinguish between them. Indeed, it seems that an upper limit for shrubs is undesirable.

A simple solution to the problem is offered by omitting the distinction between trees and shrubs altogether. Instead, a group of height classes has been introduced which is applicable to all life forms. By establishing eight such classes, a description of the vegetation can be given in adequate detail and the vexing tree-shrub problem is eliminated.

In addition, the height classes are not expressed by letters as are all other categories. Numbers are used instead. This clarifies the formulas (see below) appreciably. A number stands out boldly among letters and makes it easier to read the formula. DANSEREAU (1961) has already pioneered in this direction.

An absence of symbols for height categories in woody vegetation implies that trees are the dominant life form. This requires that height classes must be given for shrub synusias regardless of whether they occur alone, above lower synusias, or under trees. In the latter case, i.e., where both trees and shrubs are mentioned in the formula, both must be given their respective height class symbols.

The height of herbaceous vegetation is subject to strong seasonal fluctuations as many herbaceous plants die down to the ground during the period of dormancy, no matter how tall they may grow. Kansas sunflowers, for instance, will reach a height of 3 meters during the growing season, but every winter they vanish. For the purposes of mapping, the herbaceous vegetation is recorded as of the time of its maximum development which usually begins with the flowering phase.

The final group of small letters refers to the spacing of plants in the landscape, thus describing the density of the vegetation. These letters express the density by indicating the percentage of the ground covered by the respective life forms, assuming that they are projected vertically to the ground. Thus the density is in reality the degree of coverage of the individual life forms. There are six coverage classes, as follows:

c: *continuous.* This implies a continuous growth, and the plants often touch one another. The c is usually omitted and the vegetation is assumed to be continuous unless it is qualified by any one of the other letters in this group. Where vegetation types of varying coverage occur together, the "c" is used to advantage in order to show the contrast with more open stands. The coverage characterized by "c" is 76–100%.

i: *interrupted.* The plants are standing rather close together and, from a distance, may give the appearance of continuous growth. However, they are usually spaced so widely apart that they do not touch. The mapper must not confuse the coverage with the distances between trees. For instance, spruces need not be far apart before the ground between them is flooded with sunlight, whereas many broadleaf trees may be much more widely spaced before the canopy is broken at all. Among herbaceous plants, the letter "i" may be especially useful in connection with bunch grasses. The coverage characterized by "i" is 51–75%.

p: *parklike* or *in patches.* When the "p" is used in connection with woody vegetation, it signifies that the trees and shrubs grow singly or in small groves, as in so-called parklands and in savannas. In the case of herbaceous vegetation, the "p" may signify disconnected patches. The coverage characterized by "p" is 26–50%.

r: *rare.* This is applied to life forms which are more widely scattered than in "p." It may, for instance, refer to a life form associated with another one of greater continuity. Thus, occasional, widely spaced medium-tall palms may rise out of a continuous cover of grass: "GTr." A more detailed description of this vegetation might be: "G3cT6r." The coverage characterized by "r" is 6–25%.

b: *barren.* The vegetation is much reduced and the landscape appears barren. The coverage has now shrunk to 1–5%.

a: *almost absent.* Life forms now cover less than 1% of the area, or else there is no plant life at all and the vegetation is absent. This is common on shifting sand dunes, in very rocky desert landscapes, etc. The letter "p" attached to an "a" ("ap") at the end of a formula implies that open patches occur within a plant community.

The numerical values of the coverage classes are as follows:

Class		Coverage
c	=	>75%
i	=	50–75%
p	=	25–50%
r	=	5–25%
b	=	1– 5%
a	=	<1%

Both height and coverage classes vary in size, and in both cases the lower classes show a much finer detail than the upper classes. The height classes increase steadily in size whereas the coverage classes increase only in the lower categories and the three higher classes are of uniform size. It makes relatively little difference whether a forest canopy is 26 or 28 meters high. But it makes a great difference whether a synusia is 8 centimeters tall or 160 centimeters. Similar reasoning applies to coverage.

The letter symbols of this system are conveniently grouped together in Table 6.

Formulas

If a phytocenologist wishes to analyze vegetation, and has no forms (see below) on which to record his observations, he will find it convenient to combine and group the various letters and number symbols in formulas so as to produce the most meaningful description of the phytocenoses in the shortest form. For instance:

D   = a forest of broadleaf deciduous trees.
D7   = a forest of broadleaf deciduous trees which are 20–35 m tall on the average.
D75 = a forest of broadleaf deciduous trees in two continuous layers; in one layer the trees are 20–35 m tall and in the other layer the trees are only 5–10 m tall.

There is no need to record a life form more than once just because it occurs in more than one stratum. The life form symbol is repeated when the individual synusias are described separately, perhaps written one below the other in the same order in which they occur in the field, as, for instance:

B8CX
B6p
T5r
B3i T3p

In all other cases one-line formulas are composed for a detailed description of the entire phytocenose.

There are eight height classes, each characterized by a one-digit number.

Table 6

LIFE FORM CATEGORIES

BASIC LIFE FORMS		SPECIAL LIFE FORMS	
Woody Plants:		Climbers (lianas)	C
Broadleaf evergreen	B	Stem succulents	K
Broadleaf deciduous	D	Tuft plants	T
Needleleaf evergreen	E	Bamboos	V
Needleleaf deciduous	N	Epiphytes	X
Aphyllous	O		
Semideciduous (B+D)	S	LEAF CHARACTERISTICS	
Mixed (D+E)	M	hard (sclerophyll)	h
Herbaceous Plants:		soft	w
Graminoids	G	succulent	k
Forbs	H	large (> 400 cm^2)	l
Lichens, mosses	L	small (< 4 cm^2)	s

STRUCTURAL CATEGORIES

HEIGHT (STRATIFICATION)	COVERAGE
8 = > 35 meters	c = continuous (> 75%)
7 = 20 - 35 "	i = interrupted (50-75%)
6 = 10 - 20 "	p = parklike, in patches (25-50%)
5 = 5 - 10 "	r = rare (6-25%)
4 = 2 - 5 "	
3 = 0.5 - 2 "	b = barely present, sporadic (1-5%)
2 = 0.1 - 0.5 "	a = almost absent, extremely scarce (<1%)
1 = < 0.1 "	

No height class symbol ever consists of more than one digit. If therefore the formula reads "D75," it means that there is a broadleaf deciduous forest consisting of two continuous strata, one layer in height class 7 and another in class 5. The reader may recall that the "c" symbol for "continuous" is usually omitted and used mostly to emphasize contrasts (see example immediately following).

"D73p" or "D7c3p." In this case, we find a patchy layer of broadleaf deciduous shrubs under a continuous canopy of broadleaf deciduous trees. The first of the two given versions is legitimate and there is no need for a "c" symbol to follow the "7." However, it is safer and, especially for beginners, more reassuring to use the second version and place a "c" symbol after the "7." The contrast in the degree of coverage of the two strata is then established beyond any doubt.

Symbols for lianas and epiphytes are inserted in the formula after the tallest height class of woody life forms in which they occur; they are given without further qualifications: "B8CX B6p3i T5r3p."

The most conspicuous feature of the vegetation is always placed at the beginning. For instance: "DG" is a "forest of broadleaf deciduous trees with a layer of grass underneath the trees." The trees are the most conspicuous feature and therefore are mentioned first. If, on the other hand, the vegetation consists of a grassland with thinly scattered trees, then the order is reversed because the grass is more prominent than the trees. The formula now reads "GDp" or perhaps "G3 D5r."

The small letters are used to qualify the capital letters. Each capital letter has its own small letters and therefore must be followed by them immediately. If there is more than one capital letter in the formula, each will have its small letters independently of the other. For instance: "D6H" implies that a broadleaf deciduous forest is 10–20 meters tall, but the formula says nothing about the height of the forbs that grow in the forest. If the formula reads "DH2," the implication is that, in a broadleaf deciduous forest (height not given), there grows a ground cover of forbs, 10–50 centimeters tall. If the height of both the trees and the grass is wanted, then both must be given separately: "D6 H2," "D7 H2p," or whatever else the case may be.

The symbols are used in a prescribed sequence. First, the life form is shown by its capital letter. If leaf size is to be recorded, it follows immediately after the life form symbol, thus: "H1" or "Bs." The height class is given next and the coverage is shown last. The sequence is always the same: life form—leaf size (if any)—height—coverage. This sequence applies to each recorded life form individually. Thus "D6i E6b" shows a unistratal forest of broadleaf deciduous trees covering 50–75 per cent of the stand's area. There is an admixture of needleleaf evergreen trees of similar height and covering only 1–5 per cent of the area. Height and coverage are therefore given separately for both "D" and "E," which are members of the same synusia.

The number of letters used in a formula depends on the available information and on the scale of the map. Maps of very small scale should have short formulas. A little world map in an atlas will have vegetation types many of which can be described with formulas of minimum size, perhaps a single capital letter (KÜCHLER, 1951b, 1953b). The other extreme is a map of a small area, done at a very large scale. On such a map, the formulas should contain the features of the physiognomy and structure of every phytocenose just as completely as possible. This should certainly be so on the field map and in the field notes, or at least in one of these. It will give the mapper a complete record that can later be manipulated to suit the scale and the purpose of the map. Formulas can be very long, but the mapper should not hesitate to write long formulas because completeness of information is of crucial significance in several stages of map preparation, even though some of this information will not be used on the map. When mapping at large scales, it is always advantageous to establish separate formulas for each synusia of each phytocenose. This will contribute materially to the clarity of the field maps and notes. Two examples may illustrate such descriptions.

"S6i E8r B4p." This formula describes the physiognomy and structure of the following type of vegetation in northern California. The major synusia consists of a mixture of broadleaf evergreen and broadleaf deciduous trees, 10–20 meters tall on the average and covering from 50 to 75 per cent of the ground (S6i). Towering above it are needleleaf evergreen trees more than 35 meters tall; they cover only 5–25 per cent of area (E8r). Then, below the major layer, there is a patchy layer of broadleaf evergreen shrubs of 2–5 meters in height and covering 25–50 per cent of the ground (B4p).

Another complex example is "D7c4r H2p L1r." This formula describes the following vegetation in western New York. There are two layers of deciduous broadleaf plants, one continuous layer of trees 20–35 meters tall ("D7c") and one layer of shrubs 2–5 meters high and covering only 5–25 per cent of the area ("D4r"). Under the shrub layer is a synusia of forbs averaging 10–50 centimeters in height, and covering about ¼ to ½ of the ground ("H2p"). Finally, there is a very open synusia of mosses and/or lichens that are less than 10 centimeters tall and that cover 5–25 per cent of the area ("L1r").

The generalization of vegetation types on small-scale vegetation maps results in the omission of details in the formulas. For instance, the first of the examples given above may be reduced by omitting the undergrowth. Before the reduction the formula read "S6i E8r B4p"; after the reduction it reads "S6i E8r." Further reduction leads to omission of the height classes: "SiEr." Ultimately even the coverage is dropped and the formula is reduced to its minimum: "SE."

The second example may be adjusted to the desired smaller scale in successive steps as follows: "D7c4r H2p L1r"—"D7c4r H2p"—"D7c4r"— "D7"—"D."

Generalizations can be carried out in more ways than one. If a vegetation mapper must generalize his data, he should do so in a manner that the purpose of his map is served best. For instance, if the vegetation in parts of the Rocky Mountains is to be mapped for foresters, forest economists and people of similar interests, then the generalization will retain the various types of trees, their height and density. The lower synusias may be omitted and all herbaceous vegetation is ignored. However, if the vegetation of the same area is to be mapped for sheep herders, the tree synusia looses much of its significance while the ground cover of graminoids and forbs becomes all-important. Tree growth is then shown on the map simply as "forest" and all available space is devoted to the details of the herbaceous vegetation.

In this and similar ways, the vegetation mapper selects from his data only those that serve a given purpose. While in the field, he collects information on all features of the vegetation. This is done as completely as possible and in the greatest possible detail. Once his field work is completed, he is in a position to prepare vegetation maps for a variety of purposes. All his maps will be based on the same original data, but these are used selectively and, indeed, can be so used in a great variety of combinations. The author experimented along such lines in Maine (KÜCHLER, 1956b), and DANSEREAU (1961) produced interesting results in the region around Montreal, Canada.

It may be that a specific purpose is lacking and the vegetation map is to portray the general features of the vegetation of a region. This is especially true when the map scale is small. The mapper is then free to select what, in his opinion, is most characteristic of the prevailing vegetation types. Generalization always implies selection and selection is all too often a matter of judgment. The mapper will want to present the vegetation in the greatest possible detail that the scale permits without cluttering the map. This consideration and the amount and quality of the available information form the framework within which the mapper must manipulate his generalization. If he proceeds on the basis of well-reasoned arguments and if his map content is well organized, his results should be satisfactory.

Recording Data

The basis of all phytocenological work is, of course, the intensive observation and detailed analysis of plant communities in the field. Only this will permit the accumulation of information that can then be used in a great variety of theoretical and practical considerations. A simple form, the Phytocenological Record, has been devised to facilitate the recording of physiognomy and structure of the vegetation in the field (Table 7).

The phytocenological record has proved satisfactory in the middle latitudes, for natural vegetation as well as in cultural types. It has also been employed successfully in tropical and arctic environments, with vegetation types ranging from a variety of tropical rain forests to scrubby low deciduous forests, tundra, and grasslands. It is therefore adapted to a wide variety of vegetation types. It takes very little time to record the desired information on this form.

The phytocenologist who wishes to analyse the vegetation does well to acquaint himself thoroughly with the individual phytocenoses by walking around in them. He then observes the stratification of a given plant community and proceeds to write down his findings for each synusia separately, one at a time. If he is in a forest that is 16 meters tall, he observes everything in height class 6. If the forest is deciduous, he will go to the square where the vertical column of D meets the horizontal column of height class 6 on the phytocenological record. In this square he records the coverage of D. If the canopy is closed or nearly so, he writes a small "c" into the square. If a few patches of deciduous shrubs cover a rather small portion of the area, and if these shrubs are approximately 0.5–2 meters tall, they are recorded in the horizontal column of height class 3 where it meets the same vertical column of D. As the patches of shrubs cover so little ground, their coverage is more likely to be "r" and, if the leaves of these shrubs happen to be small (less than 4 cm^2), coverage and leaf size are shown together: "rs." In this way, any life form in any height class is noted in the appropriate space.

There seems to be no satisfactory method to record the coverage or any other quantitative aspect of epiphytes and climbers (lianas). Their distribution may be strongly vertical. They are therefore viewed subjectively. In the proper place on the phytocenological record, a diagonal dash (/) is shown if lianas and epiphytes are modestly represented. If they are abundant, a cross (x) is shown instead. For epiphytes, this is done in every height class in which they occur. Lianas are recorded only in the uppermost height class that they reach, and where they spread about. Of course, this may happen in more than one height class, and the record should reveal that.

The lower part of the form is used for notes on anything that seems significant. Comments on reproduction of forest trees, evidence of fire, logging, grazing, or some other form of disturbance or exploitation are entered here as well as observations on the soil, rockiness, profile, etc. Additional comments on life forms are also useful, such as stilt roots,

Table 7

PHYTOCENOLOGICAL RECORD No. 1

Location: section 29, T.12 S., R.22 E.

Date: 21 June 1964

Height above sea level: 800-840'

Base map: USGS topo.: De Soto, Kansas

Slope and exposure: 8° nw

Aerial photograph No. ZL-4W-78

Landscape: steep southern bluffs along

Type (transect, quadrat etc.) and size of

Kaw River flood plain

stand samples: quadrat - 225 m²

Structural Analysis

Life forms:	B broadleaf evergreen	D broadleaf deciduous	E needleleaf evergreen	N needleleaf deciduous	O aphyllous	S B+D: semi-deciduous	M D+E: mixed	G graminoids	H forbs	L lichens mosses	C climbers (lianas)	K stem succulents	T tuft plants	V bamboos	X epiphytes
Height classes:															
8 = >35 meters															
7 = 20 - 35 "															

6 = 10 - 20 "	c						a			
5 = 5 - 10 "	r									
4 = 2 - 5 "	r					r	a			
3 = 0.5 - 2 "	p									
2 = 0.1 - 0.5 "	r					i				
1 = <0.1 "										

coverage: c = >75%; i = 51-75%; p = 26-50%; r = 6-25%; b = 1-5%; a = <1%.

leaves: h = hard (sclerophyll); w = soft; k = succulent; l = large (>400 cm²); s = small (<4 cm²).

Notes

partially logged 8 years ago

Table 8

Floristic Analysis

Stand samples:	1	2	3	4	5	6	7	8	9	10	11	12	13	14	15	16	17	18	19	20	F
Number of species:	24																				
tree layer: D6c5r4r																					
Quercus rubra	4																				
Quercus muhlenbergii	—																				
Carya ovata	—																				
Fraxinus americana	—																				
Cercis canadensis	2																				
Ulmus americana	+																				
Tilia americana	+																				
Vitis cordifolia	+																				
shrub layer: D3p2r																					
Staphylea trifolia	2																				
Ulmus rubra	—																				
Cercis canadensis	—																				
Carya ovata	+																				
Ribes missouriensis	—																				

Species	
Symphoricarpos orbicu-latus	−
Quercus rubra	−
Rhus radicans	+
Parthenocissus quinque-folius	+
Smilax hispida	+
forb layer: H3r2i	
Desmodium canadense	2
Podophyllum peltatum	−
Asarum canadense	−
Galium aparine	−
Polygonatum commutatum	−
Chenopodium album	+
Circaea latifolia	+
Eupatorium purpureum	+
Sanicula marilandica	+

buttresses, the character of epiphytes, etc. Upon return from the field, the phytocenological record is typed and filed for use in preparing vegetation maps and discussions of the vegetation.

The reverse of the form (Table 8) is used whenever the floristic composition of the plant community is to be determined. Following standard practice, the names of the species are written into the wide column at the left and the coverage of each species is recorded in the column of each stand sample in which the species occurs.

Descriptive Refinements

The system of describing vegetation as presented above is adequate for all practical purposes. It may nevertheless happen that a mapper wishes to add a symbol for some features of the vegetation such as trunks with buttresses, stilt roots, etc., not listed here. In all such cases, new and different symbols are introduced. Any new introduction must be clearly explained in the legend of the map so as to leave no doubt in the mind of the reader. For instance, if the mapper should wish to distinguish different heights of very tall trees, the number of height classes may be increased with the use of primes thus: $8' = 35$–50 meters; $8'' > 50$ m. Such a refinement might be useful in areas like the needleleaf evergreen forests of western North America, where it was employed in site classifications.

In this manner, the mapper can enrich his descriptions of the vegetation. But he must be very judicious in making such additions and avoid them if at all possible in order to avoid confusion. A greater complexity often lowers the legibility of the vegetation map and may thereby lower its value. In fact, however, this system has been applied to a great variety of vegetation types, always resulting in satisfactory descriptions.

16

Mapping Herbaceous Vegetation

One of the most important resources of many parts of the world is their grassland vegetation. Of course, plant life is a primary resource in any landscape, but in mapping it, the herbaceous vegetation reveals significant features which require special consideration. It becomes evident that in mapping herbaceous vegetation, a uniform approach to all vegetation types may not produce the best results.

The great majority of vegetation maps treat woody vegetation in much greater detail than herbaceous vegetation. Trees are often enumerated by genera or species on maps which refer to the herbaceous vegetation with no more than "grassland"; at times there is a broad distinction between tall and short grass, meadows, bunch grass, marsh grass and others.

These observations may lead to the conclusion that herbaceous vegetation is of slight importance. This conclusion is not sound, because in an area like the North American prairie or the pampa of South America herbaceous vegetation is practically the only kind of any significance. Furthermore, in various parts of the world, forests are used almost exclusively for grazing purposes, which gives the herbaceous ground cover more importance than the tree synusia. Also, herbaceous plants are primary indicators of soil conditions and changes, which explains their value in land management. This list of arguments can be enlarged considerably.

Why, then, has the herbaceous vegetation been treated like a stepchild on so many vegetation maps? Among the possible answers, two have perhaps special significance. The first, rather intangible one is the attitude of the authors of vegetation maps. The vast majority of these authors are forest-minded because they come from regions where forests are the natural vegetation. Their eyes react quickly to changes in the floristic composition of forests, but they are rarely trained to be equally sensitive to the features of grasslands. MALIN (1947) pointed out that forest-minded people analyze all land from a forest point of view and, therefore, often speak of "treeless" areas when referring to the great grasslands of the earth; had man built his civilizations above all on grasslands, he might well have referred to the great forest regions of the earth as "grassless." Vegetation maps themselves support this argument; the contrast is striking when vegetation maps by authors from forest lands are compared with maps by grassland authors.

The second answer is probably more important than the first one; it lies in the very nature of grasslands. The individual specimen of an herbaceous plant occupies little space. Within a short distance, therefore, it is possible to meet a considerable number of species; in proportion to their size, these species may occupy no less space than trees. To show the same detail on a map of herbaceous vegetation as on a forest map would, therefore, automatically increase the scale of the former. A map at 1:100,000 showing a forest 20 meters high would correspond to a map of grasslands at 1:5,000 where the vegetation is 1 meter high. Obviously, if the same details are required, herbaceous vegetation is either mapped on restricted areas only or many more maps must be produced. One is reminded of the problems of mapping tropical rain-forests where a very large number of species per unit area makes any form of detailed mapping exceedingly difficult.

Another troublesome aspect of mapping herbaceous vegetation is the impermanence of the constituent species. The species of woody vegetation can be identified without difficulty in any season. Herbaceous vegetation, however, consists of a considerable number of annuals, and also of perennials which are geophytic or hemicryptophytic in character. This precludes their identification during part of the year. Even within the course of a single growing season the floristic composition, as far as it is readily observable, may change almost completely, although some species will remain recognizable throughout the summer and, indeed, most or all of the year. The floristic combinations of the vernal and the autumnal aspects of a given herbaceous vegetation type belong, of course, to the same plant community. But it requires a very detailed knowledge of such communities before they can be mapped satisfactorily, and in most parts of the world such knowledge is only now being assembled.

In semi-arid regions of the world, where the vegetation is often pre-dominantly herbaceous, the factor of climatic fluctuation further compli-cates the picture. In such regions the rainfall may be considerable for years, only to shrink to a fraction of its average amount for the ensuing years. The result is a more or less radical change in the floristic com-position of the vegetation. Finally, changes in the floristic composition of herbaceous phytocenoses due to human activities are rapid and far-reaching indeed.

In the deserts of Arizona and California, as of Turkestan and elsewhere, a very short-lived herbaceous vegetation of ephemerals will develop after the rare but heavy rains. Any one who maps such a region when the herbaceous vegetation is fully developed is profoundly impressed by its spectacular masses and colors. It would seem inconceivable to ignore such an important part of the native vegetation. But should it be mapped if it lasts only three weeks out of fifty-two, and does not even appear every year?

Such features seem to have discouraged authors from preparing maps of herbaceous vegetation. Is there then no prospect of preparing satisfactory maps of herbaceous vegetation?

Large-Scale Mapping

The Bundesstelle für Vegetationskartierung under the direction of REINHOLD TÜXEN has published numerous large-scale maps on which herbaceous vegetation is shown (e.g., SEIBERT, 1954). These are maps of forest regions, but the herbaceous vegetation that is characteristic of each forest community is included in all its variations. Thus, the forest types are differentiated into subtypes on the basis of the herbaceous ground cover synusias, and at the same time, the total vegetation is well presented. There seems, therefore, no major problem involved in mapping herbaceous vegetation at very large scales. It must be remembered, however, that TÜXEN and numerous other phytocenologists worked in western Europe, a region with a humid, equable climate. TÜXEN and PREISING (1951) have given directions for mapping herbaceous vegetation in their area, and their fine maps bear witness to the validity of their arguments. But it is also quite obvious to those who live in the world's great semi-arid grasslands, that TÜXEN's ideas cannot be applied there without important modifications, for it could easily turn out that, within two or three years after the area was mapped, a map would no longer correspond at all to the facts. This emphasizes the point that it may be necessary to develop different mapping techniques for different regions.

Small-Scale Mapping

As the map scale shrinks, generalization becomes a serious factor. In this, there is no difference between woody and herbaceous vegetation. If an area is to be mapped at a small scale, which implies much generalization, some material must be suppressed. If the map is to be done in a forest region, the usual procedure is to suppress the herbaceous synusias first, as on the maps by DAVIS (1943) and MOORE (1953). This may be justifiable from various points of view, but there are important aspects of land use and management which require a different procedure because the herbaceous vegetation may be quite as important as the trees, if not more so.

The maps by grassland authors show a different attitude. COSTIN (1953), on his vegetation map of the Monaro region, distinguishes a large number of herbaceous phytocenoses, but many of these are grouped together because the scale is too small to show them individually. One of the finest small-scale examples is the vegetation map of the Ukraine at 1:1,000,000 (KLEOPOV and LAVRENKO, 1942) where the herbaceous vegetation is shown to a modest degree in forest lands, but in detail on the steppes. Forests and steppes are characterized by about the same number of dominants.

At still smaller scales, KÜCHLER (1953a, 1964) attempts consistency on his maps of the United States at 1:3,168,000 and 1:14,000,000 by showing the major physiognomic divisions of the vegetation, each with its floristic subdivisions. This includes, of course, the great prairie. In spite of the condensed legends, the various aspects of the prairie are clearly discernible.

Possible Solutions to Mapping Problems

Various possibilities exist to meet the difficulties of mapping herbaceous vegetation, and in given cases it may be useful to combine some of these possibilities on one map. Such possibilities are:

1. To select a "normal" year, i.e., one which most closely approaches the averages in precipitation and length of growing season, and to map the herbaceous vegetation that persists longest in the course of such a year.
2. Where there are distinct differences between the early and the late parts of the growing season, both the early and the late aspects can be shown separately for any "normal" year.
3. Where the character of the vegetation is apt to change, due to more violent fluctuations of the climate, the "normal" vegetation can be shown with indications of "humid" and "dry" phases.

Seasonal aspects and fluctuations over the years therefore invite an elaboration of the legend items. It is permissible to show the various aspects as individual items, but it is clearer and therefore preferable to group them. Thus, for instance, legend item 1 gives the "normal" version of the phytocenose, with 1a and 1b giving early and late seasonal aspects. The same technique can be used to describe the character of the phytocenoses during dry and wet periods.

Vegetational changes from wet decades to dry ones, and back, represent a form of dynamism, but the various aspects must not be confused with seral changes. Changes due to climatic fluctuations are not an evolution toward a climax because it is the climax itself which fluctuates in harmony with the prairie climate.

When the mapper wishes to record the physiognomy of herbaceous vegetation, he should select the period during which grasses and forbs attain the peak of their development. This usually begins with the flowering phase. Where vernal and autumnal aspects are mapped, the physiognomy of the vegetation must be investigated several times during the growing season.

If the mapper has aerial photographs specially made for his area, he should insist on having them taken during the flowering phase. This will emphasize color contrasts that might not be observable during other seasons. The photographs of herbaceous vegetation (i.e., their negatives) should be of the largest possible scale. It is easy to make enlargements from small-scale negatives but they do not always show the important details with the same clarity as photographs obtained from large negatives.

It is now well established that herbaceous vegetation can be shown in appropriate detail at all scales. It would seem important, for the sake of scientific accuracy, to devote more attention to herbaceous vegetation than in the past. But it is also clear that mapping herbaceous vegetation presents peculiar problems and in many instances requires its own specialized techniques.

17

Mapping Dynamic Features

Vegetation is dynamic, i.e., it is involved in a continuous evolution. The rate of evolution is at its minimum in climax conditions, but in all other conditions it can range from very slow to fast. It is essential in phytocenological investigations to understand the processes involved in the evolution of vegetation, but such processes may be too slow for one man to observe during his life time. For this reason, authors compare various evolutionary stages and endeavor to conclude from such observations what processes are involved, their direction, and their effects. Such a procedure is, however, speculative and the results may remain debatable. Vegetation maps solve this problem, especially if done with great care and accuracy and in great detail. Some time after mapping, measurable changes will have occurred and, even though a new observer may map and study the vegetation long after the first vegetation map was made, he will find it entirely feasible to compare the old and the new situations. Then, indeed, the exact rate and direction of change can be ascertained and these, in turn, throw light on the nature of the processes involved in this evolution. The appearance and spread of some species or the disappearance of others can be observed and followed, and measured with a degree of accuracy that would be unthinkable without such vegetation maps. The causes of the changes can then be established.

The recognition of the dynamic features of the vegetation is very useful. It not only permits an appreciation of what is going on in the landscape and where a situation is headed; it also permits the phytocenologist to avoid mistakes that might have serious consequences if applied to some aspects of land use.

To use one of GAUSSEN's (1959) graphic illustrations: The vegetation evolves from the pioneer phases of a sere through a number of phases to the final or climax phase. One such sere on a north-facing slope may have phases that we may characterize as 1, 2, 3, 4, 5, 6, 7, and 8 (climax) and the phases of another sere on a south-facing slope of the same mountains may be indicated by a, b, c, d, e, f, g, and h (climax). In either case, it is quite possible that the floristic composition of the early phases has little or nothing in common with that of the climax. On the other hand, it is likely that a number of species occur simultaneously in the early phases of both seres. Thus h is derived from b and hence is related to it floristically even though b and h may not have a single species in common. On the other hand, b and 2 may have some species in common even though they are unrelated.

The evolution of vegetation may be progressive toward a climax or regressive, away from a climax. The latter case is particularly common as a result of human activities such as lumbering, herding, burning, cultivating, mowing, etc. The prevailing condition of the vegetation is therefore by no means necessarily headed for a climax, at least not so long as man continues to interfere in the natural evolution of the vegetation. It is obvious that the correct interpretation of the vegetation, particularly its stage in the evolution, is of basic importance if a phytocenological study is to result in an improvement of the prevailing conditions.

Vegetation maps have been compared with photographs, especially since the introduction of aerial photography. Both record the vegetation as it can be observed at a given moment. This gives vegetation maps a static character, but phytocenologists know their subject to be dynamic indeed. The vegetation mapper usually finds it wise to map the actual vegetation before he embarks on interpretive features such as dynamics, climax, yields or others. This is always the safest and soundest beginning, but he must realize, of course, that the actual vegetation is often quite unstable whether it is man-induced or not. His map, therefore, may soon be out of date. This is well illustrated in the United States by some of the so-called cover-type maps, which are maps of the actual vegetation. For instance, the map of Minnesota (CUNNINGHAM and MOSER, 1940) shows a pin cherry type which is transitory and soon gives way to the next seral phase. FENTON (1947) made similar observations in Great Britain.

The vegetation mapper endeavors to map the plant communities of his region in the most meaningful way. He will, therefore, try to present not just the various species combinations, or physiognomic types, or ecological units. He will include, where possible, his observations on the stability of the vegetation, on its changes, rate and direction of change, and also on the meaning of the change. In so doing, he produces a dynamic vegetation map rather than a static one.

Causes and Characteristics of Dynamism

It is necessary to consider the character of vegetation dynamism before the techniques of mapping can be discussed meaningfully. What makes vegetation dynamic? The causes of this dynamism must be understood if the interpretation of the vegetation is to be sound, and only then can the dynamic vegetation map be expected to retain its usefulness over long periods.

The environment affects the vegetation and its geographical distribution. But what is significant here is not so much the relation between a given vegetation type and a set of environmental conditions; it is rather the stability of these conditions. Secular variations, such as periods of glaciation and long-term fluctuations of the climate, have long been known. Other than that, the environment was considered stable except where man rendered it unstable. Today we know that the environment is not stable, that it changes and fluctuates, that there are many causes underlying environmental changes, and that the rate, extent, and direction of these changes may vary from place to place. Perhaps it is difficult to accept the instability of our environment, but it can no longer be denied. At best, the rate of change is so slow at some times and places that for our immediate purposes we may speak of stability. But this should be done only with the clear understanding that we are dealing in fact with slow changes, even though these may be too slow to affect our needs.

Vegetational dynamism is therefore caused above all by the instability of the environment. But it is not enough to simply observe this instability, because different conditions will result in different types of vegetation. Therefore the mapper finds it useful to observe vegetational changes as well as their causes (KÜCHLER, 1961).

Natural causes may be distinguished from anthropogenic causes, and among the former the regular or periodic ones may be separated from the irregular or aperiodic ones. The regular changes include the secular changes. For instance, the post-Pleistocene plant migrations are still in progress, at least in some parts of the world. Then there are cyclic changes covering a varying number of years for each cycle. A good example occurred on the High Plains in the heart of North America: The twenties of this century were characterized by ample rainfall; the thirties were dry; the forties were wet; and the fifties again suffered from drought. ALBERTSON (1957) and his collaborators in Kansas have described how the vegetation changed both physiognomically and floristically under the influence of these cycles. Cyclic fluctuations are known from most semiarid regions of the world, for it is here that they are experienced most acutely.

The regular changes of the environment include also the seasons, resulting in the seasonal aspects of the vegetation (KÜCHLER, 1954a). These are observed primarily in the herbaceous communities and range from the desert ephemerals, which may not even appear every year, to the grasslands and forest floor synusias. These seasonal aspects may be few or numerous. For instance in Gujarat, India, SAXTON (1924) described eight such seasonal aspects of the vegetation which develop successively in the course of the year, and this series recurs each year. It ranges from marsh to desert and back again due to the heavy monsoon rains and the subsequent drying up of the soil. The seasonal series of plankton communities offer further examples of this type.

In contrast to the periodic changes in the environment stand the aperiodic ones. These include the formation of new land on growing deltas, by landslides, melting glaciers, volcanic eruptions, shifting sand dunes, the temporary and partial destruction of vegetation by grazing animals, insects or diseases, changes brought about by windstorms, floods, fire, etc. In the case of fire, the changes depend on the vegetation type that was burned, the intensity of the fire (heat, speed, wind, etc.), the effects of the fire on the soil, especially the humus layer, and subsequent erosion. Accordingly, the succeeding plant communities may be strongly affected by the varying degree of recovery of the survivors.

For instance, in sections of the Bar Harbor fire of 1947 on Mount Desert Island, Maine, the soil was affected only slightly; the fire burned the oaks but they survived and sprouted vigorously from their undamaged roots; an almost impenetrable thicket of oak shrubs replaced the forest of tall oaks. Elsewhere, the spruces on the mountain sides were burned and utterly destroyed; there were no survivors. The dry needles on the forest floor burned, too. What soil remained was soon eroded down to bedrock, and the charred stumps rose grotesquely on their mutilated roots high above the naked granite. Five years later a few grasses and forbs and some blueberry bushes were trying valiantly to recolonize the destroyed landscape, starting in cracks and shallow depressions in the granite where soil was beginning to collect once more (KÜCHLER, 1956b). Fire alone can obviously not explain the difference between these two types of vegetation, both of which rose on a surface that seemed uniformly barren at the end of the holocaust.

There is little difference between a fire started by lightning and one started accidentally, i.e., involuntarily by man. If, however, man deliberately burns the vegetation repeatedly, and more or less regularly, perhaps even annually, then the effect on the vegetation is totally different. Fire thus becomes one of the many tools man uses in rendering the land more useful to him.

The vegetation mapper must also consider other features of land use, such as selective cutting of forests, clear-cutting and reforestation (possibly with exotics), mowing of grasslands, and grazing of both grasslands and forests. The latter may eventually vanish from the landscape as a result of grazing because the animals eat the seedling trees and thus prevent any regrowth. Californian oak woods provide good examples for this. In contrast to such anthropogenous but semipermanent vegetation types is the deliberate removal of the entire vegetation and its replacement by cultivated crops and their associated weed communities. The great significance of all these substitute communities has been well established and the vegetation mapper can ill afford to ignore them.

In short, all vegetation changes continuously, although the rates of change vary from abrupt to extremely slow. The changes brought about naturally or by man usually imply changes in the quality of the vegetation and hence of its usefulness to man. Therefore they deserve close attention by the vegetation mapper.

The term "dynamic" as applied to vegetation is here understood very broadly, implying simply that the vegetation is undergoing changes of any kind. On the map, it may be desirable to show a change that has taken place in the past; but it is particularly useful to indicate changes in progress at the time of mapping. The techniques are essentially the same in both cases.

Successive Mapping

The most accurate and reliable manner of showing changes in the vegetation is to make detailed vegetation maps of permanently established sample plots and to repeat such mapping periodically. A comparison of the maps made at different times will then reveal the changes that have taken place. The time involved in mapping the vegetation repeatedly is usually rather short. For instance, ELLENBERG allowed seven years to elapse between his two maps of the grassland vegetation along the Seitenkanal (ELLENBERG, 1952). Even though there are examples of longer periods, they are all short in the light of phytocenological evolution. One of the great problems is, of course, that vegetation mapping as a scientific field is so young. It would be most interesting to have some agency, such as a state or national academy, select one or more areas both disturbed and undisturbed, and map their vegetation every twenty years in great detail. The maps might well reveal many an unsuspected development.

Longer periods can be encompassed only through an historical approach. KRAUSE (1950) and MOLINIER (1958) give some interesting examples of this kind, but SCHWICKERATH's treatment of the area around Stolberg remains the model achievement (SCHWICKERATH, 1954). Mapping at the scale of 1:25,000 and using his own direct observations as well as historical records and documentary evidence, SCHWICKERATH presents his landscape on three individual colored maps, each with a transparent, black-and-white overlay. These three maps of the same area reveal the evolution of the landscape and its vegetation with great clarity, and if, as the saying goes, one picture is worth a thousand words, then this is even more true of SCHWICKERATH's maps with their overlays.

The first map shows the original vegetation during the "beech forest period," 2000–1 B.C., and the overlay reveals the indications of settlements during prehistoric and Roman times, as well as the changes in the landscape from early Franconian times until the year 1800. The second map shows the vegetation as it prevailed in 1800 while the overlay presents the changes that took place between 1800 and 1940. Finally, the third map shows the vegetation as SCHWICKERATH observed and mapped it in 1940. The accompanying overlay indicates the smallest units of the physical landscape: the biotopes. This permits a close correlation between the individual phytocenoses and their physical environment, revealing a distributional pattern that man was able to modify in many ways but never to obliterate. One is reminded of TÜXEN's examples of the potential natural vegetation types and their various substitute communities: the spatial pattern of the potential natural phytocenoses, neatly fitted into the mosaic of biotopes, remains the dominant feature of the landscape even through centuries of human occupation.

If on a vegetation map or its legend there is nowhere any indication of vegetational dynamism, then it may be assumed that the vegetation is relatively stable or else that its dynamic features are not important for the purpose of the map. But there are many vegetation maps where changes are shown clearly although the legends contain no particular reference to dynamism. One of the best examples is, of course, the wonderful vegetation map of Perpignan by HENRI GAUSSEN (1948). For on this map it is possible to observe the potential natural vegetation as well as the various changes that have taken place, leading to a great variety of relatively stable substitute communities. OZENDA (1963) believes this map series is of such great interest to so many users primarily because of its dynamic aspects. It is important that the reader be fully aware of all the information and its implications given on a vegetation map, and it is a part of the mapper's task to present his material in such a manner as to help his reader find all that has been shown.

Scale

Not all vegetation maps are equally well adapted to include dynamic features of the vegetation. One major limitation is the scale. In general, maps at larger scales permit more information on vegetational dynamism than smaller-scale maps. For instance, a vegetation map of a continent as commonly found in atlases cannot be expected to include the rich information on the detailed maps by KUHNHOLTZ-LORDAT (1949). Yet, an American nineteenth century atlas contains a simple vegetation map of North America which shows a large part of the interior grasslands as such but with the note that they would turn into forest if protected from fire (SARGENT, 1880). This map is therefore remarkable for two reasons: its author introduced ideas of stability and dynamism on a small-scale map, and that at a time when our ideas on vegetational dynamism were still being formulated.

The scale alone is inadequate as a criterion for the number of dynamic features to be shown because the method of mapping, the classification of vegetation, and the organization of the map content also affect what information can be shown on a map. Nevertheless, where the dynamic features of the vegetation are important, the mapper should select the largest scale that time and funds permit. The more detailed and penetrating his information as revealed in the legend, the greater is the ultimate usefulness of his vegetation map.

Legend

The legend is the key to the map; it offers several possibilities to change a static vegetation map into a dynamic one. A vegetation map can present the plant communities more meaningfully by relating them to the vegetation changes. This requires information on the environmental processes active at the time of mapping, and their effect on the vegetation. Usually, there is not a simple reaction but a set of complex chain reactions. This necessitates the determination of the most effective factors producing the most significant changes in the vegetation, and a careful organization of all features. Where succession is in progress, a sequence of plant communities can usually be established. At one end of the sequence will be the type of vegetation that prevailed when the change began. At the other end will be the vegetation type that will have taken over when the change has run its course. Between these terminal points of the chain there are one or more links. When their character and sequence have been established, the vegetation map can portray the vegetation in a dynamic fashion by presenting the vegetation types not only as they are at the time of mapping but also with regard to their place in the succession. Of course, it should not be expected that the entire series of plant communities from pioneer stage to climax is present. But the recognition of a transitory type and its place in the sequence is significant.

On large-scale maps, it may be practicable to introduce an entire chain of successional phases as part of the legend. This can be done in the form of a series of rectangles or boxes, with the initial community shown in the first box and the stabilized one at the end. Each box is followed by a description of the plant community it represents. Only part of the series may occur in the mapped area and only those rectangles are shown in color which indicate plant communities on the map. In this manner, it is possible to see at a glance what series is involved, which phases of the series are present, their proximity to the final or climax stage, and their distribution in the landscape (Figure 12).

In Figure 12, the series is called "Series 1," but there is no need to number it unless two or more series appear on the same map. Instead of numbering the series, it is also quite acceptable to name it. In such a case, the series is usually given the name of the dominant species of the climax community. In this instance, series 1 would be called "*Picea excelsa* series." GAUSSEN uses this method on his map of France at 1:200,000. In Figure 12, three phases of the series do not appear on the map and hence are left blank. The color of the two present communities is the same, but the individual hues range from light to dark, the final and most stable phase in the succession being the darkest. The communities differ from one another but are shown as different phases of the same series. (The arrows are added only when the relative quality of the phases is to be indicated; see next section, below.)

It may be that the potential natural vegetation or the climax does not occur anywhere in the mapped area. The mapper will nevertheless find it useful to show it in the legend in order to enlighten the reader on the affinities of the substitute communities. Usually, a legend item is suppressed when it is not represented on the map. In this particular instance, it is valuable to retain it, but it should be followed by a parenthetic note that it is not shown on the map unless the absence of color serves the same purpose. For example, such a legend item might read: "*Andropogon gerardi–A. scoparius* community (not on map)." Thus the

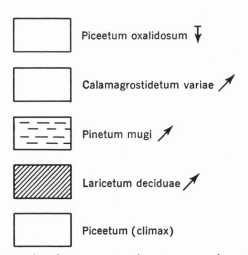

Series 1 or *Picea excelsa* series

Piceetum oxalidosum ↓

Calamagrostidetum variae ↗

Pinetum mugi ↗

Laricetum deciduae ↗

Piceetum (climax)

Figure 12. Example of a successional series as a dynamic legend item. (After Aichinger, 1954.)

legend space devoted to seral plant communities which are not on the map need by no means be wasted.

Qualitative Changes

Vegetation maps are very useful when they show improvement or deterioration in the quality of the vegetation resulting from man's use—or abuse—of the land and its cover. Not all forms of land use produce desirable results. In the United States, there are millions of acres of annual cheat grass (*Bromus secalinus*) where once perennial grasses of far greater value prevailed, and much ponderosa pine (*Pinus ponderosa*) has been replaced by worthless brush. But not all changes are bad: the valuable loblolly pine (*Pinus taeda*) in the southeastern part of this country is replacing the less desirable longleaf pine (*P. palustris*) in many areas.

In order to show such qualitative changes, AICHINGER (1954) has proposed to list the entire successional sequence and then connect the individual stages by arrows. Ascending arrows (↗) indicate changes toward a richer, more demanding, and more valuable community (progressive vegetational evolution); descending arrows (↓) indicate a change toward a poorer, less demanding, and less valuable stage (regressive vegetational evolution); finally, cut descending arrows (↓̄) indicate such regression after clear-cutting or burning a plant community.

For example, a spruce forest, rich in *Oxalis*, is located in the dolomitic areas of the conifer belt in the Alps on a shady slope where much snow occurs. When this forest is clear-cut, the top soil erodes. Snow slides, avalanches, and sheet erosion during heavy rains alter the environment to such an extent that the spruce can no longer regenerate in it. *Calamagrostis varia* spreads and enables *Pinus mugo* to invade because this pine is better able to endure the snow pressure and avalanches on the steep slopes deprived of part of their topsoil. Only slowly, under the protection of the Pinetum mugi, does a larch forest get established which, in turn, permits the return of the spruce (AICHINGER, 1954, p. 23). The sequence is shown thus: Piceetum oxalidosum ↓̄ Calamagrostidetum variae ↗ Pinetum mugi ↗ LARICETUM DECIDUAE ↗ Piceetum. The capitalized stage is the one present at the time of mapping. If, for example, a map of this vegetation showed a Laricetum deciduae, a Piceetum, a Pinetum mugi, and a Calamagrostidetum side by side, with no further information, it would be impossible to observe the relations between them. But if the legend is organized so as to show the dynamism of the vegetation, the whole story is told at once and the reader can see at a glance that all these plant communities are parts of the same sere, most of them being unstable. It is quite possible that different stages of the same sere occur side by side because different sections of the spruce forest may have been logged at different times.

Some Problems in Mapping Successions

Succession may, at times, follow a linear progression, and at other times the evolution toward the climax is very complex. SCHWICKERATH (1954) developed "association rings" to illustrate the successional complexities of the landscape. Sometimes, it may be possible to reduce very simple "association rings" to linear forms, just as a smaller map scale calls for a generalization of the portrayed plant communities. But where this is not feasible without altering or destroying the basic meaning of the "association ring," the vegetation mapper must limit himself to showing the existing communities as actual or potential natural phytocenoses and their seral phases of undetermined rank. Various "earlier" phases may possibly be distinguished from "later" phases but this requires detailed information which, in many areas, is just being gathered or is not available at all.

FOSBERG (1961c, p. 200) points out that mapping dynamism on a single map rather than on a series of successive maps, introduces into the map an element of interpretation. In addition to recording what the mapper observes, he records what he thinks is going to happen or has happened. This is very well, and may be desirable, but it should be made very clear in the explanation what part was observed and what is interpretation. AICHINGER solved this problem by capitalizing the actual vegetation.

Much has been learned about the dynamics of vegetation since the pioneering work of the early ecologists. Many North American birch and aspen forests are now recognized as transitional phases, usually following fires. The vegetation of the western ranges can be described in degrees of overgrazing, with the floristic features of the various phases well established. Some aspects of succession are particularly interesting from the point of view of the vegetation mapper. FRIEDEL (1956) observed in the Tirol, Austria, that succession need not proceed evenly through the various stages and their transitions. Under given circumstances, such successional phases can have a remarkable degree of stability. But when, in the course of their evolution, a certain threshold value in the environment is passed, one stage changes rapidly into the next one. He also demonstrated with the help of phytocenoses how the landscape evolved where the Pasterze glacier had retreated and thus exposed sizeable areas: the areas released between 1856, 1890, 1910, and 1933 can be recognized by the evolutionary stages of their vegetation (FRIEDEL, 1934). On the other hand, TANSLEY and CHIPP (1926) found that the various successional stages may not be so different from one another as they appear to be, and that the seedlings of the latest stages may already be present in the early stages, even though they are well hidden among the early dominants which grow faster and taller. Much later, this observation was confirmed by DAUBENMIRE (1943) in the Rocky Mountains, and by EGLER (1954) on abandoned fields in New England.

The dynamics of vegetation can also be mapped where one type invades another, e.g., a forest invading a grassland. Such invasions can be indicated with the help of arrows in the color of the invading community. Instead of colored arrows, black ones will do sometimes, but they become problematical on black-and-white maps. The length and width of the arrows can indicate the degree of invasion: broad arrows imply a massive invasion, thin arrows a modest one; the length of the arrows shows the depth to which the invasion has progressed.

Sometimes the problem consists in showing two or more stages of a fluctuation, as for instance the spring and summer aspects of a grassland, or perhaps its major phases during wet and dry cycles. The problem is solved by manipulating the legend items. The two stages are given together, one following the other, possibly the second one in parentheses. But each item must be clearly shown for what it is, as "spring phase" or "drought phase," etc. In this manner, the information of the map can be greatly enriched, increasing its value considerably.

Use of Color

Where the dynamism of the vegetation is an important part of the information to be mapped, it can be shown with the help of colors. LÜDI (1921) made a "succession map" of the Lauterbrunnental in Switzerland. He used one color for all pioneer communities, one other color for all transitional communities, and finally, one color each for the different climax communities. In addition, he has one more color for messicol vegetation, i.e., cultivated fields. This was probably the first cartographic attempt to portray dynamics as a major feature of a vegetation map. Much experience has been gained since LÜDI's pioneering work and it is now possible to show vegetational dynamism with the help of various color schemes.

When a given type of the potential natural vegetation has been established, it is presented in a flat color, e.g., sky-blue. All substitute communities of this type are shown in various patterns of the same sky-blue color, i.e., blue lines, blue dots, blue dashes, etc., thereby indicating which communities belong together without indicating any successional sequence. This is desirable when many substitute communities do not follow one another in a sere, especially when planted by man. GAUSSEN uses this idea in his system of color manipulation.

Some authors show the potential natural vegetation in flat colors throughout the area. Where substitute communities take its place, an overprinted pattern of a different color is used. The extent of the various potential natural phytocenoses is thereby shown, as well as the degree to which they have been replaced and by what. As the number and variety of overprinted symbols may become very large, this latter method is more useful on maps of a very large scale. Some authors use this method on small-scale maps, too; the overprinted symbols must necessarily be reduced in number in proportion to the area covered, and they must be shown in vivid colors to assure an adequate contrast with the more subdued colors of the potential natural communities. For instance, the overprinted symbols may be shown in bright red while the potential natural vegetation forms a background of soft variations of tan, green, and blue. Often the symbols are limited to the messicol vegetation and are used only where the crops assume a major economic significance in the landscape.

Where the vegetation is going through several phases of successional series, a different color may be assigned to each series. The climax is given a flat color and each stage receives a carefully selected hue of the same color. Running through the series from pioneer stage to climax, the hues should be arranged consecutively from light to dark, so that the lightest hue is closest to or at the pioneer stage and the darkest hue is at the final phase or nearest to it.

It does not seem difficult to relate the substitute communities to the potential natural vegetation with the help of colors, but this possibility seems to have escaped many vegetation mappers. For instance, MAACK (1950) on his vegetation map of Paraná set aside a whole section of his legend in which he relates the substitute communities to the potential natural vegetation by appropriate statements, but each item is given a different and unrelated color.

Care must be taken to retain a maximum number of chances for using the colors. For instance, a dark color can be made lighter by using lighter tints or else by breaking a flat color into lines and dots of varying thickness and diameter. The effect may be nearly the same. But these are two different methods of using color and they should not be confused. Only one is necessary to show succession, and the other one may then be employed to indicate other features of the vegetation. Where both methods are to be used on the same map, care must be taken to keep the line and dot patterns sufficiently coarse so that they can readily be distinguished from flat colors of light hue.

As time progresses and more research is done in the field of vegetation mapping, new ideas will no doubt be presented to map the dynamism of vegetation. But some methods have already developed and these should be employed more frequently. In a sense, this will combine experimentation with the efforts to make vegetation maps more useful, as different authors use different approaches. It is precisely this sort of applied experimentation that promises the greatest and the most rapid advances of an aspect of vegetation mapping which so far has received little emphasis. Quite independent of such considerations is the fact that every carefully prepared vegetation map, showing the character and distribution of the phytocenoses in detail, will serve as a basis for later observations, whenever the evolution of vegetation is the object of study.

18

Compiling Small-Scale Maps

All vegetation maps at very small scales have this in common: they have been compiled from source maps; they are not based directly on field work. For instance, on the vegetation map of the world by BROCKMANN-JEROSCH (1935), the equatorial scale is 1:20,000,000; therefore 1 centimeter represents 200 kilometers. Many vegetation units on the map are 3 or 4 centimeters wide and several times as long, hence they correspond to areas 600 to 800 kilometers (370–500 miles) in width and thousands of kilometers (miles) in length. It would therefore be a futile enterprise to base such a map on field work. Any sample plot, even an entire county, would be snuffed out by the reduction in scale.

Small-scale maps are therefore based on compilation. The basic idea is simple enough: the author collects vegetation maps of the component parts of his area and combines them into one new map on a smaller scale.

Source Maps

In carrying out such a project, the first step is to obtain complete map coverage for the area. This enables the author to make a detailed study of the vegetation. The more complete the collection of vegetation maps, the better; and an author should not discontinue his search for vegetation maps of a given area because he already has one. Several different vegetation maps are more valuable than just one because they support one another, or else they throw a new light on the vegetation if they are not in harmony. Where no satisfactory source material is available, the compiler can go one of two ways. He can speculate on what the vegetation is likely to be, and sometimes his reasoning and his meager evidence may permit him to hit the mark within tolerable limits. However, there always remains the very real danger that his speculation was wrong, and his map suffers accordingly. The other way open to the compiler is then to leave the doubtful areas blank and not to show the vegetation there at all. This makes the map more realistic and strengthens the reader's confidence in the remainder of the map. The latter method was successfully employed by TRAPNELL (1948) in Northern Rhodesia and by SCHWEINFURTH (1958) in the Himalaya.

Usually, it is not difficult to find vegetation maps that show one or several parts of the region to be mapped, but there will be other parts for which good vegetation maps seem to be lacking. A most thorough search is imperative and many of the elusive maps can be discovered by correspondence, by travel to libraries and mapping centers of government agencies, etc., and by a close study of the literature. The search for source maps should continue throughout the duration of the project, and if valuable additional material becomes available when the manuscript is approaching completion, such material should then be incorporated into the body of the map even though this spells new problems and delays. Many maps are accompanied by an explanatory text which often contains valuable supplementary information. Wherever such texts exist they should be collected just as diligently as the maps themselves.

Method of Classification

The second step in compiling a vegetation map is to select a classification of vegetation. This, of course, depends largely on the purpose of the map, i.e., on just what features of the vegetation the author wishes to show and in what detail. Obviously, the available classifications are not equally well adapted to given needs and it may become necessary to modify an existing classification or even to compose a new one (cf. SOCHAVA, 1954). It is very important that the author ascertains whether the selected classification can actually be employed throughout the area of his map. Any uncertainty calls for more detailed studies in order to determine the feasibility of the selected classification; if the compiler remains uncertain, he should discard it in favor of another and perhaps more versatile one. When the author is completely satisfied that the selected classification will express the ideas he wishes to convey to the reader, and that it can do this in every part of the map, then and only then can he proceed to the next step.

Translation and Generalization

The third step consists in changing all legend items of all the maps the author has collected into the terminology of the classification of the new map. This is referred to as the "translation." In many instances, this will present no particular problem, but there are times when such a translation is difficult. For example, an author may wish to present the vegetation on a purely floristic basis in an area which includes high elevations. On all source maps at his disposal he finds the vegetation above timberline described as alpine meadow. Obviously, this term reveals nothing about the species which compose these meadows. The author may then find it useful to study the literature for more information on the vegetation type in question. Correspondence with authorities on the area with the problematical vegetation types is also enlightening.

In the course of translating a map legend from one classification (the first one) into another (the second one), it is obvious that the second classification must be no more complex than the first one; usually it is simpler. If the second classification is simpler than the first one, the translation will result in the need for combining two or more types of the first classification into one broader unit of the second classification. Such combinations must be done with care, and the author should be thoroughly acquainted with the vegetation and its phytocenological character. It is not acceptable to combine any two vegetation types that happen to be contiguous in some places. The types to be combined should be related to each other and so justify the new complex. For instance, the periodically flooded forests on the delta plains of the Mississippi River show differences according to the variations in topography, even the slightest, because the length of the flooding period is dependent thereon. Yet such different types of forests can well be combined, because the inundation gives them certain common characteristics. Elsewhere, different types of pastures with the same soil and water supply are due to differences in management but the common environment nevertheless gives them common features that justify combining them. This procedure leads therefore to the formation of new complexes which are genuine vegetation entities in spite of their composite character.

The author soon learns that a compilation map is not simply a mosaic of source maps. Making translations may present little difficulty in sections for which there is only one source map that completely satisfies the author. This, however, is not often the case. It is more usual to find several overlapping source maps and that the various authors may disagree in their interpretation of what they observed. Overlapping maps may therefore be quite unlike in their common sections. If the source maps are contiguous, vegetational boundaries on one map may not be continued on the next map in the appropriate places, if at all.

Various reasons may account for such discrepancies. All maps except those at the very largest scales are generalized more or less, and every author generalizes according to his own point of view and purpose. Therefore differences between authors arise easily. If the various source maps are on different scales then the degree of generalization is also different; hence the maps as a whole must differ as well. Different methods and goals in preparing the source maps nearly always imply different results. Where such source maps cover large areas it is often impossible for one author to study all parts of the area in the same detail. If, however, different parts of the area are investigated by different authors, differences of interpretation are nearly inevitable.

Authors should not be reproached because their results are not in harmony with one another. It is entirely possible that every one of the authors was as careful and painstaking in the preparation of his map as can be expected. The differences result from the nature of the work, and especially from the varied purposes of the maps. Whatever the character of the source maps may be, the translation must be reasonable and must correspond to the facts as closely as the scale permits. The art of compiling a vegetation map consists above all in finding a way that leads from contrast and contradiction to unity and harmony.

Where detailed source maps are used it is advisable to generalize them before they are translated. This generalization must be done in any case sooner or later and doing it before the translation means that there will be less to translate, and hence fewer errors and misinterpretations are likely to be made. In so doing, it is useful to have the vegetation maps of the surrounding areas within reach whether or not their legends have been translated. This helps to interpret the vegetation more accurately over larger areas, to assure continuity from one map or one region to the next, and thus to make certain that the quality of the translation remains on the highest level.

If a type covers only a very small area, it is, in the course of generalizing, usually suppressed altogether. But there are cases when the opposite is as much or more justifiable, and instead of reducing a small area to zero, it should be enlarged enough that it can be shown on the map. This applies to all instances where special types of vegetation help to contribute to a better understanding of the map as a whole, as for example in the case of galeria forests in grasslands, alpine meadows, oasis vegetation, and others.

The translation of the source material into the terminology of the new map will be strengthened considerably by consulting soil maps and geologic maps. Where such maps are well done, they can be fine guides in cases of doubt, especially with regard to vegetation types that can form vegetation complexes and also with regard to the location of vegetational boundaries. Ordinary climatic maps are less valuable but phenological maps such as ELLENBERG's (1955) map of southwestern Germany can prove to be very useful indeed.

It is not possible to translate the vegetation units of every classification into entities of every other classification. For instance, maps based on BRAUN-BLANQUET's classification can be translated into RÜBEL's classification, but the reverse is not possible. Where maps are not comparable, translations may be very difficult or altogether impossible. However, a compiled map is almost invariably a map of small scale which is so generalized that only the broader units of vegetation can be considered, or only the higher ranks in a hierarchical classification.

KÜCHLER (1964) based his map of the United States on what he called a "classless classification," i.e., one without superior or inferior ranks. He described every vegetation unit by life forms and taxa, and this method can be applied at any scale. Furthermore, most maps describe the vegetation in such detail that the compiler can glean valuable information from them even though this may be limited to either life forms or species.

This approach was already foreshadowed by an earlier map of the same area (KÜCHLER, 1953a) and has the great advantage of being highly flexible and adaptable. It permits the translation of almost any vegetation map either wholly or at least in part. The compiler is thus in the fortunate position of being able to use practically all source maps that may come to his attention.

It may be observed parenthetically that such a "classless" method has its close parallels at large scales. The maps on which the vegetation is calibrated to a given environmental feature usually show items which are definitely not units in a classification such as that by BRAUN-BLANQUET. The publications by WALTHER (1963), LONG (1963), and others reveal that unequivocally.

Preparing the New Map

The fourth step in the compilation consists of preparing the new manuscript. This is done by changing the material on the many different translated source maps to a uniform scale. It is most readily achieved by transferring the source material to a new outline map. If the area is very large, it is desirable to use a series of base maps, all of which are drawn on the same projection and on the same scale. A good example of such base maps are the Aeronautical Charts published by the United States government, or the sheets of the International Map of the World at the scale of 1:1,000,000.

At first, the translated source map should be transferred just as it is, whether it has been generalized or not, and regardless of how the amount of detail compares with other sections of the manuscript map. Discrepancies of this kind can only be dealt with after the first draft of the manuscript has been completed. If any vegetation types were combined as a result of translating them from one classification to another, then only the new combined types (complexes) should be transferred to the map sheets of the new scale.

Where several overlapping source maps are available on which the authors contradict one another, the compiler must resolve the contradiction before he transfers the material to the manuscript sheets of uniform scale. The solution of such a problem may require a considerable amount of research and correspondence, possibly even field work, before a final decision can be made. No effort should be spared to produce the very best possible solution because this will directly affect the quality of the compiled map, and hence its usefulness.

Problems will arise when, for part of the map, the only available source material is done at an appreciably smaller scale than that of the new map. Of course, there may be a considerable difference between the scales of the new manuscript map and its eventual form when it is published. If the scale of the source maps is only slightly smaller than that planned for the printed map, the difficulties are not serious and an enlargement of the source map is feasible. On the other hand, if the scale of the source material is much smaller, then the author must proceed with the greatest caution. It becomes imperative that he utilize every means at his command to raise the scanty information to a more useful level by a most careful and detailed study of the literature and of physical maps of all kinds and by consultation with authorities on the area in question. Personal inspection of the area may contribute much, too, and the author has to allow time and funds in his budget for such emergencies.

The author will find it useful to study carefully the relations between the vegetation types and the major physical features of the landscape in the areas surrounding the problem section. This may enable him to project some of the known information into the involved area. As it is quite possible that serious mistakes are made in the process of such extrapolation, a separate map of the problem area and its surrounding regions should be prepared and submitted for criticism to all authorities familiar with the area. Major mistakes can thus be eliminated and the quality of the map can be maintained.

The result of the fourth step is a unified manuscript, one map or a set of maps, all on the same scale and projection and all employing the one selected classification.

The legend must next be organized and arranged in accordance with the classification, and all items on the map must be checked against the legend. There must be no item on the map that is not also represented in the legend, and every item in the legend must occur somewhere on the map.

The final map must not only have acceptable scientific standards; it must also satisfy esthetic standards and be well balanced. It is, for instance, quite likely that in one section of the map a great deal of detailed information is given whereas in another section very general

data have to suffice. One need only compare plains with horizontal geological strata, and hence, a relatively uniform vegetation, with a mountainous terrain where the vegetation is likely to change considerably
within short distances due to differences in altitude, slope, exposure, and
many other features. It is then not only justifiable but desirable to somewhat generalize the detailed information so as to bring it into a better
balance with the rest of the map. These and other changes and corrections necessitate a redrafting of the manuscript, possibly even more than
once. The author must prepare for such eventualities, especially when
planning and budgeting his project.

The completed manuscript gains a great deal if the author submits it
to colleagues and experts for a critical discussion. Of course, this may
well imply that sections of the map must be modified, and therefore re-
drawn, but this work is very much worthwhile. Not only does it
strengthen the quality of the map considerably, but it also eliminates a
good deal of adverse criticism that might possibly have developed later on.

Continual Proofreading

The author cannot be urged enough to spend the utmost care on *proofreading at every step and stage,* and indeed more than once at each step.
This may be a tedious activity but the need for it cannot be overemphasized. It is quite essential that all proofreading is done at least
twice because it is not feasible to simply read through a map as one reads
a book or an article. The continual shifting from the source map to the
manuscript map and back to the source map is very tiring, especially for
the eyes, so that in spite of all care many a mistake is overlooked during
the first proofreading (cf. Chapter 13).

Records

Another feature of significance is the record the author keeps as his
work proceeds. He should carefully note in detail every source he ever
consults, whether this be a map, a book, an article in a journal, letters
from colleagues, conversations, or personal inspections of the vegetation.
In certain instances, it is desirable to publish a bibliography, but this need
not contain all the different types and bits of information that accumulated
in the course of the project. However, while the compilation is still in
progress, all these data may be of great value because one does constantly
refer back to sources already used or because it is desirable to ascertain
on what sources certain items on the map are based.

A special file for problems is also very useful. Whenever a problem
arises, it is carefully described and the description deposited in the

problem file. The author can then proceed with his work and solve the problem at a more appropriate time. A problem may imply research, correspondence, and even travel. The problem must be solved before its description is removed from the file. Eventually the solution of the problem is added to the description and then transferred to a new file of solved problems; such a second file may turn out to be very useful indeed at some later stage of the project, especially when similar problems arise or whenever it is desirable to check on how a particular solution was obtained.

Problems of Field Investigation

There have been repeated references to the possibilities of travel in connection with field investigations of the vegetation types for which information is inadequate or on which the source maps disagree to an extent that the author cannot bridge the gaps and resolve the contradictions. When an author decides to compile a map he must therefore be prepared to include the possibility of such travel in his plans. If he lives in the area to be mapped, and if the various parts of the area are reasonably accessible, travel can be arranged more or less whenever it is convenient. If, on the other hand, the author plans to compile a map of, say, a distant continent, then he must approach the matter differently and with greater caution. First of all, he should travel only after the first draft of the manuscript has been completed because it is only then that he will know definitely where his map is particularly weak and in what sections field studies will be most beneficial. He can then plan his trip according to his needs, thus rendering it most profitable. He must keep in mind while planning his trip that he may possibly be unable to return to any of the places he wants to visit. It is therefore important that he knows prior to going into the field just exactly what information is needed, and while in the field, only the most detailed, comprehensive, and complete notes will assure the author that a second visit is unnecessary. The most careful planning of the trip prior to the departure is imperative.

As a matter of record, a small inset map may be planned to give an indication of the reliability or the degree of detail available for the various sections of the newly compiled map.

These, then, are the individual steps that must be followed in the course of compiling a vegetation map. The author of small-scale vegetation maps must face many difficulties. But his efforts will have their reward for the fruit of his labor will be a valuable document that can serve and benefit a large number of people.

19

Braun-Blanquet's
Table Method

The method developed by BRAUN-BLANQUET is based on the use of quadrats, or sample plots. A number of such quadrats are studied throughout the area of every individual plant community; their distribution may be regular or random. The quadrats should be relatively uniform floristically, ecologically, and in size, and care should be taken that they are located well within the area of the community. When the quadrats are too close to the borders of the community, the resulting information becomes confusing or even worthless. The sample plots should always be located in what seems to be a typical portion of the community; atypical sections should be carefully avoided. The size of a quadrat should be large enough to encompass all species which belong to the particular community that is being analyzed. The minimum size of a sample area varies with the type of vegetation, just as in the case of belt transects. In herbaceous vegetation, a quadrat may vary from 1–25 m², and the mapper is free to make his own choice. In woody vegetation consisting mainly of small shrubs, an area of 25–100 m² is preferable. In forests, the sample plots have to be much larger. Sometimes the forest flora is analyzed by using a double standard: a large quadrat (200–500 m²) for the trees and a much smaller plot for the undergrowth.

When the mapper is pressed for time, he may feel inclined to be satisfied with a single quadrat in each phytocenose. He should then use the largest plot feasible, yet the result is unreliable even if the quadrat was well placed within the community. This procedure is definitely not recommended. It is always best to study a large number of quadrats.

The quadrat method had its beginning in the nineteenth century, and many researchers have contributed to it. Building on their ideas, BRAUN-BLANQUET (1928, 1932, 1951, 1964) offered the most highly developed system yet devised, greatly stimulating basic and applied science (KÜCHLER, 1957). He first published his *Pflanzensoziologie* in 1928; this was translated into English by FULLER and CONARD in 1932, and the much-improved third German edition was published in 1964. As a large number of phytocenologists all over the world can read either German or English, it seems strange that BRAUN-BLANQUET's ideas spread so fast in Europe and so slowly, if at all, elsewhere.

This oddity is due to BRAUN-BLANQUET himself, who failed in his book, even in his third edition, to instruct the reader in his method. A 44-page pamphlet with instructions for the preparation of vegetation maps was published (BRAUN-BLANQUET, EMBERGER and MOLINIER, 1947). However, only about one quarter of this pamphlet is devoted to instructions, and these deal exclusively with suggestions for the use of color. Nothing at all is said about methods of establishing associations, etc., and how to map them. In Europe, BRAUN-BLANQUET could personally instruct his followers, and these, in turn, could teach their own students. In his second edition (p. 18), he speaks of the "tact" that a person is required to have if he is to determine the rank of plant communities. TÜXEN and PREISING (1951, p. 9) even go so far as to state that a phytocenologist must have special talents (*besondere Begabung*) to master the principles and techniques of the tables, and that a knowledge of the manipulation of the tables is to be gained by oral instruction rather than by the printed word. This sort of unnecessary and unscientific obscurantism has seriously handicapped the spread of BBAUN-BLANQUET's methods outside Europe. Most non-European phytocenologists have neither the time nor the funds to spend extended periods in France or Germany in order to receive personal instruction, and as the exact method of procedure was not published, it could not very well be tried and applied.

More than a quarter of a century after the first publication of BRAUN-BLANQUET's book, ELLENBERG (1956) showed how the tables are first prepared and then manipulated in order to identify the plant communities and their divisions in BRAUN-BLANQUET's classification of vegetation. But if ELLENBERG is convinced of the value of BRAUN-BLANQUET's system, he is also aware of its weaknesses. He shows not only the advantages and the strength of this system but also where subjectivity enters into it, and to what degree. ELLENBERG is the only one who so far has published a really instructive description of this method. The method has been widely discussed and is much used in Europe. Therefore, it is here presented somewhat more in detail in order to enable phytocenologists of North America and elsewhere to experiment with it in types of vegetation with which they are familiar. The following paragraphs are largely based on ELLENBERG's work.

There are now two major centers for mapping the vegetation according to the BRAUN-BLANQUET method: in Godesberg am Rhein (formerly in Stolzenau an der Weser, Germany, under the direction of REINHOLD TÜXEN), and at Montpellier, France, under the direction of LOUIS EMBERGER. Other centers exist elsewhere, e.g., in Belgium and in Holland. Much work must be done prior to the actual mapping, above all the establishment of vegetational units.

Mapping Seasons

The mapping is usually done in carefully selected seasons. For instance, in Stolzenau, i.e., in northwestern and central Europe, there are four such mapping seasons, which do not begin and end at fixed dates but are arranged as follows:

1st mapping season: forests with geophytes: spring.

2nd mapping season: grasslands: the last 4–5 weeks before the first hay crop.

3rd mapping season: small grains and their associated weed communities: after the second mapping season but before the harvest.

4th mapping season: other cultivated crops and meadows: after the third mapping season but before the harvest.

The mapping of pastures, heaths, moors, dunes, forests, and wastelands is not strictly related to any particular season. In Montpellier, i.e., in the Mediterranean Region, where the same method is used, the mapping seasons vary, of course, in accordance with the climatic differences between northern Germany and southern France.

Field Observation

The mapper goes into the field in order to survey and study the vegetation. He broadly distinguishes the major types, possibly even some subdivisions, and then proceeds to analyze the floristic nature of these types. This is done by examining the species composition of a large number of quadrats within each type. Such a record is rendered more valuable by indicating in it how much of the area of the sample plot is occupied by each species. One distinguishes between coverage and basal area; weight estimates are increasingly used in herbaceous communities because of their greater accuracy. In order to obtain a high degree of accuracy consistently, it is best to compare the grasses and all graminoids with the forbs, including the legumes. In Table 9, the proportion certainly is greater than 75:25 but smaller than 90:10. A proportion of 85:15 approaches a close estimate.

Table 9.   Beginning of a Raw Table *

Sample No.	1	2	3	4	5	6	7	8	9	10	etc.
Number of species	31										
Grasses:											
Arrhenatherum elatius	+°										
Dactylis glomerata	5										
Helictotrichon pubescens	1°										
Bromus erectus	50										
Festuca ovina	2										
Poa pratensis	4										
Briza media	1										
Koeleria pyramidata	3										
Festuca rubra	15										
Sedges:											
Carex flacca	2										
Legumes:											
Trifolium pratense	+										
Trifolium repens	+										
Medicago lupulina	1										
Others:											
Achillea millefolium	6										
Daucus carota	1										
Campanula rotundifolia	1										
Plantago lanceolata	1										
Heracleum sphondylium	+										
Galium molugo	3										
Chrysanthemum leucanthemum	1										
Scabiosa columbaria	+										
Linum catharticum	+										
Rumex acetosa	+										
Ranunculus acer	+										
Thymus serpyllum	1										
Cerastium caespitosum	+										
Centaurea jacea	+°										
Taraxacum officinale	+°										
Campanula glomerata	+										
Veronica chamaedrys	+										
Plantago media	+										

* The first sample of a meadow community is shown according to KLAPP's system. Space has been left to record additional species occurring in other sample plots. (After ELLENBERG, 1956.)

Now each group is divided. The legumes constitute at best one tenth of the total forbs, hence only about 1 per cent of all species. Sedges, too, are not common but obviously represent a larger share than the legumes. They may be estimated at 2 per cent. The estimated values are therefore as follows:

Grasses	83	(75–90)%
Sedges	2	(1– 5)%
Legumes	1	(+– 2)%
Other forbs	14	(10–22)%

The numbers in parentheses show the extreme estimates of persons without much practice.

When analyzing the quadrat, the species are recorded in groups as shown in the example above. The percentages are then distributed over these groups. This is best done by giving rare species only a + (spoken of as a "cross"). Then the others are estimated in the sequence of their frequency. It is often necessary, especially for beginners, to change the estimates so that in the end they will match properly, and the percentages add up to 100.

This method takes relatively more time and can be learned adequately only if the estimates are checked by actual weighing. This is most important for beginners. The growing popularity of weight estimates is based on the high degree of accuracy that can be obtained and this, in turn, has been found useful in economic considerations, the analysis of pastures and ranges, their nutritive values, etc. The method also benefits studies of ecological relations, competition, and others.

In the case of coverage, the mapper projects the species, i.e., their full lateral extent, vertically down on the ground. The area so covered by a given species is estimated, not measured, and expressed as a percentage of the total area of the plot. One distinguishes seven percentage classes in the BRAUN-BLANQUET system, as described in Table 10.

Table 10. Estimated Coverage of a Given Species per Sample Plot

Class	Degree of Coverage
5	76–100% of the area
4	51– 75% of the area
3	26– 50% of the area
2	6– 25% of the area
1	1– 5% of the area
+	Less than 1% of the area
r	Extremely small portion of the area; usually only one specimen

The use of basal area as a cover indicator is common with foresters interested in merchantable timber, and with range managers. In the case of trees, basal area is the sum total of the cross sections of all trees of the same species in a given plot, measured at about 1.5 meters above the ground. Foresters often prefer the basal area observation to tree counts because it provides a better measure of the relative importance of the tree species. In the study of herbaceous communities, the basal area measurements have been found particularly useful because they are relatively constant whereas the coverage supplied by the foliage varies greatly with the weather, the season, and from species to species. For instance, a grass species with stiff upright leaves will have a smaller coverage than one with widely spreading leaves, even though the basal area may be the same. Herbaceous plants have their basal area measured at about 3 centimeters above the ground, which is thought to correspond to the height of normal utilization by grazing animals or when mowed.

Often it is desirable to indicate also how the species are distributed within their communities, whether singly or in small or large groups, etc. This is referred to as the "sociability" of the species and is useful in analyzing herbaceous phytocenoses (Table 11).

Table 11. Estimated Sociability

1 =	growing singly
2 =	growing in tufts
3 =	growing in small groups
4 =	growing in larger groups
5 =	growing in extensive groups

Much leeway is allowed to the individual observer, as the table contains no fixed quantitative data. But experience soon helps the observer to be consistent, which is all that is necessary here. Sociability need not be shown in the tables except where it is considered to be particularly useful.

It is often difficult to distinguish between categories 1 and 5, especially when applied to trees. EMBERGER gives the following example to illustrate the problem. Category 1 indicates isolated individuals. In order to appreciate the order of sociability, one must know exactly whether or not the individuals are isolated, which is not always easy in dry countries. In North Africa, the sociability of open groves is often considered to be 5 because the trees touch one another by their roots and because there is therefore no room for an additional tree. As the density is at its maximum, the sociability must be likewise. In central Tunisia one can plant seventeen olive trees per hectare. There is no space for an eighteenth tree! EMBERGER (1963, p. 134) reports that sociability has therefore been abandoned in Montpellier and that it has been replaced by the distribution in the sample plot.

Recording and Organizing Data

The floristic analyses of all sample plots in one phytocenose are brought together in a table. Such a table has a heading which gives valuable information on the community as a whole, the names of all species recorded, and their coverage in each sample plot. Where the recording of sociability is desired, it is shown following the coverage, from which it is separated by a period. For instance, 2.3 means that a species covers between 6 and 25 per cent of the plot and is distributed through the quadrat in small groups. Table 12 shows an example of a heading with the list of species from one quadrat. It gives the date and location of the field work, type and name of base map, landscape, and topography. A descriptive name of the phytocenose is followed by its scientific (Latin) name, as well as its condition and structure. The names of the species are arranged by synusias, and every name is followed by the coverage; the sociability is given in only three instances. Each quadrat has its own number, and its size is given immediately below the number.

The observations are recorded on a table which, in its first column at the left, lists all species found. Each of the succeeding columns contains the information on one quadrat, and every species listed at the left has its coverage shown in every quadrat in which it occurs. If a species is found which does not occur in the first quadrat, its name is added to the list. The vegetation is not sufficiently homogeneous to be regarded as a type if a rather large number of new species must be added to the list with each new quadrat.

The mapper will find it useful to group the species according to some plan. For instance, in a meadow he can often distinguish such groups as grasses, sedges, legumes, other forbs, mosses, etc. If the community is multilayered, the species may be grouped by synusia. If the mapper uses such divisions on his tables, he must leave ample space after the species names of each division when analyzing the first plot. Additional species found in succeeding quadrats can then be listed in the appropriate divisions without difficulty. The quadrats, too, can be arranged in some pattern, for instance, according to increasing wetness of the soil or increasing elevation above sea level, etc. The record taken in the field with pencil is carefully and neatly copied on clean sheets with a typewriter immediately after the day's field work is completed. The basic headings on the tables can be prepared and printed in advance, so that the mapper need do no more than fill in the data on the area and its plant communities. At the time of preparing his clean copy, he can arrange the order of his sample

Table 12.   Phytocenological Record of a Forest *

Date: 30 May 1937   Base map: topographic sheet Bodenberg

Place: east of Haste,   State: Niedersachsen
         Haste State Forest, section 23   Height above sea level: 52 m

Location in Landscape: edge of broad
                         depression   Slope and exposure: 1° north

Phytocenose: moist oak-birch forest (Querceto roboris-Betuletum
               molinietosum)

Note: The trees are planted. Plot near small road that has little
        effect on light conditions in the forest

Tree layer: height: about 22 m   coverage: about 60%
              age: 115 years; quality: fair

Shrub layer: height: 1-3 m   coverage: about 60%

Herbaceous layer: height: up to 55 cm   coverage: about 20%

Moss layer: coverage: about 25%

* *

	1	2	3
Number of Quadrat	1	2	3
Size of Quadrat in m²	200		
Total Number of Species	23		
Tree layer: Quercus robur	4		
Shrub layer: Frangula alnus	3.4		
Lonicera periclymenum	2		
Ilex aquifolium	+		
Betula pubescens	2		
Betula pendula	2		
Herbaceous layer: Molinia coerulea	2		
Dryopteris austriaca ssp. spinulosa	1		
Blechnum spicant	+		
Holcus mollis	1.3		
Carex pilulifera	2		
Melampyrum pratense	1		
Deschampsia flexuosa	+		
Galium saxatile	1		
Moss layer: Polytrichum attenuatum	2.3		
Mnium hornum	+		
Aulacomium androgynum	1		
Entodon schreberi	1		
Dicranum scoparium	1		
Scleropodium purum	2		
Hypnum cupressiforme	2		
Sphagnum fimbriatum	1		
Mnium cuspidatum	+		

* After ELLENBERG (1956), slightly rearranged.

plots in any fashion he chooses and then number then consecutively. In some instances it is desirable to record the exact location of each quadrat on the base map. This is particularly useful where later checks are planned. Once the mapper has recorded all his observations on the table, he then holds a valuable document, which he should keep. It is called a "raw table" and serves as the basis of all manipulations for establishing plant communities. Table 13 shows such a raw table of an Arrhenatheretum meadow. The heading has been omitted except for the quadrat numbers and the number of species in each quadrat. The quadrats are arranged in order of increasing quantities of oat grass (*Arrhenaterum elatius*), the first species in the table; it is the most prominent grass in this meadow. Klapp's (1949) weight estimates are used, and the species are grouped as grasses, sedges, legumes, and others. The last column of the table does not refer to a quadrat but contains the frequency value of the species. Frequency is the number of quadrats in a table in which a species occurs: for instance (in Table 13), *Arrhenaterum*, 25, *Brachypodium*, 1. This is called the "absolute frequency." In order to permit a comparison of tables, the absolute frequency is usually changed into percentages. For example, in Table 13, *Arrhenatherum* has a frequency percentage of 100, *Brachypodium* only 4. At first sight, the raw table seems rather chaotic, and common and rare species are all mixed, just as they were recorded in the field. It is therefore advantageous to calculate the frequency for each species and then rearrange the whole table, listing the species in order of their frequency. Table 14 is a section of a "frequency table." The order of the sample plots remains the same but the order of the species is changed. Species with frequencies over 15 and under 3 are omitted. As a matter of expedience, the species names are abbreviated. The mapper can now discover if the material varies quite irregularly or whether he can establish some groups of species that may form divisions of the total community. Such divisions usually exist, and it should be possible to obtain them from the table. For this purpose, the species of very high frequency are of little use; they occur in so many quadrats that they cannot be employed for establishing divisions. Hence they are omitted. The same applies to species of very low frequency: they are omitted because they are too rare to aid in the recognition of divisions. However, among the species of medium frequency, there are usually some which occur together in certain quadrats and are missing from others; they seem to be mutually exclusive. Such species are referred to as "differential species." They are valuable for the comparative order of the communities, particularly because they seem to result necessarily from the table, independently of subjective experience.

At first, all species that may be assumed to be differential species are underlined with color. In Table 14, color has been replaced by straight

Table 13. Example of a Completed Raw Table *

Sample No.	1	2	3	4	5	6	7	8	9	10	11	12	13	14	15	16	17	18	19	20	21	22	23	24	25	F
Number of species	31	25	32	28	32	32	36	34	32	31	28	34	37	33	34	37	35	29	29	30	35	27	29	30	28	
Grasses:																										
Arrhenatherum elatius	+°	1	2°	2	4	4	4	4	5	8	9	10	10	12	15	15	15	22	22	24	25	25	26	30	35	25
Dactylis glomerata	5	5	15	5	12	12	4	10	2	6	12	32	15	10	6	15	15	18	1	5	18	8	8	8	18	25
Helictotrichon pubescens	1°	1			20	8	3		4	+		1	4			13	4	4		28	+	2		1		16
Bromus erectus	50		35	74					47	21					37									10		7√
Festuca ovina	2	1							1	2																4√
Poa pratensis	4	74	10	5	4	2	3	4	10	8	6	25	2	5	15	10	5	10	1	6	1	9	16	20	10	25
Briza media	1	1							2	1						2										5√
Koeleria pyramidata	3		2						3	3																4√
Festuca rubra	15		2	2	+		2	+	3	4	2	2	1		6	5	2	12	+	2	15	+	+	2		15√
" pratensis		5	3		20	3	2	8	5	2	10	10	2	2	6	10	28	12	10	2	15	15	2	2	3	23
Trisetum flavescens		2	5		8				3			6	6	4	4	10	5	5	5	8	8	16	4	2		15√
Alopecurus pratensis					2	8		10			6	4					2	2			15	10			1	9√
Holcus lanatus					1	1	1	2	1	2	2	1	2	2			2	+	+	2	2		+		15	12√
Deschampsia caespitosa							11	2		28	28						10	2	2	5	5					7√
Poa trivialis							2					+														1
Phleum pratense														1												1
Festuca arundinacea																		2								1
Lolium perenne																										1
Glyceria fluitans																			20							1
Phalaris arundinacea																			28							1
Phragmites communis																				+						1
Brachypodium pinnatum																								5		1

Table after Ellenberg (1956), page 237.

	Sedges:					Legumes:							Others:									
	Carex flacca	" acutiformis	" hirta	" panicea	" gracilis	Trifolium pratense	" repens	Medicago lupulina	Vicia sepium	Lotus corniculatus	Lathyrus pratensis	Vicia cracca	Achillea millefolium	Daucus carota	Campanula rotundifolia	Plantago lanceolata	Heracleum sphondylium	Galium mollugo	Chrysanthemum leucanthemum	Scabiosa columbaria	Linum catharticum	Rumex acetosa

The original is a large rotated frequency table (Ellenberg 1956) with column heading values: 6, 5, 2, 1, 2, 18, 14, 17, 7, 4, 10, 5, 21, 20, 13, 25, 14, 25, 23, 5, 5, 19.

237

* After ELLENBERG (1956).

Table 13. (Continued)

Sample No.	1	2	3	4	5	6	7	8	9	10	11	12	13	14	15	16	17	18	19	20	21	22	23	24	25	F
Ranunculus acer	+	+	+		-	2	2	+	+	3	-	+	2	-	+	+	+	+	+	-	+	2	+	+	+	23√
Thymus serpyllum	-	+	+	+						2																5√
Cerastium caespitosum	+°	+	+	+	+			+°											+	+	+					13√
Centaurea jacea	+°	-	6		3	2	3							4		2	2			2		+	+	2		14√
Taraxacum officinale	+°		+°	+		2	3			+			2	+		+	+	-		+		+	4	+	+	19
Campanula glomerata	+	+	-	-					-						+	+										7√
Veronica chamaedrys	+	+	+°	+	+	-	-	+	+		+	-	+		+	-	+	+	+	-	-	+	2	+	-	22
Plantago media	+	+	+	+	+			+	+				+	+	+	+	+					+	+	+		14√
Silene inflata		2				+									+			+								3√
Leontodon hispidus		-	+				4																			4√
Crepis biennis	+	+	+°		2	-		8			+	+		+		-	+		-		+		6	+		15√
Myosotis arvensis		+					+																			2
Ajuga reptans		+			+	+	-	3	-		-	+	+	+			+	+		+		+			+	16
Salvia pratensis			4						2	5					-									4		5√
Knautia arvensis			1°						2	3					+		+	+						4		3√
Viola hirta			+						2	3					+			+						+		6√
Bellis perennis			+		+			+	+			+			+	+	+	+				+				11√
Dianthus superbus			+	-	+							-				+			+	+						4√
Pimpinella saxifraga				+	+				+																	2
Galium boreale				+				-					-													4√
Cirsium oleraceum					+	12	20	20		3	3	+	+	18					+	+					3	4√
Tragopogon pratensis		2			2	-	+				+	+				-	2				2	+	-			14√
Glechoma hederacea					+		+	+			+	+										+				6√

238

Rotated phytosociological table (species rows, presence/abundance columns).

Species																	Freq.
Anthriscus silvestris	2				+				+								5 √
Filipendula ulmaria	3	2	2	+	+	+	+	+	+		+	+	+		+		4 √
Geum rivale	2	–	5	+	3	+	+	+			–	+	+	+	–	+	14 √
Melandrium diurnum	2	–		+	+	+	–				+	+	+		+		11 √
Angelica silvestris	–	2				+					–	+					6 √
Lysimachia nummularia	+		–	+	+	+	+			+	+	+	–				8 √
Prunella vulgaris		+	2	+	+	+	–			+	+			–		+	12 √
Pimpinella magna		+				+°	–			+		+					4 √
Polygonum bistorta		–								–		–				4	4 √
Lychnis flos cuculi			+	+	+	+				+	+	+		+		+	7 √
Senecio jacobaea				+	+	+			+			+					6 √
Potentilla reptans				–	–					–				–			3 √
Cardamine pratensis				+			+			+	+	–					2
Myosotis palustris				+	+		+			+		+					2
Geranium pratense					+		–			–							–
Pastinaca sativa					+			+	3								3 √
Galium uliginosum					+		++										–
Sanguisorba officinalis					+		+										2
Galium verum								–					+				3 √
Silaus pratensis									+	+				+			2
Ranunculus repens										+			+				
Euphrasia odontites									+			+		+			2
Lamium album										+				+			
Rumex crispus										+					+	+	2
Polygonum convolvulus										+							–
Chenopodium album										+	–						–
Alchemilla vulgaris														+		+	–

239

Table 14. Section of a Frequency Table *

Sample No.	1	2	3	4	5	6	7	8	9	10	11	12	13	14	15	16	17	18	19	20	21	22	23	24	25	F
Fest. rubra	15	2	5	2	+			+	3	4	2	2	1		6		2		+	2	8		4	2		15
Triset. flav.		+	+°		8	−		8	3		+	−	6	+	4	10	5	5	5	8	8	16	6	2	3	15
Crepis b.					2	−			−					+		+	+	−		−	+	−	−	+	+	15
Trif. rep.	+	+			2	+	4	+					+	+	+	+	−	+		+	+	+	+	+	+	14
Heracl. sphond.	+°	−	1°		3	2	3	+	1			26	26	+	+	+	2	+		2	+	+	+	2	+	14
Cent. jac.	+	+	6	+	+	2	−	+				−	+	4	+	2	2	+		2	+		+	+	3	14
Plant. med.					+			+			3	−	+	18	+	+	2	+	+	+	2	+	+	+	+	14
Cirs. oler.					+	2	20	5	+		3	+	+		−	+	2	+	−	+	−	2	−		+	14
Geum riv.	−	+	+	−	+	−	1	+°	+	−	+	+	+	−	+	+	+	+	+	+	+	+		+	+	13
Camp. rot.	+			+	+	−	+		+	+	2	+	+	2	+	−	2	+	+	+	2	+	+		+	13
Cer. caesp.						−	+	2	+			−	−	−	+	+	+	+	+	+	−	+	+		12
Holc. lan.			+	+	+	+	2	+	+	−	+	+	+	+	+	−	+	+	+	+	+	−	−	+	15	12
Prun. vulg.						−	−	+				−	+	2			+		+		−				+	11
Bellis per.						2	−	+	+	+	+	+	+	−	+	+	+	+	+	−	+	+	+		4	11
Melandr. d.							−									+	2	+			+	+			−	10
Lathyr. pr.					2	8	+	10	+		6	4	4	1	+			2		−	15	10		10	+	9
Alop. pr.					2	+		−	1	21	+	+			37		+		+	+	+				+	8
Lysim. numm.	50		35	74			111	2	47		28	−		1			10		2		5					7
Brom. er.							+			21														10		7
Desch. caesp.			+	+	−		+	+	1	+	+	+	−	1	+	+		+								7
Vic. sep.	+	+	+	+					−			+	−		+	+		+						+		7
Camp. glom.					2						+					+	+		+	+	+				+	7
Tragop. pr.																	2								+	7
Lychn. fl. c.	2			3					2	3				2	−	3									6	6
Car. flacca			+												+			+				+		+	+	6

Glech. hed.
Angel. silv.
Senec. jac.
Briza m.
Car. acut.
Vic. cracca
Scab. col.
Linum cath.
Thym. serp.
Salvia pr.
Anthr. silv.
Fest. ov.
Koel. pyr.
Lot. corn.
Leont. hisp.
Dianth. sup.
Gal. bor.
Fil. ulm.
Pimp. magn.
Pol. bist.
Sil. infl.
Knaut. arv.
Pot. rept.
Past. sat.
Sil. prat.

° After ELLENBERG (1956).

and wavy lines. Even after underlining the differential species it remains difficult to see any order in the table. Therefore the mapper now prepares an "extract table" (Table 15) in which he lists in two groups only the underlined species: the species underlined by a straight line are in group I, and group II contains the species underlined by a wavy line. In these groups, only those species are ultimately accepted as differential species which have a frequency of at least 50 per cent in the frequency range within these groups. The quadrats with numerous mutually exclusive species are emphasized by line frames which make them stand out boldly.

When the mapper compares Table 14 with Table 15 he recognizes that the meadow has three divisions: one in which *Bromus erectus*, *Salvia pratensis*, and others occur together, one in which *Cirsium oleraceum*, *Alopecurus pratensis*, and others occur together, and one in which these two groups are absent or occur simultaneously but in negligible quantity. In Table 15 the quadrats are still in their original sequence, but it is now useful to rearrange them because the grouping of the differential species and also of the quadrats becomes still clearer if an "orderly extract table" is prepared; this permits the mapper to see at a glance what species belong to given groups. The orderly extract table is therefore much more useful than the original extract. Accordingly, the quadrats of groups I and II are now written in the order of descending numbers of species. The number of species for each group and the resulting new sequence are already given at the foot of Table 15.

In order to rewrite the extract table in its new arrangement it is often convenient that two persons cooperate, one dictating the values which the other will write in their appropriate places. First some strips are prepared, so-called dictation strips, which will make it easier to avoid mistakes in transferring the numbers from one table to another. They must be exactly the same size as the tables. On two dictation strips (Table 16) the quadrat sequences are listed as follows: one dictation strip (A) contains the sequence as shown at the bottom of Table 15, where it is called the "new sequence." On the other strip (B), the numbers are arranged consecutively. During the transfer one person, using strip A, places this directly under the line of a species and then dictates the name, the quadrat number (new, from bottom of Table 15) and the values for the different quadrats. Strip B, containing the same numbers but consecutively, serves to keep the other person oriented when writing down the dictated values.

The result of the new arrangement is the "orderly extract table" (Table 17). This reveals that the *Bromus* group as well as the *Cirsium* group contain some species narrowly confined to their groups and others which are somewhat more widely distributed. The former are underlined in the table. The quadrats can be rearranged according to the number of under-

Table 15. Example of an Extract Table *

Sample No.	1	2	3	4	5	6	7	8	9	10	11	12	13	14	15	16	17	18	19	20	21	22	23	24	25
I. Brom. er.	50		35	74					47	21					37									10	
Camp. glom.	+		1	1												+								+	
Viola hirta			+															+						+	
Briza media		1		—											+			+							
Scab. col.	+	2	—							+						+									
Linum cath.	+		+	+					+	1					+										
Thym. serp.	—	+	+	+																					
Salvia pr.			4						2	2														4	
Koel. pyr.	3								2	5															
Fest. ovina	2	—							3	3					—										
II. Cirs. oler.					+	12	20	20			3	+	+	18		—	2	+	+	+	2	+	—		3
Geum rivale						2	—	5			3	+	+	2		—	+	+	—	+	—	+	+		+
Holc. lan.					—	—	—	2			2	+	—	—			2				2				15
Melandr. d.					2	2					6	+	+	—			+				+	+			4
Alop. pr.					2	8		10			6	+	4	—			10				15				—
Lysim. numm.						+	11	—			28											10			
Desch. caesp.							11	2			+		+			—	+	2	2	+					
Lychn. fl. c.					+		+	+			+	+							+		+		—		+
Glech. hed.								+			+		+					3							
Angel. silv.						2	2												2		—				
Car. acut.						3	10	2			4						+								
Fil. ulm.							+						+	+							—				2
Pimp. magn.							+					+°													
Pol. bist.							—					+°	—				+								4
Past. sat.														+				3							
Number of species																									
Group I	8	4	6	6	4	8	10	9	8	8					4	3								4	
Group II					4	8	10	9	2	3	9	5	9	7	6	3	8	3	8	3	10	5	3	7	10
New Sequence	1	8	5	4	14	17	23	20	2	3	21	12	22	16	6	9	18	11	19	10	24	15	13	7	25

* After Ellenberg (1956).

Table 16. Dictation Strips *

A. (for the first extract table, see Table 15).

1	8	5	4	14	17	23	20	2	3	21	12	22	16	6	9	18	11	19	10	24	15	13	7	25

B. (for the orderly extract table, see Table 17).

1	2	3	4	5	6	7	8	9	10	11	12	13	14	15	16	17	18	19	20	21	22	23	24	25

* After ELLENBERG (1956).

Table 17. Orderly Extract Table *

New Sequence	1	2	3	4	5	6	7	8	9	10	11	12	13	14	15	16	17	18	19	20	21	22	23	24	25
Sample No.	1	9	10	4	3	15	24	2	16	20	18	12	23	5	22	14	6	17	19	8	11	7	13	21	25
Brom. er.	50	47	21	74	35	37	10	2	16	20	18	12	23	5	22	14	6	17	19	8	11	7	13	21	25
Camp. glom.	+	–	–	+																					
Viola hirta	–	2	3	–	+	+	+					–													
Briza media	–	2	1	–				2										+							
Scab. col.	+	+	+	+		+		2	2																
Linum cath.	+	+	–	+	+			+	+																
Thym. serp.	–	2	–	+	+			+																	
Salvia pr.			5		4	4	4																		
Koel. pyr.	3	3	3	2																					
Fest. ovina	2	1	2	–																					

* After ELLENBERG (1956).

244

II. Cirs. oler.												+	+			+	+	2	20	+	2	2	3
Geum rivale									+	+	+	+	+	+	+	+	+	5	1	+	1	+
Holc. lan.										+			2	2	2	+	2	2	1	1	2	15
Melandr. d.									+			+	+	+	+	+	+		+	1	+	4
Alop. pr.					2	2		2	10	8	+	6	10		6	1		15	1
Lysim. numm.							+			+	+	+	28	2		+	+	5	+
Desch. caesp.							+			+	+	+	+	+	+	+			
Lych. fl. c.								+			10	2		+	2		+	+
Glech. hed.							+											+	2	10	+
Angel. silv.													4	2		+		+	+	2
Car. acut.										3		2			+		+
Fil. ulm.						+°											
Pimp. magn.									3							
Pol. bist.														4	4	1	1		
Past. sat.									+								
Number of species																									
Group I a	5	5	4	3	3	2	3	2	12				3		6	5	5	5	3	20	+	2	2
Group I b (Rest)	3	4	2	3	1	2	3	1					1		3	3	3	3	1	5	1	1	+
Group II b (Rest)								3					6	2					4		10	6	15
Group IIa	3	4	2	1	3	2	4						2	4					3	1	5	4
Improved Sequence	3	4	2	1	3	2	4	5	6	9	12	10	11	15	13	14	24	19	18	16	21	20	17	25	22	23

* After ELLENBERG (1956).

lined species, leading to a new sequence, called the "improved sequence." The improved sequence is already given in the last line of Table 17. Using this improved sequence of quadrats, the entire raw table is copied, resulting in Table 18, known as a "differentiated table." In it, the differential species as well as others are arranged in the order of their frequency. The quadrats are grouped in three columns (A, B, and C) and the species whose values are framed in a heavy line appear to be especially appropriate to serve as differential species.

Quadrat No. 19 (revised current number 16) is removed because the species list contains several notable gaps; it also includes five species which occur in none of the other quadrats. This meadow quadrat resembles the others only modestly in spite of appreciable quantities of *Arrhenatherum*. The discrepancy is presumably due to periodic flooding with resulting silt deposits. However, the mapper should be very cautious and not develop a tendency to remove everything that does not seem to "fit" with the remainder of the quadrats.

The manipulation of the tables results in the recognition of plant communities and their divisions. In ELLENBERG's example we find three groups of differential species forming divisions of the *Arrhenatherum* meadows. The first division is characterized by the *Bromus* group. The second column is marked by the group of *Geum rivale*. In the third column is the *Cirsium* group.

These units of the vegetation are obtained solely on the basis of comparing the tables on which the species are listed. Hence this is a purely floristic procedure. But an investigation of the respective sites will reveal that these units can also be described ecologically and even economically. In Table 18, they are ecologically arranged with increasing soil moisture. With uniform application of fertilizer, the forage yields increase in the same manner. However, the quality is highest in the second group.

Such vegetation units are therefore useful to the scientist as well as to the ecologist and the economist. They are vegetation units that can be mapped, and most appropriate for them is some simple name, such as "oat grass–brome meadow," "oat grass–*Geum* meadow," or "oat grass–plumed thistle meadow." As is the case with all vegetation units that are characterized floristically, these names are only symbols for the particular combinations of species. They do not mean that the species mentioned in the name of the community must dominate or even be present. For instance, ‧in Table 18, quadrat 2 (current number 8) is clearly a part of the oat grass–brome meadow although it lacks *Bromus erectus*. It is often relatively easy to recognize a plant community if it is clearly dominated by some species. But such an approach is rather superficial; the more accurate and reliable method is to obtain the total or near total of all differential species involved. This permits quadrat 2 (current Number 8) to be grouped with the *Bromus* group even though the "dominant" species happens to be absent. Ecologically and floristically, however, this is quite justified.

Field Mapping with the Key

When through the use of tables all vegetation units have been clearly established, further analyses are made in the field in order to check their accuracy. A key is then prepared which includes all plant communities that have been observed in the area to be mapped, and this key, too, must be checked in the field. The last step is the actual mapping of the types or units of vegetation according to the key, and their transitions, if any. This is done in the field, on a large-scale base map on which the outlines of the vegetation types are drawn. Cadastral maps are often used to advantage because of their large scale and accuracy. If at any time during the course of mapping doubts arise about the adequacy of the key, the mapping activity is interrupted and the key is corrected, adjusted, or supplemented, whichever is necessary. Only then may the mapping work be resumed.

When the mapper wants to draw the phytocenoses and their divisions on his base map, he begins preferably in that part of his area which has a simple topography and where the mosaic of plant communities is clear. The more complicated areas are best left to the last. He selects the community he wants to show on his map and walks through it, parallel to some line on his base map that can be readily observed and used for orientation. Where the species combination changes noticeably, a boundary is drawn. Then the community on the other side of the boundary is determined with the help of the key and the process continues. Sometimes communities merge gradually and the beginner especially finds it difficult to know where to place the boundary on the map. But he should avoid too many transitions as that makes the map more difficult to read and to exploit. A certain abstraction is necessary in any case when a stand is assigned to a particular phytocenose. In case of doubt, the area on the map is left blank and mapped again when more experience or a skilled mapper can help solve the problem. Beginners sometimes make the mistake of believing that every plant community they observe must be shown in terms of their key (which may have been prepared by someone else). But a key is by no means infallible. Even when the key is prepared with care, it is quite possible that some divisions of the phytocenoses were overlooked. When a community does not readily fit the key, its outline is mapped and its floristic composition analyzed in quadrats. It is then possible to decide how to handle this community, i.e., whether it is a new unit, a part of another one, or some transition.

Table 18. Example of a Differentiated Table *

Unit	A								B								C								
Tentative Name	oat grass-brome meadow								oat grass-Geum meadow								oat grass-thistle meadow								
New Sequence	1	2	3	4	5	6	7	8	9	10	11	12	13	14	15	16	17	18	19	20	21	22	23	24	25
Sample No.	4	10	1	9	15	3	24	2	16	18	12	20	5	22	23	19	13	17	6	11	8	21	25	14	7
Grasses (mass %)	90	55	83	85	89	70	80	90	70	75	80	75	71	85	56	89	45	86	38	75	40	89	82	33	30
Sedges "	3		2		1			2	5						4	6	4	4		10		1	3	2	10
Legumes "	+	+			+		2	+		+	+		9			+	+	+	2	+	+	+	+		1
Others "	7	45	14	14	10	29	18	10	24	25	20	24	20	14	40	5	55	10	60	15	60	10	15	64	58
Number of species	28	31	31	32	34	32	31	25	27	29	34	30	32	27	29	20	37	35	32	28	34	35	28	33	36
Ia BROMUS ERECTUS-GROUP																									
Bromus erectus	74	21	50	47	37	35	10																		
Scabiosa columbaria	-	+	+	-	+	-	+																		
Thymus serpyllum	+	2	-		+	+	+	2																	
Salvia pratensis	5		2		-	4	4	+																	
Koeleria pyramidata	2	3	3	3		4																			
Festuca ovina	2	2	2	1				-																	
Ib BRIZA MEDIA-GROUP																									
Campanula glomerata	-		+	-			+	+	+		-														
Viola hirta		3	-	2	+	+	+		2	+															
Briza media		-	-	2		+																			
Linum catharticum	+		+	+																					
IIb GEUM RIVALE-GROUP																									
Geum rivale									-	+	+			+	+	✗	+	+	2	3	5	-	+	2	-
Holcus lanatus																+	-	2	1	2	2	2	2		1
Melandrium diurnum										+	+		-	+		+	+	+	2	2	+	+	4	4	1
Alopecurus pratensis									2			2	10			+	4		8	6	10	15		1	1
Lysimachia nummularia									+	+	+						+	+	+	+	+	+	+		+

248

IIa CIRSIUM OLERACEUM-GROUP																										
Cirsium oleraceum										+	+	+		1	+	+	2	12	3	20	2	3	18	20
Deschampsia caespitosa														2		10		28	2	5			1	11
Angelica silvestris														1		+		1				+	1	2
Carex acutiformis														2				4			1	2		10
Filipendula ulmaria																+		3		2			+	
Pimpinella magna																1	+				1			+
Polygonum bistorta									+°					1								4		1
OTHERS																									
Arrhenatherum elatius	2	8	+°	5	15	2°	30	1	15	22	10	24	4	25	26	22	10	15	4	9	4	25	35	12	4
Dactylis glomerata	5	6	5	2	6	15	8	5	15	18	32	5	12	8	8	1	15	15	12	12	10	18	18	10	4
Galium mollugo	1	12	3	2	3	7	3	2	5	6	6	5	3	3	12	2	10	3	24	5	4	1	2	14	6
Poa pratensis	5	8	4	10	15	10	20	74	10	10	25	6	4	9	16	1	2	5	2	6	4	1	10	5	6
Plantago lanceolata	1	1	1	1	1	1	+	1	2	1	1	1	2	2	8	+	4	+	1	+	4	1	+	2	4
Festuca pratensis		2		5	6	3	2	5	5	12	10	2	20	15	2	10	2	28	3	10	8	15	3	2	2
Chrysanthemum leucanthemum	+	5	1	2	1	3	6	+	1		3	3	+	1	1	1	1	4	+	1	+		2	2
Ranunculus acer		3	+	+	+	+	+	+	+	1	+	1	1	2	+	+	2	+	2		+	+	+	1	2
Veronica chamaedrys	+	1	+	+	+	+	+		1			1	+	+	2	+	+	+	1	+	+	1	1		1
Achillea millefolium	1	8	6	2	2	3	3	+	5	12	1	6	2	4	+		4	+				+	+	16	1
Daucus carota	+	1	1	1	+	1		1	+	1	+	1	+	+	2		2	+	1		5	+			1
Rumex acetosa	+		+		+				1		1	1	+	1	+	1	1	+	2	2	3	+	1	2	1
Taraxacum officinale	+	+	+°		+	+°	+		1	+	+	3	+	4		2	+	1		1		+	+	3
Trifolium pratense	+		+		+	1	2	+	1	+		+	4	+	2	+°	+		1		+	+		1
Medicago lupulina	+	+	1	+	+	+			+	+	+		2	1	1		+	+	+	+				+	
Helictotrichon pubescens		+	1°	4			1	1	13	4	1	28	20	2			4	4	8			+			3
Ajuga reptans			1					+		+	1	+	+	+			+	+	+	1	3	1	+	+	1
Trisetum flavescens				3	4	5	2	2	10	5		8	8	16	4	5	6	5			8			
Crepis biennis					+°	+	+		1	1	1	1	2	1	6		+		+	1	8	+		+
Trifolium repens		+	1	+				+	+		+	2		1		+		+		+	+	+	+	

* After ELLENBERG (1956).

249

Table 18. (Continued)

New Sequence	1	2	3	4	5	6	7	8	9	10	11	12	13	14	15	16	17	18	19	20	21	22	23	24	25
Heracleum sphondylium			+			1°	+	-	+	+	-	-	+	+	-		26	-	+				+		4
Centaurea jacea		4	+°	+°	+	6	+		2		1	2	3		+			2	2			+	+	4	3
Plantago media	+		+	+	+	+	+	+	+	+	-		+		+		+			+	+				-
Campanula rotundifolia	-	-	-	+	-	+	+		+	+	-		+		-		+				+		+	-	
Festuca rubra	2	4	15	3	6	2	2				2	2	+		+	—	-	2		2	+				
Cerastium caespitosum	+		+	+	+			+	+		2	+	+	+	+	—	+			+	+°	+		+	+
Brunella vulgaris		+		+			+		+	+			+	+			+	+	+		2	-			
Bellis perennis	-	-		+					+	+	-						+	+	-		+				+
Lathyrus pratensis	+			+		+	+		+	+	+		+	+			+			+	+	+			+
Vicia sepium	+	+		+	+	+			-	+	+	-	-				-		-	+	+	+			+
Tragopogon pratensis					+				-		+		-				-		-						
Carex flacca	3		2		-				3		+		2					2						2	
Senecia jacobaea				+						+	+		2							+		+			
Anthriscus silvestris							+						2		+		+						+		
Vicia cracca	+			+	+	+	+		+						+						+			-	
Lotus corniculatus						+	+																		
Leontodon hispidus					+	+	+	-	-												+		+	+	
Ib Dianthus superbus	-					+	+		+			+												4	
Galium boreale	+		-																+		-				
Silene inflata								2																	
Ib Knautia arvensis					+	1°			+	+															
Potentilla reptans		-										-									-			+	
Pastinaca sativa																	-							+	+
Silaus pratensis									-		+	+						+						+	+

250

Species												
IIa Carex hirta	+											
IIa " gracilis												
Myosotis arvensis		−					+		+			+
Ia Pimpinella saxifraga	+				+						+	
IIb Cardamine pratensis			+									
IIb Myosotis palustris	+			+						+	−	
Ia Galium verum						+				+	+	
Euphrasia odontites		+								+		
IIa Rumex crispus	2	+										
IIa Poa trivialis			+									
Phleum pratense												
IIa Festuca arundinacea				2								
Lolium perenne												
Glyceria fluitans												
Phalaris arundinacea	20 / 18											
IIa Phragmites communis												
Ia Brachypodium pinnatum			+							5		
Carex panicea				2								
Geranium pratense	+											
IIa Galium uliginosum												
IIa Sanguisorba officinale	+	+										
IIa Ranunculus repens												
Lamium album	+ + + +											
Polygonum convolvulus												
Chenopodium album												
Ia Alchemilla vulgaris	+		+								+	

Value and Future of the Table Method

The quadrat method is a method which can save much time when properly used. It is not truly a statistical method but rather one of orderly comparisons, where qualitative criteria, e.g., the presence or absence of species, are more important than quantitative criteria. The greatest value of this method is that, with some practice, it leads necessarily, hence objectively, to an orderly arrangement of the collected data. But the mapper is reminded emphatically that the selection of these data in the field is not thereby made objective.

Once the mapper has attained some practice in using the quadrat method with tables, he is in a position to establish mappable vegetation units with a high degree of accuracy; and an accurate map of the mosaic of plant communities is, of course, the primary goal of the vegetation mapper.

The chief purpose of BRAUN-BLANQUET and his collaborators was to classify the vegetation and to establish phytocenoses as members of a hierarchy (Table 19). This is not strictly the task of the mapper. He is therefore referred to the discussion of the ways and means to assign a rank to a given phytocenose given by ELLENBERG (1956) in case he needs this information.

When a phytocenologist analyzes the vegetation of his area, using the BRAUN-BLANQUET method, he can assign the vegetational units to various ranks in the hierarchy. This, however, is a subjective procedure. Here it is where, presumably, BRAUN-BLANQUET's "tact" or TÜXEN's "special talent" is needed. The procedure becomes more objective with an increase in the size of the area, so that a rank is significant only after the vegetation of a region has been analyzed in detail and has been coordinated throughout this region. TOMASELLI (1958) showed in northeastern Kansas that ranks cannot be assigned unless such coordination has been accomplished. In other words, the stand samples cannot be coordinated when their number in a given region is insufficient.

Table 19. Vegetation Hierarchy According to the Classification by Braun-Blanquet

Rank	Ending	Example
Class	-etea	Querco-Fagetea
Order	-etalia	Fagetalia
Alliance	-ion	Fagion
Association	-etum	Fagetum
Subassociation	-etosum	Fagetum festucetosum

The ranks of BRAUN-BLANQUET's hierarchy become problematical with the expansion of the areas studied in detail. In a small region, character species and differential species are satisfactory. In a larger region, a differential species often occurs in one or more other communities that do not exist in the initial area of investigation. As the region expands, the hierarchy becomes more and more blurred, and many well-defined units grow into vague transitions. ELLENBERG (1954b) reports of attempts to integrate plant communities near Ulm in southern Germany into the system of vegetation units published by TÜXEN in northern Germany. It was found that more than three quarters of all the communities came to lie between two or three subassociations and associations, partly even between alliances and orders! According to CURTIS' continuum theory, one stand of a clearly defined association deviates increasingly from another stand of this association, the greater the distance between the stands. WHITTAKER's population gradients point in the same direction. ELLENBERG's observations were therefore not at all startling; they could have been predicted. Nevertheless, within the region around Ulm, all units could readily be determined and mapped.

The ranks of BRAUN-BLANQUET's hierarchy are only relative. As the associations became better known in their details, it was found useful to subdivide them in order to do justice to geographical and ecological variations. But when the sequence of association—subassociation—variant—facies became inadequate, the authors simply raised the ranks: an "association" became an "alliance," a "subassociation" became an "association," etc. This is a convenient way to make room for new subdivisions. But it also means that vegetation maps based on this system can soon be obsolete.

The endeavor to rank communities according to BRAUN-BLANQUET's classification can also lead an enthusiastic classifier to overclassify. ELLENBERG (1954b) points out that TÜXEN makes a clear systematic distinction between weed communities on fields with small grains and those on fields with row crops. ELLENBERG feels that it may be more desirable to consider these communities as phases of the same association because they alternate on the same field. This would be more in line with the distinction between spring and autumn phases (seasonal aspects) or with wet and dry phases in climatic cycles.

At Montpellier, the very place from which BRAUN-BLANQUET sent his trainees all over Europe and beyond, the weaknesses of his classification have been found to be so critical that for all practical purposes it has been abandoned. It is, of course, necessary to establish plant communities with the help of tables as before and as indicated above. But the communities so determined are now viewed in their ecological setting and classified accordingly, rather than by some hierarchical rank. It is felt that the instructions for making vegetation maps (BRAUN-BLANQUET, EMBERGER, and MOLINIER, 1947) are out of date, especially with regard to the principles of mapping, and that, in fact, it does not seem possible to retain the classification adopted by BRAUN-BLANQUET. It is felt that this classification does not produce a correct image of what exists in nature (LONG, 1963, p. 354).

Correspondingly, the colors on vegetation maps prepared at Montpellier no longer have the same meaning as before. Whereas in the past, similar colors were given to floristically related phytocenoses, similar colors today imply similar ecological environments. From a practical point of view, this new method offers considerable advantages and makes the vegetation maps more useful even to the layman.

At any rate, whenever a careful study of the vegetation is planned, the mapper will find it entirely satisfactory to map the vegetation in more or less independent units. There is no need for a hierarchy, nor for any ranks. This keeps the entire approach more flexible and can extend the usefulness of the vegetation map considerably. This does not keep the mapper from dividing his observed communities into smaller units as illustrated above where the tables permitted the mapper to recognize three divisions of the oat grass community. In the legend of his map, he can show the divisions in the following manner:

1. Oat grass community
   a) oat grass–brome meadow
   b) oat grass–*Geum* meadow
   c) oat grass–thistle meadow
2. ....
3. ....

Widespread experimentation with the table method in North America should produce interesting and stimulating results, regardless of whether these are positive or negative. Certainly, the method has been applied in Europe with singular success and there is no reason why it should not prove its worth elsewhere, too. But care must be taken not to overextend the application of communities established for a given region. Within such a region, the method can be most useful but in more distant regions, communities must be established anew, in order to avoid confusion and inconsistencies.

The table method remains basic to the establishment of floristically defined plant communities but this does not exclude evolution and progress. At Montpellier, this evolution is availing itself of the latest technological devices in order to assure completeness of record, standardization, and the soundest foundation for relating phytocenoses to their sites. FOSBERG (1961b) reported on it as follows:

"More time was spent at Montpellier in the Botanical Institute of the University, with its associated new Institute for the Service de la Cartographie des Groupements Végétaux, the large-scale vegetation mapping project supported by the Centre National de la Recherche Scientifique (C.N.R.S.) corresponding to the small scale one of Professor GAUSSEN at Toulouse. The Montpellier Institute is directed by Professor Louis Emberger, and the mapping project is run by Dr. G. Long. The staff of this organization are without doubt the most advanced of all vegetation students in the application of new techniques to vegetation study. Some idea of the breadth and depth of the approach planned here may be indicated by mentioning the four main departments, translated freely: field studies and collection of data, mechanographical analysis of data, experimental taxonomy, physiology of vegetation.

"The collection of data is done according to a scheme designed for use with an IBM card system. For each site studied as many as 180 separate vegetation characteristics and habitat items are recorded, in addition to a complete list of the species present, with records of eight figures, such as abundance, vitality, and distribution, of each, supported by herbarium specimens.

"This information is coded according to a very well thought-out system and turned over to the Mechanographical Analysis Department for recording on IBM punch cards. With 800 sites already studied since this system was perfected, it is now possible to establish correlations and to determine the significance of vegetational features, species, and groups of species with a reliability never achieved before.

"Since the floristic aspects are very important in the scheme it is essential to know the genetic structure of certain polymorphic species, to determine the ecotypes involved and to find means of distinguishing them, both in the field and the herbarium. This is the task of the Experimental Taxonomy Department, which is to be provided with an experimental garden.

"Inevitably study of vegetation brings out physiological questions, especially concerning the significance of the behavior of certain species under different conditions. The Plant Physiology Department is to be equipped with the most extraordinary means for unravelling these complex questions. Money and plans are already available for an "ecotron," a sort of superphytotron, similar to the famous Cal-Tech instrument for controlled environment studies but much more flexible. Dr. Eckhart, designer of the ecotron and head of the Plant Physiology Department, was sent to Pasadena to work in the Phytotron and become familiar with its advantages and shortcomings. His design preserves and adds to the advantages as well as correcting the disadvantages.

"This combination attack on vegetational problems promises to yield an insight never before possible into the nature, behavior and environmental relations, and hence the indicator value, of vegetation. Further information on these and other matters relating to the various vegetation mapping projects of the C.N.R.S. can be obtained by consulting the Bulletin du Service de la Carte Phytogéographique, a serial published by the C.N.R.S."

20

Gaussen's Ecological Method

The debt of gratitude vegetation mappers owe to HENRI GAUSSEN is unlikely ever to be paid. Trained as a botanist, GAUSSEN is at heart a geographer, and his predilection finds its undeniable expression on his beautiful vegetation maps. He has published nothing more nearly perfect than his map of Perpignan (Plate I), which has therefore been selected to serve as a basis for the following discussion.

GAUSSEN uses the scale of 1:200,000 and has devoted much of his thought and energy to a mountainous environment, the Pyrenees. It is therefore not surprising to find altitudinal vegetation belts on his maps; in this he resembles many of his colleagues. However, GAUSSEN proceeds along totally different lines, and his maps are entirely unrelated to those of other schools of thought.

What makes GAUSSEN's maps so unique and valuable is that he has succeeded in developing a method to show natural and cultural vegetation and environmental conditions simultaneously. GAUSSEN is also the only one among today's authors of vegetation maps whose work includes a significant development in the use of colors. On this, indeed, rests the originality of GAUSSEN's method, for the use of colors is no longer accidental but reasoned. This reasoning can be applied to vegetation maps anywhere on the globe. By manipulating his color scheme in a systematic, albeit intricate way, he can express more than other authors. His maps are therefore more valuable tools than one might expect from their scale.

GAUSSEN's maps are based on aerial photographs. All vegetational boundaries are carefully indicated on the photographs and then transferred to a base map on the scale of 1:50,000. The map is then taken to the field, where the floristic and physiognomic character of the individual communities is observed. Any necessary boundary corrections are made at this time. Permanent cultural vegetation, such as meadows, orchards, and vineyards, can also be checked in the field; statistical information concerning land use is taken from census data.

According to GAUSSEN, a vegetation map should show more than the vegetation. He argues that the vegetation is the most accurate and effective indicator of environmental conditions with which it is inseparably linked, and that therefore these conditions should be discernible on the vegetation map. His vegetation belts are therefore, above all, climatic belts, or rather belts of plant climates, each one expressed by a particular type of natural vegetation or its substitute communities. GAUSSEN therefore gives his colors ecological significance. This is a long step beyond the general practice to use colors simply to distinguish different types of vegetation. For instance, the beech belt of the Pyrenees implies a cool foggy climate with much snow in the winter. The vegetation includes meadows, apple orchards, heaths, tall shrub formations, and forests. If a farm is located in the beech belt, this implies that if the soil can be cultivated at all, it is useful only for hay meadows, rye, buckwheat, potatoes, and some apple orchards. If man's influence is removed, the vegetation will evolve into a climax of beech forests. The sum total of all types of vegetation, be they natural or cultural, which compose a climax and all its substitute communities (e.g., the beech climax), is called a "series." A series is therefore a term of dynamic significance because it includes the potential natural vegetation and all substitute communities that would evolve toward that same climax. But if GAUSSEN uses series as mapping units, then this implies that in preparing his map he must above all establish the character of the potential natural vegetation in all parts of the area to be mapped. This is not always a simple task.

To map an area according to GAUSSEN's method requires therefore: (1) the availability of aerial photographic coverage; (2) a full understanding of the phytocenological implications of the vegetation belts or series; (3) a thorough understanding of GAUSSEN's use of color; (4) access to census material. It took GAUSSEN years to develop his method; it is now available to everyone. The way has been shown, but it calls for much skill and practice before anyone can hope for similar results. GAUSSEN's maps are highly legible; that they contain so much information adds to their value. It must be remembered that vegetation, whether natural or cultural, is a complex matter which requires much study before its character can be understood. Similarly, a good vegetation map can be expected to require much study if it is to reveal the intricacies of the vegetation.

Color and Pattern

GAUSSEN's genius finds its expression in his manner of organizing a vast amount of information with the help of colors and their manipulation. This, indeed, is the key to the character and the uniqueness of his vegeta-

Plate I

A section from the Vegetation Map of France (sheet Perpignan), by Henri Gaussen. 1 : 200,000. (Reproduced with permission of Henri Gaussen and the Centre National de la Recherche Scientifique.)

LEGEND: SELECTED ITEMS

CLIMAX VEGETATION

Series

CL	cork oak (*chêne-liège*)
CV	evergreen oak (*chêne-vert*)
PLS	Salzmann pine (*pin de Salzmann*)
CPu	pubescent oak (*chêne pubescent*)
CS	sessile oak (*chêne sessile*)
H	beech (*hêtre*)
S	fir (*sapin*)
PS	Scotch pine (*pin sylvestre*)
PC	subalpine pine (*pin à crochets*)
alp 2	alpine meadow

Facies

B	birch-aspen (*bouleau-tremble*)

Characteristic Plants

Cneorum tricoccum

Cistus laurifolius

LAND USE

Relative Percentage of Total Surface of Canton*

>75%	C F π I
>50%	C F π I
>25%	c f π i
>10%	c f π i
<10%	. . . .

C —cultivation
F —forest
π —natural prairie
I —rough pasture and wasteland

Relative Percentage of Main Cultivated Plants in Total Cultivated Area of Canton*

	>50%	30–50%	20–30%	10–20%	5–10%
grape	V	V	v	v	
forage	P	P	p	p	
fallow	J	J	j	j	
corn			m	m	
potato		T	t	t	
rye		S	s	s	

Fruit Trees†

	100,000	10,000	1,000
olive		♉	♉
apricot	A	A	A
almond			♈
fig			♈
peach	P	P	P
plum			P
cherry		♀	♀
pear	π	π	π
apple		P	P

Other Notation

© hackberry

vineyards‡

market gardens‡

row of trees
river gravel

*Percentage indicated by type style.
†Number indicated by type style.
‡Each symbol represents 10 hectares.

tion maps. He has published detailed instructions for the use of colors so that all aspects of his method can be tested everywhere (GAUSSEN, 1949, 1953, 1957a, 1957b, 1961b; and EMBERGER, GAUSSEN, and REY, 1956).

The manner in which colors are applied indicates the physiognomy of the vegetation: flat colors indicate forests, finely ruled colors imply shrub formations, and small colored dots (fine stippling) signify grasslands. There are various possibilities for combinations. For instance, a savanna, i.e., a grassland with scattered trees and small groves, is shown by the grassland pattern (stippling), on which large dots for the trees and groves are superimposed (overprinted). Nothing is said about the density of any vegetation type, nor about the height of forests. The height of shrub and grassland communities, on the other hand, is given in nine unspecified classes, with 1 being the lowest height class and 9 the highest. These classes are shown by printing, on the ruled background, the lower case initial of the dominant of the climax, followed by the number of the height class. For instance (Figure 13), a medium-tall shrub formation in the zone of the beech (French: *hêtre*) is shown by the symbol "h6"; it is printed in black but the ruling is in blue, corresponding to the "beech climate."

The method of selecting an appropriate color is a problem of its own which GAUSSEN solved by applying several considerations concurrently. He distinguishes a number of environmental features or factors each of which has its own set of colors or colored symbols arranged in the order of the spectrum. Among the various environmental features, temperature and humidity are the most prominent. The others include the "xerothermic" factor, which is the number of dry days in a dry period (BAGNOULS and GAUSSEN, 1953), light, length of growing season, soil factors, and

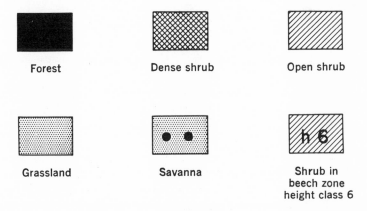

| Forest | Dense shrub | Open shrub |

| Grassland | Savanna | Shrub in beech zone height class 6 |

Figure 13

special features like winds, duration of snow cover, and others. Most of these additional features can be shown conveniently on large-scale maps, i.e., the larger the scale, the more features can be considered. To illustrate, the colors that GAUSSEN (1953) has selected for temperature and humidity are given in Table 20. The colors are combined or superimposed according to local conditions and the resulting combinations of "synthetic colors" give a good idea of the environmental conditions. A certain relation between temperature and humidity is reflected in these choices. Lower temperatures (toward the blue) render precipitation more effective (also blue) whereas high temperatures (more toward the orange and red) require high precipitation or else they result in aridity (also toward the orange). Similar colors imply similar climatic conditions; colors that are far apart in the spectrum show contrasting conditions. Where, on the same map, a given color is shown more than once, the phytocenoses involved may but need not consist of the same species. It does imply, however, that the species are likely to be interchangeable, and this applies to cultivated plants as well. The colors, therefore, have a triple function: they permit the reader to distinguish one type of vegetation from another, and they indicate climatic conditions and show the physiognomy of the phytocenoses. The map content is thereby enriched tremendously.

Table 20.   Gaussen's Color Types

Temperature			
T_1	Very cold	Polar, alpine	Dark grey dots
T_2	Cold	Leningrad	Light grey
T_3	Cool	Paris	White (no color)
T_4	Warm	Lisbon	Golden yellow
T_5	Hot	Libreville	Chestnut-orange
T_6	Very hot	Djibouti	Chestnut-orange-red
Humidity			
S_1	Very humid	Bogor	Dark violet
S_2	Humid	Tokyo	Dark Blue
S_3	Subhumid	Paris	Light cobalt blue
S_4	Subarid	Marseille	White (no color)
S_5	Arid	Zaragoza	Sulphur yellow
S_6	Very arid	Aswan	Orange

When colors are combined there is always the danger that the resulting hues and tints are difficult to distinguish from one another. GAUSSEN discovered a way to minimize this danger effectively. He argued that ordinary climatic conditions are not interesting and therefore need not be shown. If, on the other hand, conditions become extreme, and thereby more effective in limiting the spread of certain plant communities, then they are indeed interesting—and more vivid colors are used to lend the desired emphasis. The color combinations therefore contain only the colors of the more significant environmental factors, i.e., those which are more significant in the region mapped. For instance: average precipitation is of little interest. Aridity, on the other hand, sharply limits the possibilities for both natural vegetation types and their respective substitute communities. Average precipitation is therefore shown in white (no color) whereas arid conditions are shown by a vivid color which will strongly affect the synthetic color that combines the colors of the various environmental factors.

When the colors are superimposed, the various climatic regions become apparent. Each climate is a plant climate, i.e., it is represented by a characteristic series. Accordingly, on his maps GAUSSEN shows certain colors, each of which implies certain climatic conditions, hence certain types of climax vegetation. The vegetation of such an area is then shown in the appropriate color, whether the climax communities are present or not. If, for example, at a certain altitude in the Pyrenees, GAUSSEN finds a "beech climate" and gives it a blue color (being cool and moist), then this blue is used for whatever type of vegetation happens to exist at the time of mapping. If, at that time, the area is in pastures, the vegetation is indicated by patterns of small blue dots (the pattern for grasslands); flat blue would imply beech forest, and if other tree genera or species are prominent besides the beech, as for instance spruce or fir, then these additional items can be shown by letter symbols overprinted on the blue background.

Where two different types of vegetation overlap, as in transitions, the colors are given in vertical bars and the width of the individual bars is kept in proportion to the degree of dominance of the respective communities.

By experimenting with colors and relating them to climate and vegetation types, it is possible to establish color schemes which can then be applied throughout the area of the map and beyond. In this manner, GAUSSEN analyzed the climate of all of France; when he embarked on his famous series at 1:200,000 (GAUSSEN, 1948, etc.) he was ready to assign the appropriate colors to each of the various vegetation types.

Symbols

All cultivated areas are left white, i.e., without color. All crops are shown by symbols, whether they consist of annuals like wheat, soy beans, and cotton, or of any kind of perennials such as vineyards, orchards and plantation forests. Clearly, this method can be applied in the tropics as well, where plantations of rubber trees, oil palms, or tea gardens replace their equivalents of the temperate zones. In cases where the tropical rainforest is freed of its undergrowth but otherwise permitted to remain in order to give shade to cacao plantations, framed symbols for cacao are overprinted on the color of the forest. The symbols represent little windows in the forest canopy, permitting the reader a glimpse of the messicol vegetation on the forest floor.

The size and frequency of the symbols have statistical value. They correspond to the number of trees, the acreage involved, or the percentage of the cultivated area occupied by a crop, whichever is the most convenient. For instance, in the case of vineyards it is more practical to indicate them by unit areas, e.g., one symbol for every 10 hectares. On the other hand, apricot trees are perhaps better shown by varying the size of the symbol, each size implying an arbitrarily fixed number of trees. A small, lower case "a" (for apricot) may stand for 100 apricot trees, a large capital "A" may represent 100,000 trees, and between such extremes differently sized or shaped letter symbols (small or large, light or heavy print, italic or gothic, etc.) can show numbers like 500, 1,000, 10,000 trees per symbol. This method is preferable where the trees may occur on small farms where they must share the available space with other crops. Grain, potatoes, alfalfa, and other crops of this class are best shown in percentages of the cultivated area of the township, county, or some other administrative unit because their location changes from year to year as a result of crop rotation and similar practices. In the case of plantation forests, horizontal bars take the place of symbols. Grasslands and meadows which are regularly mowed are shown by a particular type of dot pattern, somewhat like colored quotation marks, on a white background. All letter symbols, horizontal bars, etc., are shown in the appropriate color, i.e., according to the ecological preference of the crop they represent. This indicates not only the optimal conditions for a given crop but also the areas where the farmer may hope for maximum results. The color and the distribution pattern of a symbol indicate also the range beyond the optimum where such a crop may be expected to succeed.

The features here enumerated do not exhaust the types and varieties of information on these vegetation maps. GAUSSEN also shows a considerable number of items which are significant only quite locally. Among these are trees planted along highways, rows of hedges, trees along streams or highways, four types of marine vegetation along the coast, salt marsh and dune communities, bogs, terraced fields, "botanical curiosa," etc. Furthermore, there is in every canton (an administrative unit) a thin frame containing four symbols of varying size and shape to indicate the percentage of the total cantonal area (1) under cultivation, (2) in pastures and hay meadows, (3) in forests, and (4) in rough pastures and wasteland. Both the symbols and their frame are in black.

Text and Inset Maps

This brings to a close the discussion of the array of data on the vegetation map itself. The wide margin around the map shows the legend of the map and that might have completed the information on the vegetation of the region. GAUSSEN, however, considered it inadequate. Two additional major items are given prominent space: (1) a schematized text and (2) a number of inset maps.

The text is valuable in that it informs the reader on every series individually. The series are usually synonymous with the climax communities and the plant climates. For each series the information given is fourfold and consists of a description of (1) the climax vegetation, (2) the land use, (3) the environmental conditions which determine both the natural climax types and their respective substitute communities, and (4) the geography of the landscape.

The value of the vegetation map as a document of regional geography is greatly increased by a series of inset maps of the same region. These inset maps are at the scale of 1:1,250,000.

Inset map 1 shows what land surveys and base maps (including their scales) were available when the vegetation was mapped. Aerial photographic coverage is also indicated.

Inset map 2 shows the major political subdivisions (departments) in black, and also the names of the local regions and districts in red. Inset maps 3–8 (A–F), in a sense, take the major vegetation map apart, according to these categories:

A. Climax vegetation. This inset map permits the reader to appreciate the extent and character of the potential natural phytocenoses, especially in the cultivated areas which are left in white on the main map.
B. Soils and their evolution. The use of colors is here analogous to that on the vegetation map, at least in principle, and features like nature of bedrock, leaching, and content of lime and humus are considered. A comparison of the soil map with the vegetation map is often very instructive.
C. Land use. Forests, pastures, orchards, etc.
D. Agriculture by crops.
E. Annual means of temperature and precipitation; other climatic features may be added if they significantly affect the distribution of phytocenoses.
F. Agricultural hazards, such as likelihood of cold winds, hail, floods, fire hazards, etc.

GAUSSEN's vegetation map of France at 1:200,000 includes not only a vast amount of information; in addition, it presents the facts as they are and indicates what might be, thereby guiding the planners and leading to a more efficient land use. It is quite the most ambitious performance yet achieved in the field of vegetation mapping and serves as a model for all who wish to study and emulate this method.

World-Wide Application

Parallel with the preparation of the series of vegetation maps of France at 1:200,000 another development is taking place, modest as yet but potentially of vast importance. This is GAUSSEN's application of his system to a vegetation map of the whole world at the scale of 1:1,000,000 (GAUSSEN, 1949, 1953). So far, GAUSSEN's efforts have resulted in six vegetation maps at 1:1,000,000 of parts of North Africa and of India (GAUSSEN, 1945b; GAUSSEN and VERNET, 1958; GAUSSEN, LEGRIS, and VIART, 1961, 1963); some sheets are accompanied by elaborate texts on the vegetation, the environment (climate and soil), and on the potentialities of the regions.

As in the case of the map of France at 1:200,000, GAUSSEN's color scheme is the essential feature of the 1:1,000,000 map series. However, evolution implies change, and it is not likely that the many map sheets of the world will be entirely uniform. Already, differences are noticeable between the first attempt at this scale, the map of France, and the latest successes in India. A world-wide approach on a uniform basis implies here that GAUSSEN's color scheme is applied evenly all over the globe. As a result, the map of Béni Abbès (GUINET, 1953) is practically monochromatic, but GAUSSEN defends this by placing the map in its proper position in the world-wide series, and the few colors assume at once a greater significance. However, the map of France is richer in colors than it should be according to the world-wide scheme.

It is quite obvious that the adaptation of GAUSSEN's color scheme to conditions prevailing in France is as nearly perfect as may be expected. For this very reason, however, it is inevitable that modifications of the scheme become more or less necessary elsewhere. This may even be true within France if conditions are particularly complex, as shown recently by OZENDA (1963) for the French Alps. The above-mentioned maps of India and Tunisia are particularly interesting in that they illustrate an adjustment of GAUSSEN's ideas to tropical or arid conditions. Such modifications in no way negate the system; on the contrary, they serve to demonstrate its flexibility. The problems were discussed at the Toulouse Colloquium and GAUSSEN (1961a) himself proposed that authors be given the freedom to enlarge the range of colors for their particular areas to whatever extent they choose, as REY (1958) had already insisted earlier, but they should strictly adhere to the world-wide scheme on the inset map which shows the potential natural vegetation. The inset maps in the 1:1,000,000 series are always done at the scale of 1:5,000,000.

The goal of the 1:1,000,000 map, according to GAUSSEN, is essentially the same as that of the other series, to wit, a presentation of the actual vegetation as well as the potential natural vegetation and the habitat conditions that govern both. The geographical character of the region and its biological potential are thereby presented in a unique manner. The vegetation maps done according to GAUSSEN's method have an unusually wide appeal which explains their popularity.

21

Küchler's Comprehensive Method

This method is based on the idea of mapping vegetation in such a comprehensive manner that the results of the field work can be applied to a maximum number of vegetation classifications. In the laboratory, therefore, the field notes can presumably be manipulated so as to fit any given classification that is based exclusively on features of the vegetation (KÜCHLER, 1955a). Accordingly, comprehensive field mapping is done only once but the result of the field work can be employed as a basis for a variety of vegetation maps, each of which is to serve a different purpose.

First Laboratory Activity

Before actual mapping in the field can begin, some work must be done in the laboratory. The first step is a careful study of the vegetation of the area to be mapped, based on the literature and all available maps showing vegetation and features of the landscape such as topography, soils, drainage, macro- and microclimate and land use.

Simultaneously, the second step consists of the acquisition and careful study of a complete set of aerial photographs of the area. The photographs should be as recent as possible. The scale of the photographs is often 1:20,000, but if photographs are to be specially taken for a new vegetation map, it is much better to have them done at 1:10,000 or larger and printed on glossy paper.

Investigation of the photographs reveals different types of vegetation. The contrasts between the various types range from strong to very subtle but every contrast should be noted. A good stereoscope, preferably of the mirror type, is a great help because the most detailed analysis of the vegetation is essential. Every area which is at all different from neighbor-

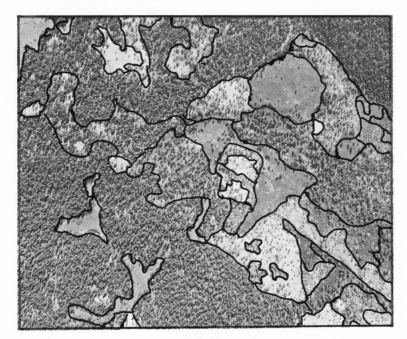

Figure 14

ing areas is bounded by a line of ink drawn directly on the photograph (Figure 14). Omissions on the ground that it will be easier or better to establish the line when in the field should not be tolerated.

All boundaries of every vegetation unit should be on the photograph before going into the field. This means that there is a definite line on the photograph which can be checked in the field. If the line is acceptable it need not be touched. If the location of the line is unsatisfactory, it can be shifted but such a shift can be made only for specific reasons. Thoughtful observation is then required before a line can be moved on the photograph to a more accurate position.

If, however, the line had not been drawn at all, in the hope of establishing its location while in the field, the difficulties may be serious and the results unsatisfactory. For instance, it is difficult to walk about in a forest of mixed composition and determine where to draw a line. And if a place has been selected for a line, it may be difficult to locate it on the photograph.

The decision where to draw a line on the photograph, separating one type from the next, is not always easy to make. Certain considerations made prior to drafting these boundary lines will save much confusion.

One such consideration concerns the problem of transitions, which has been discussed in Chapter 10.

Another problem relates to the smallest size of an area to be shown. When is an area too small to be considered? At times, a given type of vegetation contains an "island" of a different type. Should this be ignored? That depends on the scale of the map which is to be based on this field investigation. If the scale is not known, it may be assumed to be approximately half of that of the photograph. The problem is easy to solve if the scale is known at least approximately. One need only enlarge the minimal area of the final map to the scale of the photograph. If the "island" is smaller than this minimal area, then it should be ignored; if it is as large or larger, then it should be shown. The minimal area on the final map, if in color, should be at least 1 millimeter in diameter if round and not much less than 1 millimeter wide if the shape is long and narrow. On black-and-white maps the minimal area is usually much larger, depending on the type of patterns to be used.

It is very useful to calculate the actual field size of the minimal area. For instance, the map is to be published at the scale of 2 inches to the mile (1:31,680), and the minimal area is to be 2 millimeters in diameter. Then a distance of 2 millimeters on the final map corresponds to 2 × 3.168 or 6.336 millimeters on the aerial photograph (scale 1:10,000) and to 63.36 meters in the field. This is roughly 200 feet. In this particular instance, the minimal area to be considered in the field should therefore have a diameter of not less than 200 feet.

When all boundaries are drawn on the photographs, it is important to make sure that all marginal boundaries are continued on the adjacent photographs.

Further preparations for field work include the acquisition of appropriate equipment and a well-trained staff. Equipment includes pencils, fountain pens and ink, paper, clip boards, notebooks, binoculars (the more powerful, the better), a Haga altimeter, an Abney level or a draftsman's triangle (right angle, isosceles), measuring tape, topographic maps, and whatever is necessary for the personal comfort of each member of the party. Cameras are not strictly necessary but very desirable. If more than one camera is available, one should be used for color film and one for black-and-white film. For photographs in forests the camera with black-and-white film, placed on a tripod, assures the best results. A good exposure meter prevents serious failures. Photographs are useful when analyzing the field notes in the laboratory. In the notebook a special section should be set aside to record the photographs, i.e., the number of the plant community on the phytocenological record (cf. Chapter 15), with numbers of film and individual exposures. It is also useful to take along a topographic map on which the exact place where a photograph is taken can be shown by an angle; the vertex of the angle indicates the photographer's location and the two sides of the angle embrace the width of the photograph. The number of the photograph is placed as closely to the vertex as convenient.

Information gathered in the field should be placed on note paper, such as forms of the phytocenological record, specially prepared for its purpose. A master copy (Tables 7 and 8) can be made in the laboratory and copies should be available in plentiful supply. It is best to have an adequate supply of printed forms where such vegetation mapping is done. The number on a given form corresponds to the number of the described phytocenose as recorded on the aerial photograph and later on the base map (see below).

A major consideration for vegetation mapping is the careful selection of an appropriate staff. Under certain circumstances a party of one is adequate. However, this means that this one person must know how to observe physiognomy, landforms, and many other details. He must have a very thorough knowledge of the flora; he must carry notebook, aerial photos, clip board, camera, binoculars, and often a raincoat, lunch, and other items. It is much better to have more than one person in the party. A party leader with two assistants approaches the ideal. If the party consists of more than one person, one should be a well-trained taxonomist. Ideally, such a taxonomist has specialized in the flora of the region to be mapped. His only equipment is the latest edition of a standard flora covering the region, such as *Gray's Manual of Botany* (FERNALD, 1950) for the northeastern United States or *A California Flora* (MUNZ and KECK, 1959). It is best to have the names of all species based on the same manual, as there are variations from one manual to the next, and the use of different sources leads to confusion.

The entire party should be thoroughly familiarized with the aims and methods of the field work. All members of the group should be well acquainted with the physiognomic and floristic methods of analyzing plant communities. There are many cases calling for relatively arbitrary decisions in the field, and an intelligent discussion among the staff members helps in making the decisions as reasonable as possible.

Field Work

With staff and equipment assembled, the party can proceed to the field. Here it becomes necessary to visit every individual area outlined on the aerial photographs. It must be remembered that the information is to be as complete as possible but that aerial photographs show only the surface layer of the vegetation. What grows under the canopy of a forest can only be discovered by direct observation. In deserts and at the high altitudes of alpine terrain, the paucity of vegetation types and the simplicity of their structure and composition permits one, after much practice, to recognize types accurately from a distance, e.g., across a valley, if strong binoculars are available. In all other cases it is imperative that each vegetational area outlined on the photograph be inspected.

Upon arrival in a given area to be inspected, the first task is to walk about in it, preferably from end to end and across, observing the vegetation critically. Thereupon all relevant data are entered on the blank which is carried on a clip board.

It is necessary to know in advance just what to look for, and then, in the field, to look for it with unwavering consistency. Once it has been established which aspects of the vegetation to consider, it is absolutely necessary to consider them uniformly throughout the region mapped, with no exceptions. For instance, it is not permissible to observe and record in the field notes the height of the vegetation in one area and then ignore it in another area. If the height of the vegetation is to be recorded, it must be recorded in every area, i.e., for each individual synusia of every phytocenose. This insistence on being consistent at all times pays big dividends later on, when the field work has been completed and the maps are being prepared in the laboratory.

Recording good notes is at times difficult in the field. To make sure that the notes remain legible for some time, the script should be reasonably large. It is very desirable to type the field notes as soon as possible. This is important because pencil notes become increasingly difficult to read and are blurred after some time. On the other hand, it is not good to rely on a fountain pen because in wet weather writing with ink is difficult, the paper absorbs moisture, the ink runs, and the notes are soon quite illegible.

It is, of course, necessary that every area outlined on the aerial photographs can be correlated with the field notes. For this reason, every areal unit which appears on a photograph must be numbered, and the same number must appear in the field notes where the vegetation of this area is described.

When the vegetation of a given area has been inspected critically, its salient features are recorded on the prepared forms. The first step is to fill in the first section of the phytocenological record and to give the area its number (Table 7). No number may be written on the photographs until a given area has been inspected. Then its number is written down on the form and on the photograph simultaneously. The next number is not set down until the next area has been inspected and analyzed. In this manner, area follows area, each with its own number. If an area is inspected in which the vegetation is the same as in another area already inspected, it nevertheless receives its own number, and the character of the vegetation is recorded anew. This is not necessary for such types as barren, urban, etc.

Upon inspection of the phytocenose, the mapper proceeds to describe it both physiognomically and floristically. The physiognomic classification (cf. Chapter 15) reveals the structure of the plant communities, i.e., height and coverage of every synusia, and, in addition, such special features as may be present. If physiognomic formulas are used they should always be recorded as accurately and as completely as possible.

Often the physiognomic formula reveals characteristics of the vegetation that are not evident from the floristic description. For instance, if the flora is described as *Betula papyrifera* 5 and *Abies balsamea* 5, we can only see that the vegetation consists of two dominant species each of which covers more than three-quarters of the area. This may seem confusing. But the physiognomic formula "D6E4" gives the explanation. "D6" stands for a broadleaf deciduous forest 10–20 meters tall, and "E4" means small needleleaf evergreen trees (2–5 meters). The formula reveals therefore that the vegetation consists of two layers, an upper one consisting of broadleaf deciduous trees (paper birches) and a lower one of needleleaf evergreen trees (balsam firs).

The density of the vegetation is estimated as outlined in Chapter 15. Such estimates rarely present difficulties. The height of the various layers of vegetation can be measured, and after some practice it can be estimated with a considerable degree of accuracy. It is very useful to know the height of 10 centimeters, ½ meter, and 2 meters with regard to one's body (e.g., one's knee may be ½ meter above the ground), as these are critical heights "within reach" of the mapper.

For measuring the height of trees, an Abney level provides the simple solution. Where such an instrument is not available, a measuring tape and a plastic draftsman's triangle (right angle, isosceles) suffice. The height of the tree equals the observer's distance from the tree when he looks along the hypotenuse of the triangle and its extension toward the tree top (Figure 15). The height of the observer's eye above the ground should be added to the distance from the tree for greater accuracy. Care must be taken that the lower side of the triangle is horizontal. To assure the best results most easily, the height of the observer's eyes above the ground is marked on the bark of the tree (point G in Figure 15). Then the observer moves away from the tree until the tree top coincides with the upper tip of the triangle. To make sure that the lower side of the triangle is horizontal, it may be placed on the tripod as high as the observer's eyes. The triangle's lower edge must then point to the mark on the tree which indicates the height of the eyes above the ground. If the tree stands on a slope, observations are made along the contour.

It takes very little time to become acquainted with the physiognomic classification, and its application in the field is simple and quick. The

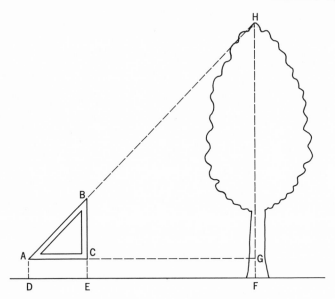

ABC: triangle   AG: distance of observer from tree
AB: hypotenuse   FH: height of tree
BH: extension of hypotenuse   DEF: ground
A: position of observer's eye   ACG: must be horizontal
                        AG = GH
           AD = CE = GF: height of observer's eye above ground

Figure 15

structural analysis on the phytocenological record permits an accurate recording of all necessary details.

The description of the physiognomy and the structure of the vegetation
is adequate if all observational data are recorded on the forms of the
phytocenological record. When the mapper has no such forms at his disposal, he will use formulas, as shown in Chapter 15. Where the phytocenological record is used, the collected information can easily be transcribed into formulas whenever this is desired.

The following points should be kept in mind in analyzing the flora.
Each species must be identified by its scientific name, and its coverage
must be determined, i.e., estimated. The distribution within the area of
herbaceous species may also be recorded.

The values of the coverage and distribution of species and the method
of recording them are given in Chapter 19, Tables 10 and 11. The mapper is, of course, free to record the basal area instead of coverage. Both
are equally acceptable but one method may be preferable to the other
under certain circumstances.

The taxonomist is usually able to identify all species on sight. When he is in doubt, he can nevertheless give the species a name that can be entered on the record, followed by a question mark. He can then collect a specimen and identify it accurately upon returning to the camp and to his botanical manual. The correct name should then be entered on the record at once. Doubt may remain because of a lack of diagnostic characteristics due to immaturity or old age. It may also remain because of the taxonomic complexity of the genus, making the specific or subspecific identification the concern of the specialist on the genus. If some doubt about the accuracy of the name persists, the question mark is retained on the record. Only scientific botanical names should be used to identify the plant species, or else the value of the entire work may be seriously impaired.

The floristic composition of stand samples is recorded on the back of the phytocenological record (Table 8). It is always best to break down the phytocenoses into their constituent synusias, each of which is described physiognomically and floristically. Hence, for a given sample, the mapper records first the tree layer. He writes "tree layer" or simply "trees" in the first column. Then, under the heading of "tree layer," all species are listed that have attained tree size. Each species is recorded by its botanical name only and its coverage is given in the column of stand sample No. 1. As other sample plots may contain tree species that do not occur in plot No. 1, the mapper should leave some space for additional names before proceeding to the next-lower synusia. Climbers are listed here if they reach into the tree layer.

The shrub synusia is handled just like the tree synusia. All woody plant species that are not of tree size are here recorded just as the tree species were recorded before. Again each species is listed by botanical name and coverage. If there is a synusia of dwarf shrubs, e.g., "D2i," then the mapper must not hesitate to enter such a separate synusia.

The procedure is the same for whatever other synusias there may be. However, many phytocenologists prefer to list herbaceous species with both their coverage and their distribution even though the latter is not recorded in the other synusias. The moss layer is the place in which mosses and lichens are recorded provided they are not epiphytes.

If a form is inadequate to record all species, the work is continued on a second form. This second form receives the same phytocenological record number as the first one, with "page 2" written after the number. On the first page, under Notes, the mapper should write "continued on page 2" to indicate that page 1 is incomplete.

Finally, under Notes (Table 7), all sorts of remarks may be made that help to throw light on the recorded phytocenose. Comments such as "old burn" or "recently logged" will prove very helpful when the character of the vegetation is to be interpreted, especially if it can be established what forest type was burned or logged. Comments on topography, geology, soil, water conditions (bog, etc.), or any other site quality should always be made in the greatest possible detail. There may be no particular need for any remarks but the mapper is urged not to ignore anything that is at all relevant.

The result of the field work is a set of phytocenological records and a series of aerial photographs on which the vegetation types are outlined. Each individual outlined area on the photographs must have received a number which corresponds to the number in the records where the particular type is described. The critical observations, especially with regard to the lower layers of the vegetation, may have necessitated the addition of further boundaries on the aerial photographs. It may also be that boundaries first drawn in the laboratory had to be shifted or removed upon field inspections. If any boundaries have been added or changed on the photographs during the field work, such a change should be made on all photographs on which this boundary appears. This change may have to be repeated on two or even three other photographs, especially if a change on the photograph was made near a corner; this should be done in the field.

Second Laboratory Activity

The field work concluded, the party returns to the laboratory. The work of the taxonomist comes to an end. If no typewriter was available during the field work, the first step is to type all records exactly as they appear on the field note forms. They are the basis of all information. If it seems desirable to rearrange the various items on the lists, then this should be done afterwards. It is always possible to make any number of changes. But it is of fundamental importance to have the original field data typed just as they were first set down. The contents of the notebook should be typewritten also. As each phytocenose is described and typed on its own form, it is best to type the qualities of its site and all relevant information recorded in the notebook in the space for notes on the form. The forms are of the same kind as those used for collecting data in the field.

The next step is the preparation of the base vegetation map. This is a map which shows the exact outline of each individual vegetation type, i.e., each area shown separately on the photographs, and the numbers of the areas. In order to make this map it is best to transfer the lines (boundaries of phytocenoses) on the aerial photographs to a topographic map. It is not feasible to trace the lines directly from the photographs on white paper because of the distortion on the photographs. The topographic quadrangles with streams, roads, lakes, coastlines, houses, and other features help overcome this difficulty. Once all boundary lines have been transferred to the topographic map, they can be traced on white paper, or preferably on a stable base to maintain the constancy of the scale. On this drawing it is best to add rivers, and lake and ocean shores, if any, to assist in orientation. Then the numbers of all vegetation types, i.e., of all

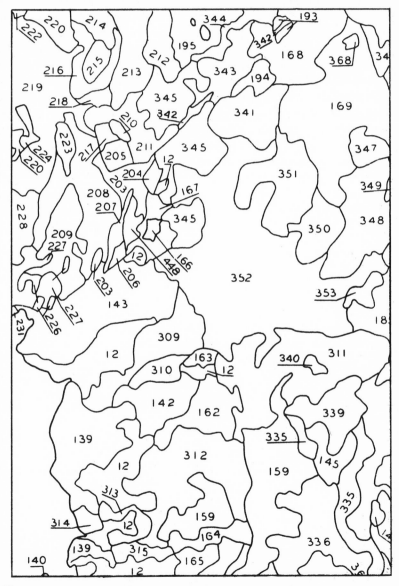

Figure 16. Base map, showing outlines of vegetation types and their numbers.

areas shown on the photographs, are entered on this map. Scrupulous checking (proofreading) upon completion is quite essential.

The result of all this labor is a base map of the vegetation of the selected area (Figure 16). It shows the exact outline of every vegetational unit and the number of each unit, which refers to the corresponding number in the records with its detailed description of the vegetation type. All the basic work has now been completed, and the outline map, with its numbers, and the records form the foundation for the vegetation map (or maps) to be drawn.

The preparation of the final vegetation map depends on what particular classification is to be selected. This may be physiognomic or floristic, or a combination of the two. Perhaps forest trees are the only objects of interest, in which case all undergrowth and herbaceous vegetation can be ignored. It all depends on the purpose of the map, and according to this purpose, the information on the records is manipulated so as to produce the most useful categories. When these categories have been established, one need only go through the records, assign each unit to the appropriate category and then trace the new map off the base vegetation map, merging all units which are adjacent to each other and of the same category. Obviously, the comprehensive information on the records lends itself to a great variety of possibilities, and herein lies the chief value of this method.

22

The California
Vegetation - Soil Survey

The California Vegetation-Soil Survey developed into an important project under the leadership of A. E. WIESLANDER. WIESLANDER evolved a method of classifying the vegetation of California during the decade preceding World War II; this classification was published by one of his close collaborators (JENSEN, 1947). Later, the CALIFORNIA FOREST AND RANGE EXPERIMENT STATION published detailed instructions on classifying and mapping the California vegetation, containing WIESLANDER's latest ideas on the subject. Our description of the California method is based directly on the revised instructions and later publications by the CALIFORNIA FOREST AND RANGE EXPERIMENT STATION (1954, 1958).

The California Vegetation-Soil Survey is now handled cooperatively by the University of California (Berkeley and Davis) and the Pacific Southwest FOREST AND RANGE EXPERIMENT STATION. The State of California assists in the project and finances work done on state and privately owned land. The UNITED STATES FOREST SERVICE also assists and finances work on land owned by the federal government.

Classification System

The vegetation is classified and mapped at two levels (GARDNER and WIESLANDER, 1957): first, according to major kinds of vegetation, called "vegetation cover classes," which can be delineated by stereoscopic interpretation of aerial photographs (Table 21); and second, according to the dominant plant species, called "species types," which are delineated by a combination of photo-interpretation and ground observation.

There are certain minimum requirements for recognition of the foregoing vegetation and other elements. These follow on the next page.

1. The presence of commercial conifer species is indicated wherever their coverage is 5% or more.
2. The presence of non-commercial conifer species or hardwood species is indicated wherever their coverage is 5% or more, except when in association with commercial conifer species. In the latter case, their coverage must be 20% or more before recognition is given.

Table 21

Symbol	Definition
C	*Commercial conifers:* All conifer species that are considered generally valuable for lumber, pulpwood, or related uses.
K	*Noncommercial conifers:* Conifer species not now considered as merchantable.
Ho	*Old-growth hardwoods:* Stands in which mature (11″ dbh and over) hardwood trees comprise more than 50% of the hardwood canopy.
Hy	*Young-growth hardwoods:* Stands in which mature hardwood trees comprise less than 50% of the hardwood canopy.
S	*Shrubs:* All shrubs, such as manzanita, scrub oak, chamise, mountain mahogany, California yerba santa, wild buckwheat, bitterbrush, sagebrush, and rabbitbrush.
N	*Non-timberland:* Land unsuited for producing commercial conifer timber crops and on which the tree canopy covers less than 5% of the ground.
N+	*Non-timberland:* Land unsuited for producing commercial conifer timber crops but supporting stands of trees (commercial conifer species, non-commercial conifer species or hardwood species) on terrain that would feasibly permit harvesting of the trees.
N—	*Non-timberland:* Land unsuited for producing commercial conifer timber crops but supporting stands of trees on terrain so steep or with such adverse surface conditions that there is little likelihood of the trees being harvested.
F	*Bushy herbs:* Herbaceous plants that are bushy in size and character of growth.
G	*Grass:* Includes all grasses and other associated herbaceous plants (not under cultivation). Relatively moist "wet meadows" with a herbaceous growth of low rushes and sedges are included.
M	*Marsh:* Areas of very poorly drained or partially submerged soils supporting tules or other vegetation characteristic of such situations.
BO	*Burned over:* Applies to timberland, brushland, or woodland areas that have been obviously burned over and a woody vegetation cover is not yet established. Areas classified as having a woody vegetation density of 5% or greater are not designated as burned-over. Grassland or woodland-grass areas are never designated as burned-over.
CO	*Cutover:* Applies to areas of timber cropland that have been obviously logged for timber.
B	*Bare ground:* Areas of soil that are practically devoid of vegetation. Litter-covered ground is included.
R	*Rock:* Areas of solid rock or land that is very rocky in character. Talus and lava flows are typical. Sand and gravel bars and beaches subject to infrequent inundation—by very high flood waters or storm waves—and which are essentially devoid of vegetation are included. Also included are sand dunes or placer tailings.
A	*Agricultural:* Land being cultivated for farm crops, regularly cropped natural haylands, irrigated pastures, and fallow fields. Includes intensively grazed non-irrigated pastures.
U	*Urban-industrial:* Residential, business and industrial areas. Mines and mills are included.

3. The presence of shrubs is indicated wherever their coverage is 5% or more except when in association with a tree cover. In the latter case, the coverage of the shrubs must be 20% or more before recognition is given.
4. The coverage of all other elements must be 20% or more to be indicated.
5. Agricultural or urban-industrial areas will not be shown in combination with other elements.

In addition, age and density of commercial timber species are recorded by letter symbols as shown in Tables 22 and 23.

Table 22.   Age Classes

Symbol	Definition
O	*Old growth:* Stands in which mature trees comprise 80% or more of the commercial conifer crown canopy.
OY	*Old growth–young growth:* Stands in which mature trees comprise from 50 to 80% of the commercial conifer crown canopy.
YO	*Young growth–old growth:* Stands in which mature trees comprise from 20 to 50% of the commercial conifer crown canopy.
Y	*Young growth:* Stands in which mature trees comprise less than 20% of the commercial conifer crown canopy.

Table 23.   Density Classes

Symbol	Definition
1	*Dense:* Coverage more than 80%.
2	*Semidense:* Coverage from 50 to 80%.
3	*Open:* Coverage from 20 to 50%.
4	*Very open:* Coverage from 5 to 20%.
5	*Extremely open or none:* Coverage less than 5%.

These data in the form of letter and number symbols are written in the form of fractions where each item has its place (Figure 17).

Qualified foresters, range specialists, and pedologists carry on the technical investigations of this survey. Besides their professional education and experience, these men have received special training in the principles techniques, and procedures of the California Vegetation-Soil Survey. Each team is balanced, so far as practicable, in professional skills: for example, a forester and a pedologist form a team. Both operate out of the same field headquarters, but each carries on separately the job of classifying and mapping both vegetation and soils, following a closely integrated procedure. Technical responsibility for the vegetation work rests with the forester, for the soils with the pedologist.

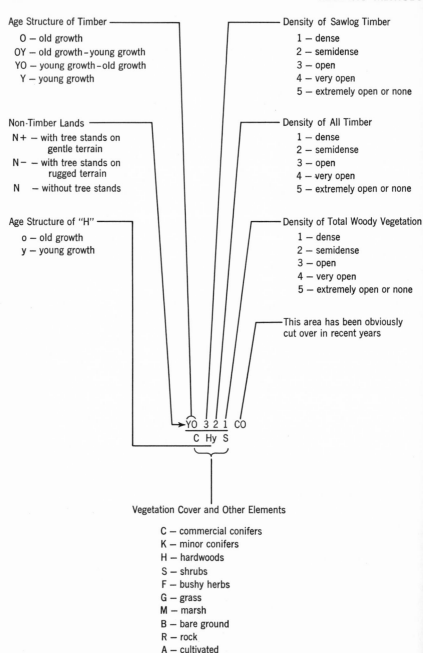

Age Structure of Timber
   O – old growth
   OY – old growth – young growth
   YO – young growth – old growth
   Y – young growth

Non-Timber Lands
   N+ – with tree stands on
         gentle terrain
   N– – with tree stands on
         rugged terrain
   N – without tree stands

Age Structure of "H"
   o – old growth
   y – young growth

Density of Sawlog Timber
   1 – dense
   2 – semidense
   3 – open
   4 – very open
   5 – extremely open or none

Density of All Timber
   1 – dense
   2 – semidense
   3 – open
   4 – very open
   5 – extremely open or none

Density of Total Woody Vegetation
   1 – dense
   2 – semidense
   3 – open
   4 – very open
   5 – extremely open or none

This area has been obviously
cut over in recent years

YO 3 2 1 CO
   C Hy S

Vegetation Cover and Other Elements

   C – commercial conifers
   K – minor conifers
   H – hardwoods
   S – shrubs
   F – bushy herbs
   G – grass
   M – marsh
   B – bare ground
   R – rock
   A – cultivated
   U – urban-industrial

Figure 17. Example of classification symbol.

Reconnaissance and Photo-Interpretation

The first step in this work is a general reconnaissance of the area to be mapped. Field crews compare the appearance of vegetation on the ground with that on aerial photographs of the area and express their observations on the vegetation in terms of the cover classification of types or elements (Table 23). They become familiar with the lay of the land and get ready for the next step: photo-interpretation. Most photo-interpretation is done in the laboratory. The interpreter outlines, on the photograph, mapping units that differ in (1) broad types of vegetation, (2) density of woody vegetation and (3) other landscape features, like barren areas or rock. He looks especially for areas which are relatively uniform in cover or vegetation. This is important because the uniformity of plant cover in undisturbed areas usually indicates uniformity or similarity of soil.

Field Investigation and Mapping

Boundaries between different soils, however, are not mapped until the third step in the survey: detailed field investigations. This is the time when the mappers check their photo-interpretations against the actual field conditions, determine plant species composition, classify soils, and collect factual information needed to guide land management. The field crews identify the species of shrubs and trees in the mapping unit, and the classes of herbaceous cover there. They measure the age and height of commercial timber species, and on selected 1-acre plots make detailed observations of the vegetation. Where grass is an important part of the vegetation, they take a systematic sample of 1-acre plots to determine the composition and total cover of herbaceous vegetation (see below). They collect specimens of many plant species and submit them to the herbarium of the University of California, where the specimens provide a verified record of the geographical distribution of plants in the state and aid plant scientists in many research projects.

At the same time that the field crews map the vegetation, they map the "soil series" as the principal units used in the natural system of soil classification. Soil series are separately named and standardized within the state and the nation. They are distinguished by a number of physical, chemical, and morphological characteristics and by the type of parent material or parent rock from which the soils are derived. Soil series are divided into soil phases. These divisions show differences within each soil series, such as depth of soil, slope, rockiness, or erosion, which will help in making land use decisions. The field crews also collect soil samples for laboratory analyses and for greenhouse tests of soil fertility.

All of this information, on both vegetation and soils, is mapped in the field by means of aerial photographs. A lightly frosted acetate overlay is taped to the photograph; it is attached on one side only so that the mapper can lift it conveniently. Mapping is usually started at one edge or corner of the assigned area (usually a 7½-minute quadrangle unit). It is desirable to begin mapping along a road where detailed observations of vegetation and soils may be readily made. Then, as the mapper becomes more familiar with species, timber sites, and soils, he will find it easier to map the areas through which he must travel on foot.

The delineation boundary and cover classification symbols for each area are checked by comparing the photo features with the ground features. They must be correct as of the time of field mapping. Corrections are made where photo-interpretation is in error or where actual changes have taken place since the date of photography. These changes may be due to fire, logging, or land clearing, or growth of vegetation and other natural phenomena. Erroneous delineations and symbols are erased and corrected.

Vegetation types by species composition (referred to as "species-types") are natural bodies of vegetation classified according to the dominant species growing together in an ecological association. Each woody vegetation element shown on the photograph is classified by one or more species. The herbaceous elements usually are classified by physiognomic or ecological groups of plants but by species in some cases. Species-types are designated by the species symbols. One or more species symbols is shown for each vegetation element (except grass and forbs). The species symbols are listed in order of decreasing abundance. In order to be recorded as part of a species-type, a species must have a coverage of 20 per cent or more of the element it represents.

With certain exceptions, species symbols have been standardized. They have been derived from the initial letters of common or scientific plant names. Various combinations of large capital, small capital, and lower case letters are used. Special distinguishing marks are also used, including the prime ($'$), caret ($_\wedge$), underscore (__), and overscore ($\overline{}$). Some herbaceous elements are not classified by species. They are symbolized, however, in the proper order. The following symbols are used: *Gr*, grass other than wet meadow; *Md*, wet meadow; *Hb*, bushy herbs such as bull thistle, fireweed, etc. (forbs); *Mr*, marsh.

Miscellaneous elements such as bare ground, rock, cultivated areas, and urban and industrial areas are also symbolized: *Ba*, bare ground; *Rk*, rock; *Cu*, cultivated (never used in combination with other symbols); *Ui*, urban and industrial (never used in combination with other symbols).

Each area delineated on the photograph will be mapped as to species-type. The species-types or miscellaneous elements are given recognition to the minimum-sized area of 10 acres (4 hectares). Large areas of the same cover classification may be subdivided to a minimum of 40 acres (16 hectares), i.e., subdivided into two or more areas, each 40 acres or more in size to show difference in species of any vegetation element. No subdivisions will be made, however, if the species are the same, and the only difference is in the order of abundance of those species.

The boundaries delineated on the photographs provide most of the boundaries for species-types. Where the species-type boundaries correspond to the cover classification boundaries, they are copied as solid lines on a frosted acetate overlay, which has been taped to one edge of each mapping photograph. The boundaries delineated on the photographs are not copied on the overlay unless they indicate a difference in species-type (or timber site or soil) shown on the overlay by a difference in symbols on each side of the boundary. Boundaries between areas of different species-types which do not correspond to boundaries delineated on the photographs are shown as dashed lines on the overlay. The proper vegetation, species or miscellaneous element symbols are written on the overlay directly in the area to which they apply. They will be arranged in such a manner that there can be no question as to their proper order. If it is not possible to list the symbols within the area to which they belong, they should be written as near to the area as possible and arrowed into it (Figure 18).

In most areas, species-types of the present conifer timber stands will be the same as those of the original virgin or old-growth timber stand, so special designation is unnecessary. In some areas, logging, burning, or land clearing may have eliminated one or more or even all of the species of commercial conifers composing the original old-growth stand. In such areas the species symbols of the conifers eliminated or reduced to less than 5 per cent density are shown on the overlay in red pencil in parentheses.

A species-type complex is an association of two species-types so intimately mixed that they cannot be indicated separately at the scale of mapping. Species-type complexes are symbolized by listing the symbols for each species-type and separating the groups of symbols by a line.

Timber sites are also mapped while the vegetation mapping is in progress. Timber sites may be defined as the timber-growing capacity of an area. Timber-site mapping is concerned with the subdivision of timber cropland on the basis of differences in site and classifying each area as to site quality. Timber-site classes are based on the age-height relationships of trees; they are presented by number symbols according to the systems of DUNNING (1942) or McARDLE (1949). The timber-site class of an area is determined by referring age-height measurements of suitable trees to proper site curves which are supplied by the Forest Service. In addition,

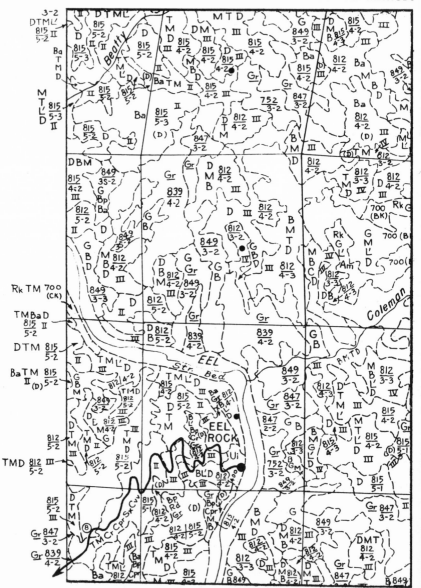

Figure 18. Soil-vegetation map. (After California Vegetation-Soil Survey.)

the kind and depth of soil and other factors of site are considered in classifying the timber sites. For the best results in classifying sites, the mapper must select the proper species, and only average, sound, dominant
trees, that are representative of the area. Their age should be between 70
and 120 years if at all possible. Tree height is measured by means of an

Abney level and tape. Tree age is determined from a ring count of an increment boring at breast height, adding 10 years for the time required to grow to breast height.

The California Vegetation-Soil Survey includes mapping of the soil by soil series. These soil series are defined as "a group of soils having soil horizons similar in differentiating characteristics and arrangement in the soil profile, except for the texture of the surface soil, and developed from a particular type of parent material." National standards are followed in this survey. Soil series are differentiated mainly on the basis of significant variations in the morphological characteristics of the soil profile and in kind of parent material or parent rock. The most important of these are the kind, thickness, and arrangement of the soil horizons; color, texture, structure and consistence of the horizons, and the chemical nature of the horizons, such as reaction, lime content, and mineralogical composition. Each soil series is given a name, usually a place name from the area where the soil was first described.

Due to the generally close relationship between soils and the type of natural vegetation they support, particularly in upland areas, the intensive delineation of vegetation accomplished in this survey results in the delineation of most soil boundaries. This is especially true where soils are significantly different. The correspondence of soil and vegetation boundaries must be checked in the field, of course, and significant exceptions mapped out. Road-cut banks provide opportunities for soil profile examinations. Where road-cut banks are not available, holes must be dug to gain the same information. The number of holes that must be dug will, of course, depend on the frequency of exposure of soil profiles by road and trail cuts and on the complexity of the soil pattern. Surface indicators (vegetation, topography, rock outcrops, etc.) are often correlated with soil series and soil depth phases, and can be used as aids in mapping and in determining the frequency needed for soil profile examinations.

Constant correlation of landscape features with their appearance on the aerial photographs will provide a basis for extrapolation into nearby areas that are not traversed in the field. Analysis of photo features will in many cases aid in the projection of soil characteristics and the location of soil boundaries. Field experience has shown that certain plant species are indicative of certain kinds of soils. In some places these plant indicators will be of great help to the mapper. Each mapper should be on the alert to observe differences in vegetation that are related to soil differences.

Preparation of Final Map

The results of the field work are taken to the laboratory where cartographic draftsmen transfer the boundaries and other data to base maps at a scale of 2 inches to the mile (1:31,680). These are standard 7½-minute quadrangle maps, each covering about 36,000 acres (14,400 hectares). United States Geological Survey quadrangles are generally used as a base, and Forest Service planimetric maps where they are available.

The information obtained by the California Vegetation-Soil Survey is published on maps, reproduced in blue-line form (Figure 18), supplemented by separate legends and descriptive material that explain map symbols and tabulate other information. These are the soil-vegetation maps. In some areas, these maps are supplemented by the so-called timber stand–vegetation cover type maps (Figure 19) for forest economists, and by generalized maps of upland soils.

Value and Future of the Procedure

The emphasis on woody species and especially on conifers of commercial value betrays the limited character of these maps. They are prepared above all for persons and agencies concerned with silviculture, forest economics, or some other aspect of forestry. A more scientific approach would place forests, grasslands, and deserts (which cover a large part of California) on an equal plane and a less commercially minded approach might well place the creosote bush (*Larrea tridentata*) on the same level as the Douglas fir (*Pseudotsuga menziesii*), as both dominate large sections of the Californian landscape. The California Vegetation-Soil Survey has never reached into the desert. Nevertheless, the basic plan of WIESLANDER's method permits the extension of its application into nonforest phytocenoses.

The work done in the CALIFORNIA FOREST AND RANGE EXPERIMENT STATION (1955b) does, indeed, include studies of ranges. The herbaceous communities are therefore receiving now more detailed attention in the mapping projects than they did at first. Special methods have been devised to map the vegetation of grasslands. Herbaceous plants are recorded by generic or species names and, on printed sheets, are entered in six groups:

1. Desirable annual grasses
2. Undesirable annual grasses
3. Desirable perennial grasses
4. Undesirable perennial grasses
5. Desirable forbs
6. Undesirable forbs

Density figures are estimated in percentages for the vegetation as a whole in each sample plot. The most intensive observations require 100 "point"

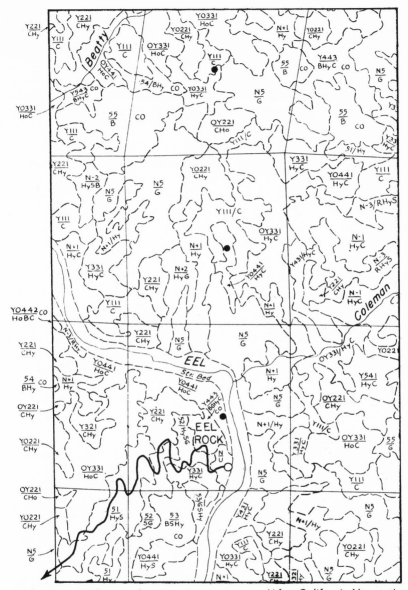

Figure 19. Timberstand—vegetation cover map. (After California Vegetation-Soil Survey.)

records per acre, at each of which one herbaceous genus or species is recorded, and ten density plots per acre. The points and plots are evenly spaced along five transect lines per acre (cf. the step-point method described in Chapter 14). The six groups of herbaceous plants as given above reveal the strictly utilitarian approach just as in the case of forest mapping. They remind one of KUHNHOLTZ-LORDAT's method of mapping vegetation from the point of view of sheep (cf. section on KUHNHOLTZ-LORDAT in Chapter 23). Immediate application to grazing dominates the process of mapping herbaceous vegetation.

The vegetation of California is now being mapped for given purposes, provided it consists of forests or, secondarily, of grasslands. Desert vegetation is ignored. The utilitarian approach is carried to such a degree that a scientific basis for the study of the Californian vegetation is given only in a limited form. Phytocenoses cannot usually be established securely on the basis of this work because, for instance, in forests only species with a coverage of more than 20% are recorded by name. Only a comprehensive recording of *all* synusias by life forms and taxa will permit an adequate recognition of phytocenoses. This is quite essential even from the point of view of forest management and silviculture. The interpretation of "commercial" conifers is almost certain to change as more uses are found for species now classed as non-commercial. Granted that funds may not be available for this project unless an immediate use can be demonstrated, it is now widely recognized that silviculture is rapidly becoming a form of applied science and as such can succeed only if based on a strictly scientific foundation. Perhaps appropriate modifications will someday permit this method to produce scientific results too, and to be applied as well in the Mojave and other deserts.

But the west coast states are natural forest lands to a very considerable extent and WIESLANDER's pioneering work is now bearing fruit. Its growing popularity is indicated by two facts: more government agencies map more and more vegetation by means of this method, and private interests such as lumber companies, paper corporations, etc., are now also employing the techniques of the California Vegetation-Soil Survey, mapping vast areas. Furthermore, these mapping activities have spread beyond the California boundaries and while it may be necessary to make adjustments to local conditions in areas far removed from California, such adjustments present no difficulties.

In a sense, the California Vegetation-Soil Survey resembles some of the procedures of the Soviet Academy of Sciences (cf. KOSMAKOVA, 1960) and other governmental agencies elsewhere. There is an air of mass production about them. A prescribed method and a standardized editorial policy are strictly adhered to and ultimately make the vegetation maps not so much the personal achievement and triumph of an individual author but rather the result of an efficient, well-organized institution. The advantages are obvious: the vegetation of large areas is mapped uniformly; the size of such areas is usually far beyond the capacity of any given author. The uniformity offers the great value of comparability of many different landscapes. A large staff can be trained in a short period to do the mapping according to printed rules and regulations. Governmental agencies for vegetation mapping such as the California Vegetation-Soil Survey are therefore to be welcomed, encouraged, and supported.

23

Other Contributions to Methodology

The Vegetation-Site Map

An important map was presented by ELLENBERG and ZELLER (1951), showing the close interrelation of vegetation, climate, soil, and geological features. This "vegetation-site map" is a document of unusual interest because it promises to develop into one of the most practical types of vegetation maps. The purpose of the map is to show site conditions in their relation to the cultivation and production of crops produced in fields and meadows, in orchards and vineyards. It is, therefore, an excellent basis for agricultural planning in all its ramifications. It is equally useful for teaching purposes at agricultural colleges and in courses on phytocenology and ecology.

ELLENBERG and ZELLER mapped the vegetation of Kreis Leonberg, an administrative unit roughly comparable to a small American county, at a scale of 1:50,000. The area involved is approximately 350 square kilometers (roughly 10 by 14 miles) and quite hilly. A vegetation map showing the potential natural vegetation and its substitute communities is adequate for most purposes of site description and analysis but ELLENBERG and ZELLER desired additional refinement in order to distinguish sites that are optimal for given varieties of tree fruits and grapes.

In their attempt to supplement their vegetation map with data on soil properties, they observed, as PALLMANN (1948, p. 7) had done before them, that minor characteristics of the soil can be more significant for high crop yields than those important in soil systematics. They decided that only those features of the soil are important in this kind of work that affect growth and yield of crops. Due to the considerable local relief, the geological origin of the soil also becomes a major feaure of consideration.

Where soils are characterized by two layers, one above the other, the two layers are shown in alternating bars. This is done only where the surface layer is so thin that the lower layer appreciably affects the crop plants. For instance, a layer of clay may rest on a layer of sand.

Climatic data are deemed most important but meteorological stations cannot supply the needed information because they are too widely spaced and too few in number. Adequate climatic information can only come from the plants themselves. Hence, phenological observations are indispensable. By singling out several key species and observing key ontogenetic phases while cruising through the landscape in a car, the phenological zonation of the region becomes evident. Of course, such a record is valid only for the tested species and for the season and year of observation. But by repeating such phenological observations the following one or more years, and by adjusting the phenological boundaries to the various sites, it is possible to show the resulting climatic zones within the local landscape with sufficient accuracy. Such phenological zones are the kind of climatic information most useful to the farmer who needs to know just what particular variety or varieties of apples, cherries, etc., will promise consistently the highest yields. In addition, but separately, there is a description of the climatic zones that occur in the mapped area. The manner of their numbering reveals that they form a part of a system which is employed on phenological maps of the state of Württemberg-Baden in southwestern Germany, an area equivalent to the combined areas of Massachusetts and Connecticut (ELLENBERG, 1955).

An inset map, centered on Leonberg, shows the distribution of climates in southwestern Germany so that the area of the main map is integrated into the larger region surrounding it. The climatic types are based on phenological observations and are, therefore, quite literally "plant climates." ELLENBERG (1955) distinguishes twelve types of local phenological climates in southwestern Germany:

1.	Very hot:	Warmest vineyard locations
2.	Hot:	Vineyard climate
3.	Very warm:	Vineyard–orchard climate
4.	Warm:	Orchard climate
5.	Moderately warm:	Winter wheat–orchard climate
6.	Moderate:	Orchard–winter wheat climate
7.	Moderately cool:	Winter wheat climate
8.	Cool:	Spring wheat–winter wheat climate
9.	Moderately cold:	Winter wheat–spring wheat climate
10.	Cold:	Mountain meadow–spring wheat climate
11.	Very cold:	Mountain meadow climate
12.	Extremely cold:	Coldest mountain locations

This table of phenological phytoclimates at once reveals the local character and hence the limited range of application of the individual types. For instance, the winter wheat climate is quite central in this table and in much of Kansas winter wheat is also the dominant crop. Yet, the Kansas type of winter wheat climate and the number of climatic types in a Kansan region of similar size are quite different. Nevertheless, within their particular region, the phenological climates are perhaps the most valuable climatic record for any kind of biological consideration.

The relation of yields to slopes and exposures, to passages of cold air by air drainage, etc., is well established. Gentle and steep slopes are therefore distinguished on the map, as well as the direction of their exposure. This shows the farmer and the planner where the most and the least amount of insolation may be expected and over how large an area. If a danger like a late spring frost is common to the entire area, then there is no need to show it on the map. But if there are individual sections where steady strong winds from one direction prevail during the main vegetative period, i.e., while the shoots are growing, such areas must be indicated because the wind's effect on the crop yield is so great.

The vegetation-site map is therefore a map of phytogeocenoses showing not only the potential natural vegetation and its substitute communities but also the climatic, edaphic, and geological features of the various biotopes.

The legend of the map comes in four columns, correlating the plant communities to the properties of the soils and the geological base of their respective sites with the help of colors and symbols.

The colors are the means of presenting data, of which the reader is conscious first and foremost. They must therefore show here the major qualities of the biotopes. ELLENBERG and ZELLER established a scale from one end of the spectrum to the other and related it to the water conditions of the sites. Dry and relatively warm sites are shown in red hues; sites with alternating moisture conditions are purple; medium-moist and relatively favorable sites are shown in yellow or brown; moist areas, especially those endangered by flows of cold air, are green; finally, wet and usually cool sites are given in blue. The degree of lightness or darkness of a given color relates the site to its utility for agricultural purposes. The darker a color, the less adapted is the site to cultivation (e.g., dark red, dark green, dark brown, etc.) and the lighter a color, the better adapted is the site.

A variety of letter, number, and other symbols is used to indicate local features of importance to land use and planning.

The vegetation-site map permits a deep insight into the prevailing environmental conditions; but ELLENBERG and ZELLER went further in order to assist the farmers and planners in their use and exploitation of the information on the map and in the evaluation of their farm sites. For this purpose, they prepared a table on which they arranged all site-type combinations in their relation to every crop raised in the mapped area; the yield expectancy for each relation is then expressed by a number (from 1 to 10). Number 1 implies the least favorable conditions for a given crop on a given site, and No. 10 the most favorable. The crops are shown in groups of varieties that have similar ecological requirements.

If, for example, a planner wishes to determine the possibilities of producing sweet cherries commercially (i.e., not for home consumption), he need only place a transparent paper over the vegetation-site map, trace each site, and mark it according to the numbers of the column for sweet cherries in the table. This will result in a map of a "sweet cherry potential" that will tell the planner at a glance where sweet cherries are likely to be profitable and where they should be discouraged. Once the vegetation-site map is available, the maps of crop potentials can be done by unskilled help and, therefore, be produced inexpensively. But their usefulness is very great.

For the preparation of the vegetation-site map and its associated table, the phytocenologist requires the cooperation of a wide variety of collaborators, especially experts on the ecological requirements of crop varieties, agronomists, and others. At present, the needed and very detailed information is not available outside some very small portions of our world, but as more data accumulate the contribution made by ELLENBERG and ZELLER will be emulated in ever-widening circles.

Of course, the vegetation-site map presents only the physical-biological conditions of a region. On the other hand, the advice of planners, county agents, and others is guided not only by information on site conditions but also by economic, financial, technical, social, historical, and human considerations. Nevertheless, whenever information is adequate for the preparation of a vegetation-site map, then such a map should surely be done, for its cost is no more than a fraction of the gain to all persons involved in the productivity of the land.

Parcelle Mapping

From France comes a method of mapping vegetation that has proved valuable, especially for agronomists. It evolved at Montpellier in the Mediterranean region of France. This is an area which has been inhabited and cultivated for a very long time, and the historical aspect strongly enters into this method of mapping. The natural vegetation, of course, has vanished long ago, but land use varies with time, and the history of the land can be read by interpreting its vegetation. This history, indeed, may not be ignored in the evaluation and the utilization of the land.

The minor cadastral divisions of France are sections. They must not be confused with an American section of 640 acres (1 square mile). The French sections are divided into units called "parcelles." These are small parcels of land of irregular outline and comprising only a small number of acres. In the cadastral records, every parcelle has its number and description with regard to land use, e.g., meadow, field, forest, etc., with various degrees of elaboration. This land classification is periodically revised because of changes in land use and because taxes, governmental farm supports, etc., are based on it. To map the vegetation of parcelles implies, therefore, mapping at very large scales.

The method of mapping the vegetation of parcelles was introduced by KUHNHOLTZ-LORDAT (1949) who, as director of the Agricultural College at Montpellier, was interested in aiding local farmers to obtain better yields. He saw the need for vegetation maps at 1:20,000 as produced at Montpellier (Carte des groupements végétaux de la France) but found that this scale was too small(!) for many agronomic purposes. He, therefore, uses scales of 1:1,250, 1:2,500, and 1:5,000. A scale of 1:10,000 is considered to be so small as to form the extreme limit within which his observations can be shown, but this scale is too marginal and is usually discarded in favor of the larger scales.

KUHNHOLTZ-LORDAT felt that the usual variety of vegetation map may fulfill its usual tasks. But there are others. For instance, the plant communities are usually shown in a scientific manner which is as it should be. However, when the mapper makes a vegetation map of pastures, should he show the vegetation from the point of view of the scientist or perhaps from the point of view of the sheep that have to find their food there? Obviously, a sheepherder would find it more desirable to have a map which shows the distribution of grasses and forbs arranged in the order of their desirability for sheep. Furthermore, the actual value and the agricultural and fiscal potential of any parcel of land is strongly affected by the manner in which it was managed during the past; for while a farmer can improve his land considerably, he can also ruin it.

The cover of the landscape is divided into fields, pastures, and forests, which are called by their Latin equivalents. Thus, the cultivated field is termed *ager*, applying to orchards, vineyards, olive and chestnut groves, and the like. Pasture is referred to as *saltus;* this comprises all grass and brushlands, as well as forests used for grazing. Finally there is the forest, called *silva*. This term implies only those forests which are protected from fire and are not open to grazing.

Under pressure of circumstances, many once-flourishing vineyards have been abandoned in southern France. They turn into pastures and eventually into forests wherever they are provided protection against fire and overgrazing. And these abandoned lands have received particular atten-

tion. Well-managed and cultivated farms may well be left to continue
as they are but the abandoned, impoverished, and rather unproductive
old vineyards could bear a thorough study so as to permit their reintegra-
tion into a more harmonious and fruitful landscape. The new type of vegetation map records their various stages of evolution toward the climax
forest of oaks, including the degrees of erosion and the species which
are characteristic for each individual evolutionary phase of the vegetation. As, in different parts of the region, different species may imply the
same phase of vegetational evolution, they are considered homologous
species and are given the same color. The colors therefore have a
dynamic quality.

KUHNHOLTZ-LORDAT's method of mapping the vegetation of the parcelles
is here presented as it was developed in and as it applies to the Mediterranean part of southern France.

Mapping is done on copies of cadastral sheets. At first, the mapper
makes a general survey of the area and examines which species may be
used as homologous indicators of dynamic phases of the vegetation. Each
group of homologous species is then assigned a color and both are recorded on the margin of the map. Then each individual parcelle is
examined and properly described. A systematic procedure is advisable
so as to avoid any oversights. KUHNHOLTZ-LORDAT recommends the following sequence:

1. Note the topography. If there are no contours on the map, indicate
   slopes by conventional symbols or arrows.
2. Map the homologous species in the following order: herbaceous
   species—dwarf shrubs (chamaephytes)—leguminous shrubs—other
   shrubs—species of forest trees including seedlings—water features.
3. Prepare a clean copy oriented with north at the top and showing in ink
   the outlines of every color and every symbol. Whenever the map tends
   to become crowded, it is better to present a part of the information
   on transparent overlays.

The ager's value is shown by what it produces. There is no difficulty,
and a symbol suffices: a little circle for an olive tree, a grey dot pattern
for vineyards, etc. These are plants that remain for long periods.
Orchards may be less permanent but, as the cadastral scale is large, it is
best to mark the orchards as such and in addition mention the type of
fruit. From a phytocenological point of view the information is more
interesting and complete if the weeds are listed with the crops.

The saltus consists of a series of postcultural phases evolving toward
the climax forest. The sequence begins usually with herbaceous communities of considerable nutritive value for sheep, followed by others
that are much less valuable. These latter communities are burned periodically because the young shoots are more palatable. Then follow

shrubby communities, in spite of the fire, or indeed, because of it; they are usually preforest communities (preclimax) maintained as saltus (pasture) by their management. A common feature of the saltus is the occurrence of chamaephytic communities of thyme, lavender, etc., on stony ground. The many stones may have been brought to the surface by the plough, or else they accumulated as the finer soil particles eroded away. This floristic type of vegetation mapping is based on the value of the plant communities and their place in the sere. The various phases have been given colors as follows: the first rich postcultural communities are tan (light and dark); the following stage, periodically burned, is shown in purple; the chamaephytic communities are yellow on the map, and orange, red, and yellowish green are used for the preforest stages.

The silva can be shown in its floristic detail and according to its value. There are some well-managed closed forests but many more forests consist of short, widely spaced trees. This permits much light to penetrate between the crowns, resulting in an undergrowth of heliophytic shrubs and sometimes even of an herbaceous ground synusia. In mapping the silva, the forbs and grasses are shown first, next the shrubs, and finally the trees. Deciduous tree species have their own color, i.e., some shade of green; pines are shown in black symbols.

To illustrate the manysided usefulness of the parcelle vegetation maps, the value of different vegetation types to beekeepers may serve as an example. Apiculture thrives most where nectar-producing plant species occur in masses, especially if each plant bears many flowers and the flowering season is long. In the region of Montpellier, *Rosmarinus officinalis* belongs in this category, with *Thymus vulgaris, Lavandula stoechas,* and *Dorycnium suffruticosum* nearly as important. RENAUD (1949) has prepared a vegetation map of some parcelles near Montpellier (Domaine de Fontcaude) with overprinted bee symbols. No such symbol indicates that the vegetation discourages apiculture, one symbol encourages it, and two symbols promise optimal conditions. An analysis of the map reveals that the postcultural stages include few nectar-producing species, at least not in sufficient quantity. There are no forests on this map, but it is well known that beekeepers do not frequent forests except perhaps when the chestnuts and the acacias are in bloom. On the other hand, the preforest stages of the saltus turn out to be rich in species that attract bees, especially two such stages: one with much *Rosmarinus,* and one with much *Thymus, Lavandula,* and *Dorycnium.* The map reveals at a glance the location and extent of the most favorable communities as well as their composition and their place in the sequence of the succession. This helps beekeepers decide where to place their apiaries; it also suggests to them what type of vegetation to look for in other parts of their region.

The use of KUHNHOLTZ-LORDAT's method of mapping the vegetation of parcelles is now spreading through France. It is said to be easy to learn; it is also a fast and inexpensive method. Its strongly historical character makes it interesting to many people other than agronomists. Especially in the field of phytogeography and, indeed, in human geography, this method should receive a warm welcome.

Mapping Marine Biocenoses

One of the least explored aspects of vegetation mapping is that of marine vegetation. Until recently, marine biological research was strongly focused on taxonomy, physiology, autecology, and similar features, but the idea of mapping marine biocenoses signifies a rather new development. When modern scientific methods were employed to explore marine biocenoses, the logical result of marine-vegetation maps became inevitable. ROGER MOLINIER prepared such maps for Grand Ribaud (1954) and the Cape Corse area (1960). PÉRÈS and PICARD (1955) published a map of the Gulf of Marseille, and other maps of the French Mediterranean benthos are now in preparation. More recently, MOLINIER and PICARD (1959) published their techniques for mapping the vegetation on the floor of the ocean, thereby stimulating similar mapping projects elsewhere. MOLINIER (1961) then summarized all relevant material and brought it up to date at the Toulouse Colloquium. The following paragraphs are based directly on the observations and conclusions of these authors.

One of the basic differences between terrestrial and marine vegetation is that on land the maps are usually limited to show phytocenoses whereas maps of the ocean floor present biocenoses. This is only natural, considering the great importance of animal species which are sessile or nearly so. Indeed, when MÖBIUS first introduced the term "biocenose," he was dealing with just marine communities. Of course, plants are particularly important in the upper marine zones if the substratum is relatively solid. But where the latter is mobile and in greater depth, the animal species are often of greater importance than the plants.

Another important difference between terrestrial and marine vegetation is the stratification above and below sea level. The rapid decline in the intensity of sunlight with growing depth results in a series of more or less clearly observable strata, all of which are quite thin when compared with the altitudinal belts of terrestrial vegetation. In fact, the lowest altitudinal vegetation belt on land can be of a vertical extent several times that of the entire photic zone in the ocean, which rarely exceeds 200 meters in depth. This is particularly true of many parts of the humid tropics.

It has been found that methods of studying the terrestrial vegetation can also be used on the ocean floor for the purpose of establishing biocenoses. Marine biocenoses are distinct not only in terms of their physiognomy and floristic and faunistic composition but also with regard to ecology and distribution on the ocean floor. Transitions, of course, occur in the sea as they do on land. As in the case of most terrestrial vegetation, the marine biocenoses are recognized on the basis of qualitative criteria rather than absolute counts or weight determinations. However, the use of the quadrat method is limited to biocenoses on a solid substratum. On a mobile substratum, dredging (see below) seems to give the only satisfactory results.

In using the quadrat method, the minimal area should not be less than 25 cm², but it rarely exceeds one square meter. It is also convenient to indicate the vertical distribution within the community with the help of some abbreviations. MOLINIER and PICARD (1959) distinguish two strata and epiphytes, thus:

SE: *strate élevée* (upper stratum)
SS: *sous-strate* (lower stratum)
 E: *épiphyte*

Another item requiring special attention is the use of sociability classes for animal colonies. The latter may be massive, ramified, and spread over the ground, or branched in arboreal fashion. An entire colony is considered a unit and the sociability figures apply to the distribution of colonies rather than individual organisms. But the following distinction is also important:

1. Separate colonies occupying a given area together. Their sociability is recorded in the usual manner, i.e., in five classes (1–5).
2. A single colony may occupy an area quite as large. It is often necessary to examine such a colony very carefully in order to establish whether there really is only one colony to begin with, or perhaps several colonies. Where a single colony occupies such a large area, its sociability is shown by a cross surrounded by a circle: ⊕. The cross indicates a sociability close to zero as there is only a single specimen; the surrounding circle indicates that the area involved is covered by a single colony only. Of course, in the tables that always go with the quadrat method, the ⊕ is preceded, as usual, by the coverage coefficient.

Where biocenoses have been established by actual inspection on the ocean floor and by the sample plot method, the extent of such biocenoses can be determined by additional sampling without need for further descents. When repeated sampling reveals a change in the composition of the biocenose, the mapper must dive again and take new records.

The dredge used in obtaining biological specimens is not an instrument which scoops up part of the ocean floor. Rather, it is a device, called a drague, consisting of four heavy metal bars joined to form a rectangle and equipped with two knives which correspond to the two longest dimensions. At one end, a net is attached which is lined with cloth so as to retain samples of small organisms. The samples are taken at regular intervals along parallel lines; then the process is repeated along parallel lines that cross the first ones at right angles, so as to form a grid. Only a dense grid will give much detail and this is necessary where the biocenoses are of small extent and change frequently. Where the biocenoses are uniform over large areas, the grid may be wide. Even though the outline of areas occupied by given biocenoses can thus be established satisfactorily, it is wise to take additional samples within the individual grid squares.

MOLINIER and PICARD propose some ideas concerning the cartographic representation of the marine biocenoses with the help of colors. Starting with GAUSSEN's ideas on the use of colors for relating vegetation to the characteristics of the environment, MOLINIER and PICARD found it advisable to limit themselves to a single sequence. The practice of superposing colors to indicate the combined effects of several environmental factors did not seem feasible to them. But they also found that sea level is an unsatisfactory boundary and that it is desirable to show terrestrial phytocenoses and marine biocenoses on the same map. They related terrestrial phytocenoses to xericity, but as crucial as this factor is on land, it is obviously meaningless in the ocean. The authors therefore change at sea level to another climatic factor of equal if not more decisive significance: insolation. Their color scheme is therefore arranged as follows: for terrestrial phytocenoses red to green, with red at the most xeric end of the sequence; for marine biocenoses from green to purple, with green for the lightest parts of the ocean, i.e., closest to the shore and to the surface of the sea. From here the colors change to blue and purple with growing depth and distance from the shore. Within such light zones, expressed by appropriate colors, different biocenoses are shown by different shades of the zonal color. Transitions and dynamic aspects are shown by alternating color bars.

MOLINIER's (1954, 1960) maps are done on the basis of direct inspection and observation. This, however, is feasible only down to a depth of approximately 40 meters. As the depth increases appreciably beyond this contour, it becomes ever more necessary to rely on mechanical means of obtaining the data required for a map of biocenoses.

The Place-Name Method

LEO WAIBEL, one of the most eminent German geographers during the first half of the twentieth century, combined a deep insight into the geography of vegetation with broad experiences in four continents and many fields of learning. His highly original imagination was stimulated by the least observation; and when, by chance, he came across a quotation by CARL TROLL (1936, p. 275) from the *Enciclopedia universal ilustrada* (1929) to the effect that the term "savanna" as applied to various tropical grassland types is not of Spanish but West Indian aboriginal origin, his fertile mind at once swung into action and the ensuing research led to his famous vegetation map of Cuba (WAIBEL, 1943).

The method of employing place names in the study of the natural vegetation was not new to WAIBEL, as it had been developed in Germany to a high degree of perfection. But no part of the Western Hemisphere had been investigated in such a manner that its place names could be successfully employed for the preparation of a vegetation map and, at least on this side of the Atlantic Ocean, WAIBEL's contribution was a real piece of pioneering.

In contrast to the usual ways of studying and mapping vegetation by analyzing the various plant communities, WAIBEL consulted a large variety of sources which included historical accounts, old and new maps, reports of botanists, military surveys, soil maps, geological maps, geographical descriptions, analyses of the location and site of settlements, especially with regard to their central or marginal location on certain vegetation types, archeological data, and accounts of travellers. Another most important part was the careful study of the Cuban place names and their etymological interpretation. This latter part is, of course, the core of WAIBEL's method and certainly proved to be more enlightening than might have been anticipated. His investigation of the Carib term "savanna" was particularly useful, as were all Spanish and Indian terms of vegetation types related to savanna, such as semi-savanna, mixed savanna, parkland, havanna, sabana nueva, sabanita, sabanilla, sabanazo, sabaneton, quemado, ceja, ciego, sao, and others.

The result of his endeavor was a vegetation map of Cuba at the scale of 1:2,000,000 on which he distinguished the following details:

1. Hardwood forests, 1906–1907
2. Pine forests
3. Parklands, 1906–1907
4. Sabanas
5. Cacti-thornshrub formation
6. Swamps
7. Former hardwood forests
8. Scattered pine trees
9. Former parklands
10. Cultivated lands or original vegetation unclassified
11. Strand or littoral vegetation (on map only, not in legend)

The map also shows the consecutive numbers 1–169 and their location, one number each for the names of places that were used in the reconstruction of the original vegetation. The date "1906–1907" in legend items No. 1 and 3 is the date of the American military map of Cuba at 1:62,500 which shows the distribution of hardwood forests and parklands as of that date.

WAIBEL's work was a library investigation and did not include any field work. Circumstances did not permit WAIBEL to check his results by studying the Cuban landscape, but a vegetation mapper who desires to emulate WAIBEL and test his method in some other region should definitely plan on numerous field checks, carefully prepared and executed. WAIBEL's method implies research in history, geography, phytocenology, and Indian linguistics. This multiple approach is most stimulating to the imagination and of particular value to regional geographers. Indeed, if a vegetation map is to be related to historical or regional studies, it is fair to say that WAIBEL's method holds out a special promise for satisfying results.

The Belt Method

SCHMID (1940, 1948) introduces what he calls chorological units or vegetation belts on his vegetation map of Switzerland. These belts are composed of species that occupy similar areas (SCHMID, 1954, 1961). This approach is closely related to the *Arealkunde* by MEUSEL (1943). It is based on a careful investigation of the area occupied by every species of the country. By comparing these areas, it becomes evident that many species occupy the same area whereas other species are grouped together in another area. They seem to be mutually exclusive and form "belts" which can extend over very long distances. For instance, SCHMID sees certain belts reach throughout the Alpides from the Alps to the Himalaya Mountains and cites the larch-pine forests at the alpine timberline as an example, containing in its various parts such genera as *Rhododendron, Vaccinium, Delphinium, Prenanthes, Aconitum, Anemone, Ranunculus,* sometimes even the same species.

Some species occur throughout a belt, others in several individual parts of the belt, and still others in only one part (SCHMID, 1940, p. 78). All these make up the species combination of the belt. Of course, there are many species which are not limited to one belt: they are termed "bizonal" if limited to two belts, and "plurizonal" if spread over more than two belts. Obviously, the plurizonal species do not lend themselves to the establishment of belts.

Belts are concrete units and the floristic difference between two adjacent belts is much greater than the difference between any two sections of the same belt, even if these sections should be hundreds and even thousands of miles apart. A belt contains a large number of heterotypical phytocenoses, conditioned by climatic and other local circumstances. Every phytocenose is assigned to the belt with which it shares the largest number of species. A vegetation belt is a chorological, geographical, and historical (geological, geomorphological, climatic, etc.) unit. In contrast, the biocenose or phytocenose is a synecological entity which greatly depends on the adjustment of its constituent species to one another.

The floristic and semistatistical method of BRAUN-BLANQUET reveals associations, alliances, orders, and classes. But it never leads to chorological entities like the vegetation belts. For these are heterotypical by definition, containing various biocenoses that result from climatic and local conditions (SCHMID, 1940).

The method of mapping the vegetation of, say, Switzerland, consists therefore in comparing the areas of distribution of all species involved and in grouping them according to their common occurrence. The resulting belts can be checked in the field and, in the case of Switzerland, correspond to reality to a remarkable degree.

SCHMID's method has been applied at similar and larger scales elsewhere (SAPPA and CHARRIER, 1949; SCHWARZ in MOOR and SCHWARZ, 1957; GALIANO, 1960). But the larger the scale and hence the smaller the area to be mapped, the more difficult is it to distinguish between SCHMID's belts and phytocenoses. Eventually, the belts vanish and only the component phytocenoses remain. Indeed, on the map of the Creux du Van area by SCHWARZ at 1:10,000, the vegetation belts are not mentioned at all. The method is therefore best adapted to medium and small scales (SCHMID, 1948, 1949).

SCHMID's method of vegetation mapping is certainly most interesting, particularly because it is based ultimately on historical and evolutionary considerations, on routes of travel and migration during climatic fluctuations, on phytopaleontological observations as well as synecological relations including both the relations of species to the physical environment and to competing species and communities. This broad foundation makes SCHMID's method very stimulating; it should be the object of further experimentation.

Profile Maps

A vegetation map shows the mosaic of plant communities in the landsscape. This implies continuity throughout the entire territory with no blank spots anywhere. In contrast to this, WAGNER (1957) proposes to map the physiognomy and structure of vegetation by portraying these on individual profiles. These profiles reach across the map from east to west, parallel to one another and closely spaced. A small number of conventional symbols representing physiognomic and structural features is used to compose the profiles. The spacing of the profiles is even throughout the map, controlled by the tallest synusia that occurs anywhere within the mapped area. The map consists therefore of a set of profiles separated by white (blank) ribbons. In a sense, this method presents a series of line transects expressing the physiognomy and structure through symbols. Where numerous parallel and evenly spaced roads or trails are available, this method should permit a mapper to progress very rapidly.

Sliced Maps

From India comes the suggestion of sliced maps (KHAN, 1954). In essence, this is simply a series of overlays, such as has often been used in the past. KHAN, however, proposes to systematize the overlays for the purposes of the Indian Forest Service and includes a schematic use of colors and symbols. KHAN (1954, p. 113) shows five map sheets, all of the same area. Sheet A is called the "base map"; the remaining four sheets (B–E) are termed "flying sheets." The flying sheets are pasted onto the base map along the margins as indicated, and a particular feature of the vegetation or the site is allotted to each one of the five maps. The base map (A) is above all a topographic map and, with flying sheets B and C, presents topography, soil, and ground-cover synusias. Flying sheet D shows the middle synusia, and flying sheet E the uppermost synusia. The maps are at the scale of 1:15,840, or 4 inches to the mile, which is adequate to show all needed details. All vegetational features are recorded in the field with the belt transect method. KHAN also proposes a color scheme according to which one or two colors and their various shades and hues are assigned to each of the five maps. The use of symbols is more flexible.

It will be interesting to see to what extent such a scheme can be applied uniformly to all of India and what modifications must be introduced locally. KHAN observes repeatedly and quite correctly that there is a real need for maps showing the phytocenoses because they form the best foundation for sound silviculture and forest management. But his sliced maps seem to cut right through the phytocenoses and some way must be found to overcome this difficulty. Perhaps topography and soils can be combined on one of the flying sheets B or C, leaving the base map A for the phytocenoses. As the phytocenoses are the very basis for all management and research considerations, they should be placed on map A.

V

APPLICATION OF VEGETATION MAPS

24

The Utility of Vegetation Maps

Basic Science and Applied Science

The areal extent and delimitation are essential characteristics of every phytocenose, which thus becomes evident as a geographical entity and can be mapped. What are vegetation maps good for? Ozenda (1963) has this to say in reply: "We may have two extreme points of view. Either we answer: 'For nothing, at the moment,' alleging that the proper function of university research is, in fact, to be theoretical in character, or basic. To have a particular solution in mind from the beginning of a research project may keep us from seeing a variety of possibilities because we specialized too soon.

"Or else we answer: 'For everything,' referring the questioner to long lists of possible users both public and private whom the phytogeographers have so often invoked but not always convinced.

"We prefer to stay between these two extreme positions. At any rate, it is not for the vegetation mapper to say what his map is good for, and even less to force it on a given user. His task is simply to make his map accurate and clear, and perhaps more simply still, to make it. That is already a lot."

In contrast to Ozenda and his basic research, Walther (1960) is more pragmatic, viewing vegetation in a man-made and -managed landscape. He points out: (1) Phytocenoses are the result of scientific research and systematics and serve as standards of reference for managerial planning and research. (2) Phytocenoses indicate site qualities and their effects on vegetation. (3) Management can employ phytocenoses as living construction material. (4) Where management is to improve or alter the vegetation, vegetation maps become indispensable, and phytocenological studies, including yield studies, are equally necessary.

WALTHER's is the approach of applied science, of applied vegetation mapping. He sees phytocenoses as units that are simultaneously floristic, geographical, ecological, dynamic, and economic. He observes they can be defined by characteristic and differential species and are clearly distinguishable from one another. Within their sites, they grow under relatively uniform conditions, and they possess a given biological potential or yield potential and their own possibilities for further development. They are therefore standards of reference in scientific phytocenology as well as in all branches of economics that exploit vegetation in any form.

Vegetation maps show units of vegetation and, directly or by implication, the sites on which they grow. But their real economic value is realized only when vegetation and sites can be analyzed in such a manner that measures of improvement can be based on them.

At very large scales, i.e., 1:10,000 and larger, a vegetation map can show all significant features of the vegetation with sufficient accuracy. Such maps should therefore be prepared wherever scientifically or economically important changes of the vegetation may be anticipated in the near future.

If, on the other hand, a map of the potential natural vegetation is planned, a scale of 1:24,000 * or less is usually adequate because it lacks the man-made details. The great significance of such maps lies in the fact that they portray areas of equal biological potential or what REY (1962c) called "isopotential zones." Such zones consist therefore of ecologically equivalent biotopes and form the natural divisions of the landscape. As any yield potential rests on site qualities, and each biotope has its own possibilities for use and development, it follows that any land use is closely tied to the natural divisions of the landscape. These, in turn, can be read directly on a map of the potential natural vegetation. The important point here is that those in charge of land use should have a map that reveals the areas of biological potential. Whether these areas happen to be occupied by one or another kind of substitute communities at a given time is of secondary importance.

Return on Investment

Good vegetation maps are expensive. Any really good and useful map, especially if printed in color, requires much knowledge and skill, much energy and patience during all phases of field work, compilation, drafting and printing. As a result, large funds are needed. The production of vegetation maps in most countries to date has not been so significant as

---

* 1:24,000 (2,000 feet = 1 inch) is the scale of the topographic sheets of the U.S. Geological Survey.

might have been expected. One is led to believe that such maps are too expensive compared with their usefulness.

It is therefore a startling revelation to find that in parts of Europe ever since World War II many excellent vegetation maps are being published, and now more than ever. Today the United States is unquestionably the wealthiest country on earth. Nor is there any doubt that nations like France, Germany, Belgium, and others have had their economies seriously crippled by war and destruction, occupation, and huge payments of all kinds. One can argue that during the post-World War II period Europeans could ill afford what appears to be a luxury, whereas the production of vegetation maps in the United States should meet with few obstacles, if any.

An investigation of this matter reveals that good vegetation maps are far from a luxury, that, indeed, they appeal to the economy-minded. By bitter experience, the Europeans have been forced to economize to a degree that amazes many observant Americans. Under this pressure of harsh circumstances the Europeans have discovered that good vegetation maps will save them millions of dollars. It has been found that these expensive colored maps cost but a fraction of the expenses incurred without their use.

Even in the United States it has become necessary to be economy-minded and to practice frugality. To achieve the most stable, secure, and profitable use of the land, it would be well to consider the European experiences and results with great care. To ignore them cannot be justified any longer. When vegetation maps are based on scientific phytocenology, their value can be demonstrated from the broad approaches of state planning down to such fine details as selecting an appropriate site for bee hives. In the words of MOLINIER (1951): "Phytocenology does not perform miracles, it does better than that. A miracle, by definition, is both incomprehensible and exceptional. But phytocenology is in the front rank of all considerations concerning land use because of the possibilities it makes available to man."

Purpose and Utility

The eventual use of a vegetation map or the purpose for which it is prepared has a strong bearing on the character of the map. It directly affects the classification of vegetation and influences the observations in the field. The effect of a given purpose is often to emphasize certain features of the vegetation while neglecting or even ignoring others according to their relation to the purpose of the map. The purpose, in turn, links the map with the people who are to use it.

Botanists are by no means the only ones interested in vegetation maps, and whether or not their actual number is increasing, their proportion among those who use vegetation maps is declining. On the other hand, there are growing numbers of geographers, zoologists, geologists, plant and animal ecologists, pedologists, and an ever-increasing multitude of people concerned with land-planning, forestry, agriculture and conservation, with climatology, communications, investments and fiscal problems, education and military matters, who are discovering the practical value of vegetation maps as applied to their respective fields.

Vegetation maps satisfy three groups of interests: (1) They are inventories of plant communities existing at a given time and place; they show the areal distribution of vegetation types in the landscape and thereby the extent of what is actually available and what is valuable and desirable, and what is not. (2) They are tools for analyzing the natural environment and the relations between it and the various phytocenoses. To a considerable degree, the distribution of phytocenoses in the landscape can be explained by the physical and chemical qualities of each site and, in turn, these qualities can often be deduced from the vegetation. (3) Through proper use and interpretation of the information on vegetation maps, it is possible to plan future action with regard to optimal land use, where "optimal" implies the best adaptation of land use to the requirements of the people at any given period, and also qualitative and quantitative maxima of production without damage to the soil and water economy of the landscape. "A qualified analyst looks through a vegetation map into the habitat of plants even as a physician looks through an X-ray screen into the human body" (Tüxen). Vegetation maps permit man to work in harmony with nature rather than against it or in ignorance of it.

Vegetation maps are therefore used for a wide variety of purposes. It does not follow that there are as many types of vegetation maps as there are purposes to which they are applied; but it does mean that vegetation maps are highly flexible instruments. They can be prepared according to a variety of methods, and as soon as the purpose for drawing the map has been clearly established, it is then possible to select an approach to the preparation of the map that will assure the most satisfactory results. The nature of the purpose controls the comprehensiveness of the vegetation map and often restricts its usefulness.

Indexes to the Landscape

The immediate usefulness of a vegetation map rests on the fact that it shows the distributional aspects of vegetation, and that the individual plant communities indicate the complex features of climate, soil, and water. Instruments, even the most accurate ones, can give no more than a fraction of the information needed. Of course, the climatology, geology, and physics and chemistry of the soil have been and will continue to be important in the study of the landscape, and phytocenology is simply a later addition to this group of sciences that permits us to appreciate the intricacies of our environment. But phytocenological methods are superior in analyzing the complexities of sites and site types because they make vegetation the basis of investigation, and it is, after all, the cultural vegetation and its welfare on which man's interest is now so eminently focused. Plants are rooted in the soil and exposed to the daily weather conditions of all seasons and can therefore report the nature of the environment much more comprehensively than any instruments ever can. The presence or absence of given species, their appearance, the pattern of their distribution, their association with other species, and many other features, all tell a story which is of fundamental value to all who deal with the land and what grows on it. Indeed, nothing permits one to appreciate the character of the land more readily and completely than the vegetation itself.

To illustrate: It is difficult, even for trained pedologists, to establish the areal extent of wet soils of similar nutrient value. An endless number of chemical analyses is inevitable. But the vegetation reveals at a glance the entire environmental complex, including soil type, the physical and chemical characteristics of the soil water, as well as the climatic and biotic features of the habitat.

Environmental Calibration

As has been pointed out before, vegetation maps reflect the qualities of the environment. They can also give quantitative information, but this requires that the mapped plant communities be calibrated with respect to a particular feature of the environment. The plant communities thus become measuring instruments for certain value ranges in the water, energy or nutrient economy of the landscape.

Such calibration is done by relating floristically defined plant communities to measured conditions of a given environmental feature. Plant communities are carefully recorded in the field and factor measurements are made in each recorded community. The floristic tables of these communities are placed in order of increasing or decreasing values of the environmental factor. It then becomes evident which species or species combinations correspond to which factor values. As a result, given species combinations portray a given feature of the environment quantitatively. This opens new vistas for vegetation mapping with calibrated units of vegetation which portray clearly outlined areas of given environmental values (TÜXEN, 1958; WALTHER, 1960).

KNAPP (1949) illustrates this graphically with an example from the northeastern Vogelsberg region in central Germany. The depth of the water table is to be related to the floristic composition of meadow communities. Twenty quadrats of one square meter each are examined and their vegetation recorded. In the table the quadrats are arranged according to the measured depth of the water table, the depth increasing from left to right. The observations were made in the fall, a period of high water table. At that time the first two quadrats were flooded with 6 and 2 cm of water, respectively (Table 24).

The table reveals that the species can be arranged in three groups. The plants of group I do not react to the depth of the water table, at least not within the ranges of fluctuation as it occurs on these sites. Only those species which occur quite consistently have been listed here. The species of group II are absent from the drier sites. The first ones mentioned are found only on the wettest places and the farther down on the table a species is listed, the farther it penetrates into drier sites. The same applies to the species of group III, but they are all lacking in the wetter places.

As a result of these observations, it is possible to use the plant communities as indicators for the depth of the water table. If, for instance, *Potentilla erecta, Trifolium repens, Succisa pratensis, Nardus stricta, Juncus conglomeratus,* and *Carex leporina* occur together, then it may be concluded from the table that the water table is at a depth of 17–20 centimeters below the surface (at corresponding water level, management, and other environmental features). The degree of accuracy of the possible estimates was shown when, in a number of places, the depth of the water table was first estimated, then measured. The results were as follows:

Estimated	Measured
17–20 cm	18 cm
10–12 cm	12 cm
21–25 cm	23 cm
5 cm	5 cm

Such observations are of particular significance since they permit us to ascertain the relative depth of the water table in other seasons, too, even during dry months, and to judge its rise during periods of high water level. An excellent example of a vegetation map with quantitative information was published by WALTHER (1957), relating phytocenoses to the depth and fluctuations of the water table.

Vegetation maps are not a panacea for all land-use problems. LONG (1963) points out, for instance, that in the area of the Sologne in central France the natural vegetation does not indicate whether the soil is free of gravel or contains as much as 10 per cent of it. However, the commercial production of asparagus is made impossible by 5–10 per cent gravel in the soil. MOLINIER (1951) rightly emphasized that vegetation maps are important tools in solving land-use problems, but they are not the solution. However, as more knowledge is accumulated concerning the preferences, requirements, and tolerances of plants and plant communities, it becomes easier to exploit a vegetation map to capacity. And as our knowledge of the indicator value of phytocenoses grows and deepens, the interpretation of a vegetation map becomes more efficient. It follows that the greater the number of published vegetation maps the more economical is the use of the vegetation maps published later.

Qualified Personnel and Utility

Essentially, there are two prerequisites for the preparation and application of vegetation maps: (1) a properly trained staff to handle the field work and all cartographic aspects, and (2) qualified persons to interpret the map. Persons concerned with land use will avail themselves of whatever techniques can help them solve their problems. Among these, vegetation mapping is very important. The vegetation maps reveal the biotopes and perhaps what environmental factors may exert a controlling influence on them at given times. But this is often the limit of their competence. If site qualities are to be analyzed in detail, the vegetation mapper must have been trained in all relevant fields (which can hardly be expected), or else he has to rely on appropriate specialists, above all on pedologists. Furthermore, the mapper is not often qualified to determine how his map is to be exploited. This must be left to the users: agronomists, silviculturists, and others. If the mapper intends to prepare a report that is to supplement his map, and go beyond the information on the map, he is well advised to make his report a cooperative venture, enlisting the collaboration of specialists from the relevant fields. Indeed, it is well to plan the entire mapping venture so as to insure the closest collaboration between the mapper, cartographic and printing technicians, and the eventual users. Thereby, the finest quality and the greatest usefulness of the map are most likely to be attained.

Unfortunately, there are at the present time few schools for training appropriate personnel, and this lack of skilled technicians is felt keenly. This is an important consideration because vegetation maps are intricate instruments which cannot readily be used by the layman. The rapidly increasing application of vegetation maps in some countries means also that there must be a growing number of people who can prepare, analyze, and interpret them so that the information on the map can be made available and be exploited to the fullest advantage even by people who are not trained in the study of vegetation. Whenever an order for a large-scale vegetation map is filled in Europe, whether for government

Table 24. Depths of Water Table Versus Floristic Composition *

Depth of Water Table in cm:	-6	-2	0	2	5	8	10	12	16	17	18	19	21	23	25	26	26	28
I.																		
Carex panicea	—	+	—	—	—	2	—	2	2	—	—	2	—	—	2	—	—	—
Lotus uliginosus	.	.	.	+	+	—	—	—	+	+	+	+	—	—	—	—	—	—
Cardamine pratensis	.	+	+	+	+	+	+	+	+	+	+	+	—	+	+	+	+	+
Deschampsia caespitosa	—	—	.	.	—	3	3	2	—	—	+	—	—	+	—	—	2	2
Lychnis flos cuculi	.	+	+	—	—	+	+	+	+	+	+	+	+	+	+	+	+	+
Valeriana dioica	.	+	.	.	.	—	—	—	+	+	.	+	+	+	+	+	+	+
II.																		
Iris pseudacorus	+	—	.	.	.	.	.	.	.	.	.	.	.	.	.	.	.	.
Veronica scutellata	+	+	+	+	.	.	.	.	.	.	.	.	.	.	.	.	.	.
Agrostis canina	3	2	3	3	—	+	.	.	+	.	.	.	.	.	.	.	.	.
Ranunculus flammula	2	2	2	2	3	3	3	2	—	.	.	.	.	.	.	.	.	.
Calliergon cuspidatum	3	4	3	3	3	3	3	2	+	.	.	.	.	.	.	.	.	.
Carex fusca	3	2	2	+	—	+	+	+	+	.	.	.	.	.	.	.	.	.
Galium palustre	—	+	+	+	+	—	+	+	+	+	+	.	.	.	.	.	.	.
Ranunculus repens	+	2	2	—	+	—	—	+	—	—	+	.	.	.	.	.	.	.
Juncus conglomeratus	+	—	2	2	—	—	—	+	—	+	+	2	.	.	.	.	.	.
Carex leporina	+	.	—	.	—	+	+	+	+	+	+	+	r	.	.	.	.	.

III.

(Phytosociological table — species, rows read vertically; abundance/cover values arranged in columns)

```
— 3 — 2 r — — + — + + + + 3 — + — — +   · +
— 3 + 2 r — — + + — · · — + 3 + + — — + + ·
— 3 — 2 · — — + + + + + — + 3 + + — + + r +
2 2 — 2 + — + + — + + r · + 3 — · + — + · ·
2 2 — 3 · — — + + + · · · + 3 · + + + + · ·
— 2 — 2 · — — + + + — + + + 3 + + — — · · ·
2 3 + 3 + — — + + + · r · · · 2 + + + r + · ·
2 2 — 3 · + + + — + · + + + 3 + + r · · ·
2 2 2 — 3 + — + + + · — r · · — · · + · · ·
2 3 + 3 · — — + + + · + + · 2 + + — · · ·
2 3 + 3 · + + + — — + + + + 2 — + · · ·
2 2 — 3 + + + + · + — · + · 3 + · · · ·
2 2 — 2 · + + + + · · · + + · · · ·
— 2 — — + + — + · + — · — · · · ·
2 2 2 + + — + + + + — + · · · ·
+ — — + · · · · · ·
+ 2 2 — + · · · · ·
— · · · · ·
```

Species:

- Climacium dendroides
- Festuca rubra var. genuina
- Holcus lanatus
- Aulacomnium palustre
- Galium uliginosum
- Luzula campestris
- Ranunculus acer
- Filipendula ulmaria
- Molinia coerulea
- Cirsium palustre
- Rhytidiadelphus squarrosus
- Selinum carvifolia
- Sanguisorba officinalis
- Polygonum bistorta
- Nardus stricta
- Succisa pratensis
- Trifolium repens
- Potentilla erecta
- Hylocomium proliferum
- Trifolium pratense
- Avena pubescens
- Chrysanthemum leucanthemum

* After KNAPP (1949).

agencies or for private organizations, the map is accompanied by a detailed written report with analysis and interpretation of all features relevant to the purpose of the map. The vegetation map can then be usefully employed by a large number of people, even if they themselves lack the training in preparing and interpreting such maps.

So great has been the demand for vegetation maps in Europe that research may lag behind. The available manpower is employed almost entirely to fill the steady and ever-growing current of orders. Clearly, it would be wise to make adequate funds available for large scale and continuous research programs. The deeper the insight into the problems of vegetation mapping, the greater are the returns on the invested capital. It is a false economy indeed that places its resources at the disposal of immediate exploitation without availing itself of the much greater gain which unhampered long-term research assures. But at last, more people are beginning to appreciate that the vegetation map is a new application of science serving the economy and the welfare of the nation.

On the following pages, a series of examples will be given to illustrate the utility of vegetation maps, but it is neither feasible nor necessary to point out all possible uses to which vegetation maps may be put.

Many examples in the following chapters have been taken from the European scene because there vegetation maps are applied most intensively. Indeed, some of the examples may seem startling to the American reader, who does not suspect such a wide range of applications. On the other hand, it is the purpose of these paragraphs to point out the great variety of uses to which vegetation maps may be put so that all countries may benefit from them as much or more than Europe has so far.

25

Scientific Investigations

The recognition of phytocenoses and their distribution in the landscape is fundamental for an understanding of vegetation. Indeed, establishing a natural order of the biogeocenoses is a goal of primary significance in basic science as well as in many of its applications. Size and extent of the plant communities, structure and composition, and relations to each other and to the landscape make up the very basis of phytocenology. Phytocenoses are an expression of site qualities; this aspect recently developed into a crucial and revealing field of research because of its many practical applications. In particular, vegetation maps clarify our knowledge of the living conditions and the ecology of phytocenoses because the close relations of plant communities to environmental features (soil, exposure, altitude, etc.) can often be observed directly on them.

In discussing the significance of vegetation maps in research, OZENDA (1964, p. 335) said: "In the study of vegetation and its relations to the environment, the vegetation map is a tool of exceptional value. It may even be considered indispensable. This will be increasingly so because the evolution of modern forms of scientific expression tends to progressively play down texts and to replace them with more synthetic and more readily exploited forms of representation. In fact, the vegetation map expresses more facts than a text can, it expresses them more clearly, i.e., it can be used easier and faster, and it expresses them more objectively."

Phytocenose-Biotope Relationships

A problem of great importance is to establish the degree of consistency with which given phytocenoses are tied to certain biotopes and to discover the causes of this consistency. Progress in such research can be materially aided by vegetation maps and indeed, simplified and expedited better than by any other means. The results of such investigations must

317

always be verified in the field and on the vegetation map. This strengthens both the research method and the usefulness of the map. The recent developments in mapping aquatic vegetation open up an additional and vast field of research that is just beginning to be appreciated.

An Objective View of the Landscape

One of the significant features of a vegetation map is that it forces the author to include every part of the landscape. As the map covers the entire area, communities and biotopes are observed which might have been missed by spotty observations. A phytocenologically sound vegetation map therefore prevents a subjective emphasis on favored communities. In addition, the mapper discovers most effectively to what extent the units of his classification of vegetation actually correspond to the communities he observes.

For instance, ZONNEVELD (1963) and his collaborators mapped the vegetation of the Biesbosch, a freshwater tidal area in the Rhine delta region in the Netherlands. The map was made for purely practical purposes: to serve as a basis for melioration. Nevertheless, it not only revealed important scientific problems but contributed directly to their solution. The most significant results of mapping the vegetation and of the research based on it are that they—

1. increased our knowledge of the phytocenoses;
2. revealed new combinations of species to form phytocenoses with ecological indicator value;
3. extended our knowledge of the autecology and synecology of several species and the phytocenoses they form;
4. contributed materially to our knowledge of the geomorphology and evolution of a region and the features of sedimentation;
5. showed the stages of deposition and maturation of the soil, used in delimiting the maturation phases on the soil map and potentially important in classifying the area for land use;
6. clearly revealed the suitability of the area for planting reeds, rushes, willows, and poplars;
7. greatly facilitated the evaluation of cultural measures and their results;
8. permitted an insight into the original natural landscape in spite of strong human influences;
9. revealed the effect of aeration of the soil and of the flooding intensity on the morphology of life forms;
10. showed the relation between the aeration of the substratum and the ability of phytocenoses to tolerate flooding;
11. gave a new insight into the nature of succession in a highly dynamic environment.

Ecological Research

KRAUSE (1950) has concerned himself at length with vegetation maps as ecological research tools, especially in analyzing the causes responsible for the geographic pattern of vegetation as we observe it today. He gives the following example.

He asks, Why does a species occur at a particular site? Using heather (*Calluna vulgaris*) as an example, he observes on his vegetation maps that it occurs as a member of the "Calluneto-Genistetum" on the sandy plains of northwestern Germany, on the sandstone mountains of central Germany in the *Calluna-Antennaria* association, and as a *Calluna* facies in drained peat bogs. He demonstrates that *Calluna vulgaris* finds on all three sites essentially the same relations between its own specific constitution and certain site qualities, which are repeated throughout, although each time in a different guise. Such generalization of many individual cases is one of the goals of scientific research. In an instance like the above, some of the critical requirements of the species are revealed, as well as certain important site qualities leading to the plant communities of which *Calluna vulgaris* is a prominent member.

Terminology Improvement

A significant aspect of vegetation mapping is the need to formulate an exact terminology and to define precisely the vegetation entities that can be classified. Indeed, such entities sometimes remain unknown and unrecognized until they are to be mapped. There must be no doubt about the terms used on the vegetation map. The mapper is therefore obliged to test the extent to which the units of his classification actually correspond to the plant communities he observes. For instance, when the vegetation of the dunes near Haarlem (Holland) was mapped, it was found that the classification of vegetation by BRAUN-BLANQUET could not be applied (DOING KRAFT, 1963). The entities of "landscape-units," eventually adopted, differed from one another by—

1. characteristic or differential species (according to local disjunctions of areas)
2. dominant species or combinations of dominant species
3. characteristic or differential vegetation-units
4. dominant vegetation types
5. floristical differences within the same vegetation-unit
6. definite combinations of vegetation types
7. definite proportions in surface of constituting vegetation types
8. physiognomical differences (relative surface of open spots, shrubs, woods, etc.)

Evidently these landscape-units correspond to hitherto uninvestigated differences in geomorphology, geology, local climate, soil profiles, and the local distribution of species.

This map proved to be useful for studies of the biogeography, history, and origin of the dunes, for the protection of nature, and for management.

Evolutionary Processes and Site Differences

Where vegetation maps of a given area are made at long intervals, the differences between the maps imply changes which lead to a whole series of questions. The invasion of the area by a species, its progress or failure to progress into certain sites, its effects on the soil and on the competing plants, the differences between deliberately introduced species and those that freely migrated into the area, and a host of other problems are revealed by comparing the vegetation maps. By exposing such problems, the vegetation maps give research an impetus which would have been less likely without them.

Vegetation maps also direct the attention of the phytocenologist to the cultural vegetation of forests, fields and pastures, plantation forests, and semi-natural communities like many heaths and range pastures. These substitute communities are the result of human activities which are revolutionary for most site qualities and tend to obscure the true nature of the sites. Here it is the large-scale vegetation maps that comprehensively record the subtle variations in the communities of weeds in the fields or of the herbaceous ground cover on the forest floor and thereby point to the site qualities as they change from place to place. No instrument clarifies the changes in vegetation and site more effectively than the vegetation map.

Logical Generalization

SCHMITHÜSEN (1963) demonstrated how the definition of entities is related to the problem of generalization. Thus, a large-scale vegetation map, perhaps only in its first draft, shows all units of the actual vegetation. The first step beyond this is to express these units as abstract entities, the step from phytocenoses to types of phytocenoses *sensu* SUKACHEV (1960). Once these abstract units are established, the generalization that goes with decreasing map scales is a logical problem, not a technical one.

While therefore the problem consisted at first only in a precise description of actual vegetation entities, it is now different: it consists in combining entities into logical complexes of phytocenoses, i.e., the units must be shifted to another plain of operation. The new entity, the complex, implies that, in a given area, a given combination of phytocenoses prevails. Such complexes can be shown on maps of smaller scales. If the scale is further reduced, the complexes must be merged to form complexes of a higher order, and, theoretically, this process can be continued to vegetation maps at very small scales, world-wide in scope.

If the vegetation is described by means of a hierarchical classification, e.g., that by BRAUN-BLANQUET, the generalization may logically proceed from lower to higher ranks. As the scale shrinks, the lower ranks are merged into the next higher one; etc. However, this procedure may soon fail, because the high ranks may form intricate mosaics on small areas. Thus DOING KRAFT (1963) found it difficult to show alliances even though his scale was 1:25,000! The usefulness of this approach is therefore limited.

Generalization should always proceed in a logical manner. This implies that the units used on a generalized map should be of the character of the units of the original, non-generalized map. If actual vegetation is to be shown, it should be not only on the original map but on the generalized map as well. The same applies to potential natural units, to ecological units and all others. GAUSSEN combined two methods by presenting the potential natural vegetation with subdivisions of actual vegetation. This method permits a generalization down to at least 1:5,000,000 as shown on the inset maps of the vegetation maps of Tunisia and southern India. On large scales, the actual vegetation can be shown in any desired detail.

Zoology

A special point can be made of the usefulness of vegetation maps to zoologists. Phytocenoses with their associated animal life form biocenoses. A vegetation map is therefore of fundamental significance to all concerned with the distribution of animals in the landscape, with wild life management, hunting, insect control and a host of other problems.

Asking the Right Questions

It is a condition for the usefulness of vegetation maps, that the individual plant communities be comprehensively recorded and that their character and their relationships be appreciated by the mapper and by the reader of the map. Awareness of the order in the plant cover of the landscape as revealed on a vegetation map will make an observer more sensitive toward nature and will offer him distinct problems. The discovery and clear formulation of problems is one of the most crucial features of all research and botanists, especially phytocenologists and ecologists, find vegetation maps therefore a nearly inexhaustible treasure.

Much research remains to be done if vegetation maps are to attain the degree of perfection that we can reasonably hope for. But vegetation maps already serve as a basis for the scientific and economic exploration of entire nations (LAVRENKO and SOCHAVA, 1956; BERTOVIC, 1963; NEU-HÄUSL, 1963). It seems quite clear that vegetation maps will have to serve mankind for many generations as essential tools in many branches of theoretical and applied science.

26

Geographical Research

Throughout the civilized world, ALEXANDER VON HUMBOLDT is celebrated as the father of modern geography; he is also the recognized founder of modern plant geography. The extraordinary breadth of his interests made it inevitable that he should train his vivid imagination and his unusual power of observation on the innumerable forms and combinations of plant life in Europe and the tropical regions of America. As HUMBOLDT was generally accepted as a geographer, his fundamental contributions to plant geography made this field an integral part of physical geography, and the names of geographers like GRADMANN, SCHMITHÜSEN, TROLL, WAIBEL, and many others attest to the vigor of the Humboldtian tradition to the present day, at least in his own country. These geographers and their many unnamed colleagues find their counterparts among botanists with a genuine geographical interest like CAIN, ELLENBERG, FOSBERG, GAMS, GAUSSEN, HUECK, SHANTZ, SHREVE, and TÜXEN. Such men reveal the close ties between the two sciences of geography and botany, and it is not at all surprising that the great majority of them have contributed to our store of vegetation maps.

The vegetation map is the logical meeting ground of geographers and botanists, and the study of vegetation, or phytocenology, has become an auxiliary science for geography, even as physical geography has assumed the same character for botany. Progress in one science has therefore been stimulating progress in the other. To a certain extent there has been a division of labor, for such facets of plant geography as the geographical and genetical evolution of species have been studied primarily by botanists. Geographers, on the other hand, have shown a particular interest in the ecological aspects of plant geography. This is only natural, since it is one of the tasks of geography to synthesize the geographical regions from data supplied by its auxiliary sciences like climatology, geomorphology, pedology, geology, and, of course, the study of vegetation, or phytocenology.

Geographers consider vegetation an integral part of the landscape. Their approach to vegetation, therefore, is to study vegetation as a feature which gives an area its basic character and as a means to differentiate regions and their components of landscapes and landscape types. The study of individual plant species is usually of secondary interest to geographers, a study which they readily leave to their botanical colleagues. But the results of botanical research in phytocenology have proved to be of great significance for geographical research. It is inevitable that the work of botanists and geographers should overlap, and although their goals are not the same, it is stimulating and beneficial for one to be informed about the methods of the other.

Direct Areal Observation

The map is the geographer's most important tool, and he more than anyone else will appreciate SCHMITHÜSEN's (1942) observation on the particular advantage vegetation maps have over other maps. This great advantage consists in the fact that the mapper can actually walk along the boundaries of every plant community and outline and establish the actual area occupied by a given vegetation type. This areal feature is rather unique because climatic maps, for instance, are based on data obtained at a limited number of points of observation. Similarly, geological and soils maps rest on inspections of occasional outcrops, drillings, or borings. Topographic maps go beyond this by having contours extending the critical information from points to lines. Only the vegetation units are open to and based on areal observation. In any regional or landscape study, this is a significant advantage which has not been fully appreciated so far.

The difference between geographical and botanical research concerning vegetation is that phytocenology studies vegetation types as biological entities and for their own sake, whereas geographical research endeavors above all to grasp and to express the various phytocenoses as components of the landscape. It is therefore of primary importance that vegetation types be arranged in physiognomic-ecological units which must be identifiable in the field. Wherever it is feasible, these units should be refined floristically, i.e., their divisions and subdivisions should be based on species combinations.

Cultural Geography

The use by geographers of plant-ecological information as revealed on vegetation maps is not limited to studies of plant life in the landscape or to relating it to other branches of physical geography. The study of vegetation has also been employed to deepen our appreciation of various features of cultural or human geography, such as economic and historical geography, the distribution and density of population, and others. Such studies are fruitful in both the simplest and in the most complex civilizations. For the primitive life and land use of the Indians in the Amazon Basin, the distribution and character of vegetation types is about as vital as the cultural and semi-natural vegetation in Kansas or in Sweden is for the inhabitants of these countries.

The comprehensive study of the landscape or the region is the very essence of geographical research and gives the entire field of geography its unity and strength. No other field of science disputes this position, even though individual aspects of the landscape or region are examined by a variety of other sciences (e.g., geomorphology, pedology, etc.). This comprehensive approach of geographical research implies that both the natural (physical and biological) features and the anthropogenic or cultural features are considered together and without prejudice. In a study of the cultural geography of a region, the natural features reappear in new relations and combinations with cultural aspects that do not necessarily depend on them. In this new totality of the landscape, the natural and cultural vegetation plays an important role.

A biotope is the smallest component of a landscape; it has comparatively uniform features throughout its area and hence a relatively uniform type of natural vegetation. Every biotope implies a certain potential for plant life in general and for land use (economic development) in particular. For each type of natural vegetation there are one or several crop types for optimal land use. Man devotes his land to field crops, hay, pasture, or forest but, whichever he chooses, each of these will have certain ecological features that correspond to the type of natural vegetation on the site of which they occur.

At times, a map of the cultural vegetation can show the contrasts between biotopes even better than the natural vegetation, as SCHMITHÜSEN (1942, p. 139) has pointed out: the forest of an alder bog can merge rather imperceptibly with the forests on the adjacent drier sites. But in the cultural landscape, a meadow replaces the alder bog and then the moist site will contrast sharply with the surrounding forests or fields with their lower water table. As land use becomes more highly developed, more complex, and more carefully attuned to the physical and biological features of the landscape, the natural biotopes are reflected in the cultural landscape with increasing clarity and in ever finer detail.

JOHNS (1957) in his study of Dartmoor in southwestern England investigates the vegetation of the region as a basic part of the landscape. He shows how the plant communities reveal the character of the landscape and demonstrates how the gentle changes of topography and other features result in numerous gradual transitions between the recognized communities. Certain types of vegetation, on the other hand, such as *Sphag-*

num bogs, are clearly outlined because they seem to occur wherever the water factor exceeds a certain threshold value. His work is primarily descriptive as, indeed, it should be. Once the vegetation has been mapped and described in detail, the observations and the collected information can then be used as a basis for qualitative and possibly quantitative studies of the physical and biological character of the region and its relation to human use at the present time or under pressure of changing economic demands and policies.

Jes Tüxen (1963) uses vegetation maps and the principles on which they rest to explore the cultural past of the landscape around Stolzenau an der Weser, Germany. This is a remarkable study in historical geography. But while on one hand the results are revealing, it is, on the other hand, not feasible to emulate this research in areas where archeological and palynological data are not available or at least appreciably less so than in Europe. The difficulties are greatly increased if the research area is mostly cultivated and modern agricultural techniques have eliminated the weed communities through the consistent use of herbicides.

Comparative Geography

The insight into the landscape achieved through maps of natural and cultural vegetation can be deepened considerably by making comparative studies of two or more regions. For instance, in many respects the wormwood steppes of the Aralo-Caspian Plain are startlingly like the Great Basin sagebrush; the relations of the California chaparral to the Corsican macchia have been pointed out many times; the páramos of the northern Andes reappear on the East African volcanoes, and the Dakota Prairie has its counterpart in the Ukraine. But such comparisons can be refined considerably by observing on the vegetation map just how the vegetation types are distributed in the region and how they can be related to soils, microclimate, topography, and land use. Comparative studies of this type result in a greater appreciation of the characteristic features of the geographical region and reveal new problems, stimulating research. For instance, such a comparative study was made by EMBERGER (1958), in which he compares the vegetation of two distant regions (Mediterranean Basin and southern Australia). He enriches and strengthens his work by linking the vegetational comparison with a climatological one. This permits an excellent insight into the similarities and differences of the two regions.

Large-Scale vs. Small-Scale Maps

The geographer profits from vegetation maps of all scales. The small-scale maps are largely synthetic maps compiled from a variety of sources such as various maps of larger scale, the literature, reports, observations, etc. The task of small-scale vegetation maps is to give a broad view. Through them it is possible to follow the major vegetation formations beyond the borders of a region and to trace their ties with neighboring formations. This fits a region into its proper place on the continent and into the biosphere of our planet. The large-scale maps, on the other hand, show the details of the vegetation in defined units that can be observed in the field. The larger the scale, the more units can be differentiated. Here, then, is the key to the character of the biotopes and their distribution. Even the finest variations in the landscape can be discerned with the help of the large-scale vegetation map, as was beautifully demonstrated by FRIEDEL (1956). The geographer is here enabled to grasp the nature of his region because the biotopes are the ecological units, the building bricks in the structure of the landscape. Their identification and extent, their distribution and character belong to the goals of every regional analysis because they are the essential standards of reference for a large number of geographical phenomena.

Maps at large scale, i.e., of small areas, are usually based on field work and have an important advantage over small-scale maps. They can be adapted more readily to local needs and can express the features of the vegetation peculiar to a given region without having to fit them into a continental or world-wide scheme. Large-scale vegetation maps show, therefore, a higher degree of individuality and flexibility than small-scale maps, and hence are more easily adjusted to a particular purpose, to a given landscape, and to the originality of their authors.

Much geographical research is concerned with climate. The vegetation map as a climatic document is discussed in Chapter 27.

Whatever its scale and purpose may be, an accurate vegetation map is essentially a significant geographical achievement because of the sensitive relations between vegetation, climate, soil, and land use. Indeed, KRAUSE (1955, p. 48) emphasized that the greatest success in the interpretation and use of vegetation maps may be expected from one who possesses a thorough knowledge of the nature of vegetation and who, simultaneously, is a comprehensively trained geographer.

27

Vegetation Maps as Climatic Records

Vegetation-Climate Correlations

Late in the nineteenth century, SCHIMPER (1898) made a major effort to coordinate the geographical distribution of climates and vegetation types. His forests, grasslands, and deserts expressed wet, periodically wet, and dry climates respectively, and his views were widely accepted. Later, CLEMENTS (1916) even went so far as to say that the climate controls the vegetation to such an extent that within the region of a given climate all types of vegetation evolve toward a uniform climax.

The close relations between climate and vegetation are expressed *inter alia* by such terms as "savanna climate," "rainforest climate," "tundra climate," "steppe climate." In all these instances, the climate is characterized by the vegetation. The reverse happens, too, and such terms as "cloud forests," "alpine meadows," etc., imply a forest vegetation where clouds and fog prevail, and meadows of a climatic type characterized by a short, cool growing season, ample moisture, a long-lasting snow cover, etc.

The climate, like all features of the environment, is highly complex and difficult to describe in exact terms. Its major components are temperature, precipitation (both rain and snow), and wind. Atmospheric humidity, direct and diffuse insolation, and a host of other factors contribute to the complexity. These features vary with the seasons from continual high intensity to total absence as, for instance, in the case of insolation; Kordofan and northern Greenland illustrate some of the extremes. But the seasonal variation of a climatic factor assumes a new character when viewed in combination with others. Thus climatic conditions even within a given latitude may be almost totally unlike. A comparison of the climate at Bakersfield, California, with that at Charlotte, North Carolina, in the same latitude illustrates this: Bakersfield experiences its rainfall maximum during the winter and has a pronounced summer drought, whereas the rainfall maximum at Charlotte occurs during the summer with no dry period in any season. The contrast in the vegetation is profound.

Sometimes, individual climatic factors have been used to explain phytocenotic changes. Thus, KÖPPEN (1931) used the arctic timberline as the boundary between his D and E climates. In northern Russia, he found this coincided with the 10° C isotherm of July. TROLL (1943) noted sharp vegetation boundaries in the high Andes of Peru where the temperature rises above 0° C during the day and drops below 0° C at night every day for most months of the year. This is a temperature condition outside the range of tolerance of most species and as a result, where this type of climate sets in, the relatively rich vegetation of lower altitudes changes abruptly to much impoverished phytocenoses of widely spaced cushion plants, dwarf shrubs, and very tough bunch grasses.

In a similar fashion, an increase in the annual precipitation is illustrated by the increasingly luxurious character of the vegetation. A traveller journeying from eastern New Mexico to eastern Tennessee along the 36th parallel will observe an impressive change from a few grass species of short stature to one of the tallest and richest forest types anywhere in the middle latitudes. The contrast is even more extreme if the observer travels along the 10th meridian (western longitude) from central Mauritania to southern Liberia, or from the barren sand dunes of the Sahara into the tropical rainforest of Upper Guinea.

The most complex pattern of vegetation is usually found in mountainous regions where a great local relief combines with different exposures to sun and rain-bearing winds. An increase in altitude implies a decrease in temperature, an increase in relative humidity, a decrease in absolute humidity, frequently an increase in cloudiness and precipitation (often followed higher up by a decline of both), and an increase in the intensity of insolation and radiation and also in average wind velocity. The contrasts in exposure are often so great that in many mountainous regions a regular terminology has evolved in the local dialects to describe these contrasts, as for instance *adret* for the sunny slopes and *ubac* for the shady ones in the region of the western Alps. The effectiveness of exposure to sunlight varies often with latitude. In arctic regions, the vegetation on a south-facing slope benefits from the increased intensity of insolation and the resulting higher temperatures; it is therefore richer than on northern slopes. However, in the Front Range of the Rocky Mountains in Colorado, the southern exposure means a poorer vegetation: shrub and grass as compared with the forests on the north-facing slopes. Here the insolation on the southern slopes is more powerful, due to the lower latitude; the heating and hence drying effect produces semi-arid conditions whereas the cooler and therefore moister northern slopes retain enough moisture to support forests. In equatorial regions, there is usually little difference between northern and southern slopes with regard to insolation because the amount of energy received is more alike on both sides.

The moisture conditions of mountainous regions are not only dependent on altitude but also on exposure to rain-bearing winds. The starkest contrasts are produced where steady sea winds blow throughout the year more or less in the same direction. This is particularly true of the tradewind belts. In the outer tropics, where normally a rainy season alternates with a pronounced dry season, the trade winds deposit heavy rain on the windward side of coastal mountains. Such orographic rainfall is, of course, relatively independent of the seasons. In the high elevations, vegetation will be about the same on both sides of the mountains because ample moisture is available. But in the lower altitudes, as for instance in Jamaica, the mountains bear a dense tropical rain forest on their northeastern flanks while the southwestern foothills are covered with strongly xeromorph communities, rich in cacti and thorny shrubs.

OZENDA (1963) showed the close coordination of vegetation and climate in the French Alps in tabular form (Table 25). The names of species represent phytocenoses of the potential natural vegetation, not simply a forest composed mainly of that species. The changes in altitude with the corresponding climatic changes are well documented by changes in the vegetation, and this applies equally well for the dry and humid phases. Phytocenoses between the dry and the humid phases are transitional in their ecological requirements and tolerances. Such a neat documentation of the close correlation between vegetation and climate is, of course, quite schematic and generalized. But local variations in climatic conditions can often be demonstrated with the help of vegetation just as accurately or even more so.

Even wind as an individual climatic factor can sometimes find expression in the vegetation. However, this is the case only when it is so strong and persistent that it inhibits tree growth in areas where the available heat and precipitation are ample to support forest communities. The best-known examples are the Hebrides, Shetland, and other islands that face similarly frequent and severe storms.

Divergences in Mapping

The number of correlations in the distribution of climate and vegetation might well lead one to believe that everywhere climate and vegetation are so closely coordinated that a vegetation map and a climatic map are essentially identical. This, however, need not be the case.

Table 25

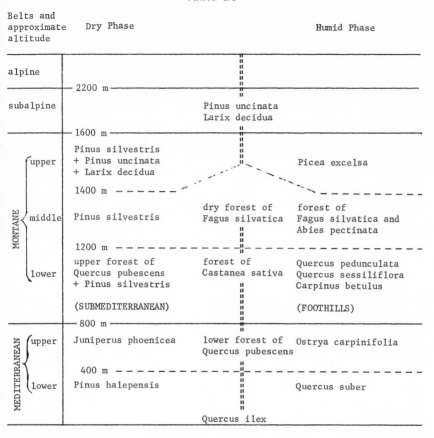

Belts and approximate altitude	Dry Phase		Humid Phase
alpine			
— 2200 m —			
subalpine		Pinus uncinata Larix decidua	
— 1600 m —			
MONTANE — upper	Pinus silvestris + Pinus uncinata + Larix decidua		Picea excelsa
1400 m			
middle	Pinus silvestris	dry forest of Fagus silvatica	forest of Fagus silvatica and Abies pectinata
1200 m			
lower	upper forest of Quercus pubescens + Pinus silvestris (SUBMEDITERRANEAN)	forest of Castanea sativa	Quercus pedunculata Quercus sessiliflora Carpinus betulus (FOOTHILLS)
— 800 m —			
MEDITERRANEAN — upper	Juniperus phoenicea	lower forest of Quercus pubescens	Ostrya carpinifolia
400 m			
lower	Pinus halepensis		Quercus suber
		Quercus ilex	

After OZENDA (1963).

Both climate and vegetation are very complex, and each can therefore be described in a variety of ways. Climatic maps cannot present all climatic features individually. They are usually based on only one or two features, more or less ignoring all others. Thus a change in vegetation may be brought about by climatic features which are not recorded on the climatic map. If, for instance, a climatic map is based on mean annual precipitation, and the vegetation of two areas differs because of a difference in the seasonal distribution of rainfall, then a vegetation map is not likely to agree with the climatic map. Parallels between a climatic map and a vegetation map can exist only if those climatic features which are responsible for vegetational changes are recorded on the climatic map. All other features are likely to be irrelevant.

The complexity of the climate finds its counterpart in the complexity of the vegetation. Floristic composition, structure, and all other features of phytocenoses are susceptible to change because of altered climatic conditions. But it is not feasible to predict with certainty just which feature will change for which reason. It may now be one and then another.

LIVINGSTON and SHREVE (1923) published a massive book in which they collected an extraordinary variety of climatic data, mostly on maps, in an effort to discover what climatic features controlled the geographical distribution of vegetation in the United States. In spite of the painstaking work, examining every conceivable climatic factor, the authors had the rare courage, in the end, to admit defeat. They concluded that the geographical distribution of vegetation in the United States cannot be explained by individual climatic features.

An important item which prevents vegetation maps and climatic maps from being alike is the reaction of vegetation to changes in the soil. The climate may be uniform over large areas but within such climatic regions several soil types may occur side by side. The soils may differ appreciably within short distances because of unlike parent material, different degrees of maturity, different water conditions, etc. The reader need only remember the great contrasts between the vegetation of oases and the surrounding deserts, or between galeria forests and the surrounding grasslands. In each case, the macroclimate is identical in the contrasting types of vegetation. It is therefore possible that there may be nearly as many phytocenoses as there are soil types. The conclusion seems inevitable that vegetation maps and climatic maps are unlikely to agree and that, due to more frequent changes in the soil, vegetation maps tend to be more complex than climatic maps.

The evidence is contradictory. On the one hand, climatic types seem to imply vegetation types and climatic changes seem invariably to produce changes in the vegetation. On the other hand, vegetation maps cannot reasonably be expected to agree with climatic maps unless, perhaps by chance, the latter are based on the particular climatic factor that affects the particular feature of the vegetation shown on the map.

The apparent dilemma disappears with the realization that there is no need for a mirror-like agreement between vegetation maps and climatic maps. It is enough that vegetation maps reveal climatic differences. Within one vegetation map, the effects of different climatic factors may be revealed by different phytocenoses. The task is not necessarily to produce a vegetation map which will faithfully reflect climates. It is rather to interpret the vegetation map in such a manner that observable climatic effects on the vegetation can be clearly discerned, whatever they may be.

A close consideration of vegetation maps as a climatic record reveals three types of vegetation maps. The difference between them lies in the degree of coordination between vegetation and climate. The three types may be termed (1) aclimatic, (2) quasi-climatic, and (3) climatic vegetation maps.

Aclimatic Vegetation Maps

Aclimatic vegetation maps are prepared without any reference to any aspect of climate and they reveal none. An example of an aclimatic vegetation map is that of the Patuxent Research Refuge at 1:7,920 (STEWART and BRAINERD, 1945). This map covers only a small area and the climate may be assumed to be uniform throughout. Therefore the various types of vegetation portrayed on this map do not differ from one another for climatic reasons. Of course, it may be argued that this map does indicate climatic conditions after all. For in what sort of climate other than that of the Patuxent area would these vegetation types exist? From such a point of view, all vegetation maps reveal the climates of their respective areas. However, this is not a useful argument. If a vegetation map is to be considered a climatic record, then differences in the vegetation as presented on the map must go hand in hand with corresponding differences in climate. In other words, a vegetation map shall be included among the climatic records only if one and the same map reveals areal changes in vegetation and parallel climatic changes. This is not the case on aclimatic maps.

It may be argued that maps at so large a scale as that of the Patuxent Research Refuge cannot reasonably be expected to show climatic variations of sufficient contrast to result in different phytocenoses. But a vegetation map is not aclimatic simply because its scale is large. For instance, the vegetation map of southern Florida (DAVIS, 1935) was published at the much smaller scale of 1:400,000 and it, too, is aclimatic. The area includes Florida from the Keys in the far south to just north of Lake Okeechobee, and the number of vegetation types is considerable. Yet, in spite of the large territory and the complexity of the vegetation, it is not the climate but features like the depth of the water table, the soil structure, the geology, etc., that determine the character of the numerous phytocenoses.

The maps of Patuxent and of southern Florida have one thing in common: both maps portray the vegetation of areas which are only slightly above sea level and have little relief. This at once eliminates the climatic contrasts due to topography. If southern Florida has a large area, it is nevertheless a low land, much of it barely above the warm seas that surround it on three sides. The marine influence reaches right across the peninsula and assures such a uniformity of climatic conditions that the variations in the vegetation must necessarily result from non-climatic causes.

Quasi-Climatic Vegetation Maps

As in the case of aclimatic vegetation maps, the quasi-climatic vegetation maps, too, are based more or less exclusively on phytocenoses. Vegetation is usually the only criterion for the location of the boundaries between individual types. However, it may be that the soils or some other environmental features, such as outcrops of geological strata, are employed in order to locate vegetational boundaries more precisely. Maps portraying the distribution and extent of substitute communities imply that considerations of land use may have entered into the preparation of the map. At any rate, climatic data were not taken into account during the preparation of the map.

Unlike the aclimatic vegetation maps, however, the quasi-climatic vegetation maps do reveal climatic features. They do this incidentally and by implication. They may do so in one part of the map and not in another, and they may reveal the effects of different climatic factors in different parts of the map. While it may not be the purpose of the vegetation map to show these climatic features, the reader is nevertheless enabled to glean climatic relationships from such a vegetation map. Quasi-climatic vegetation maps are therefore genuine climatic records to a varying degree and in preparing such maps, it is often difficult to foresee how much climatic information will be revealed by the vegetation.

The complexity of climatic conditions in areas with appreciable local relief is well known. It is therefore not surprising that vegetation maps of mountainous areas are almost necessarily quasi-climatic in character. Altitudinal vegetation belts are common, as are the contrasting conditions on north- and south-facing slopes. The effect of the differences in altitude and exposure is a matter of degree. At one extreme stand high mountains of alpine character with bold contrasts in climate and hence in vegetation. As altitudes get lower and the slopes gentler, the contrasts in climate and vegetation become more modest and the boundaries become blurred until at last, in gently rolling plains, the differences fade into the finest phenological nuances.

In areas with considerable local relief, climatic conditions change frequently and within short distances. This is equally true of the mosaic of plant communities. Quasi-climatic vegetation maps are therefore relatively independent of the map scale where the relief is reasonably bold. As one studies the aclimatic vegetation maps, it becomes clear that little or no relief is quite the rule.

A large scale must not be interpreted to imply an aclimatic character of the vegetation map. A good illustration is the map of the foothills of the Harz Mountains near Bad Harzburg, Germany, by Tüxen (1954c). This map is done at the scale of 1:10,000 and is based on the classification of vegetation by BRAUN-BLANQUET. Most readers will know that the preparation of vegetation maps with the BRAUN-BLANQUET method is focused on a sort of semistatistical approach, analyzing and distinguishing the phytocenoses according to their floristic composition. There is nothing in this method which relates the vegetation to climate. Once the vegetation map has been completed, however, the relations to the climate may become evident. On TÜXEN's map, the altitudinal differences are too small to affect the vegetation much, but the contrasts in exposure of the steep slopes are clearly reflected in the pattern of plant communities.

Thus the Querceto pretreae-Betuletum grows only on the south- and southwest-facing slopes, leading TÜXEN to the conclusion that these slopes are the warmest and also the driest part of the mapped area. The distribution of the Luzulo-Fagetum cladonietosum is traced back to the exposure to strong winds which, in turn, blow away the leaf litter on the ground, thereby contributing to the desiccation and impoverishment of the soil.

The Luzulo-Fagetum festucetosum altissimae, on the other hand, is limited to northeastern and some northern exposures, where the mean temperatures are lower, evaporation is reduced, and the wind accumulates the leaf litter, increasing the humus and the soil moisture and thus illustrating the effect of climatic factors on the soil and, through it, on the vegetation.

The Melica-Fagetum avoids the dry windy exposures and is limited to north- and northeast-facing slopes, with one variant reaching somewhat toward the northwest. Lower temperatures and higher humidity are the chief climatic factors stimulating this community. Other phytocenoses owe their extent and distribution to edaphic rather than climatic factors.

Phenological features such as the progress of fall coloration of the foliage tie in well with the phytocenoses and their distribution by climatic types. Phenology thus supplies TÜXEN with an unsought but gladly accepted support in his attempt to establish correlations between the distribution of phytocenoses and local climatic variations.

TUXEN's map shows nothing but a number of plant communities and also contours. The latter allow the reader to appreciate the local relief and to correlate it with the vegetation. Wherever a given phytocenose is restricted in its distribution to a particular exposure, it is assumed that the climatic conditions prevailing there are responsible for this distribution. All other types of distribution must be presumed due to edaphic or biotic causes. In general, this theory may work well but it does not exclude the possibility that a plant community is limited to one exposure and occurs there primarily for edaphic reasons, the exposure with its climatic qualities being more or less coincidental.

Tüxen's legend contains no indication of the interrelations between the distribution of phytocenoses and the local climate. To establish such interrelations, the reader is obliged to deduce them from the map, where his success will be proportional to his experience and knowledge of local circumstances. Or else, he must refer to the text which accompanies the map. Not everybody is so familiar with the climate of the northern Harz foothills, the prevailing wind directions, etc., that he can get the full benefit of the map without consulting the text. The map is therefore not independent. It may, of course, be argued that such independence was not intended, that the map was expected to be accompanied by the text. But as it was the stated purpose of the author to study the vegetation as an expression of the complex local climate (Tüxen, 1954c, p. 456), at least the more relevant observations might have been extended from the text to the map legend, thereby greatly enriching the map. In other words, an expanded legend could have made this vegetation map a climatic record of more immediate usefulness, and this could have been done with ease since Tüxen's text contains the necessary data in a well-ordered presentation.

The attempt to achieve such immediate usefulness was crowned with more success on the vegetation map of the Nanga Parbat group in the northwestern Himalaya at 1:50,000 (Troll, 1939). Some of the climatic correlations with the vegetation are here incorporated into the legend. As a result, the map is more independent of a text and the reader of the map is made more aware of several climatic implications of the vegetation.

All major groups are correlated with altitudinal belts, but only a partial effort is made to explain the climatic significance of these belts. That average temperatures and temperature ranges decline with increasing elevation is a matter of course, but the altitudinal effect on precipitation can only be guessed. What different climatic conditions prevail in some of the altitudinal belts of the vegetation is therefore implied rather than stated. Other belts are said to be hot and dry, or they are moist, etc. Many of the divisions of a major vegetation belt are directly related to exposure, but such is the contrast between northern and southern slopes that some phytocenoses can climb more than 1,000 meters higher on the sunny south side than in the shadier north, e.g., the *Artemisia* community. The pine-spruce forests, the birch groves, and two phases of alpine meadows with willows and with *Rhododendron* respectively occur primarily on northerly exposures with much shade and more moisture. On the other hand, two phases of alpine meadows with different juniper species prefer a sunny southerly exposure.

Not all phytocenoses on this map are related to the climate, some definitely to the substratum. In some instances, the rockiness of the slopes is more significant than the exposure as in the case of the little pistacia tree community which occurs on both north and south facing slopes of the hot arid valleys below 2,000 meters. Like Tüxen's map of the Harz foothills, Troll's map of the Nanga Parbat is a good climatic record in a limited way, but with the added advantage of a more interpretive legend.

A last example of quasi-climatic vegetation maps may be selected from the smaller-scale maps. The vegetation map of central Asia at 1:1,000,-000 (Lavrenko and Rodin, 1956) comes in seventeen sheets, and the Tashkent sheet (K-42) may serve to illustrate a different method. On this map, a large number of phytocenoses is spread over a terrain which ranges in elevation from less than 200 meters along the Syr Darya to over 4,500 meters. There is great uniformity in the lowlands and great complexity in the mountains. Both altitudinal zonation and exposure contrasts are clearly noticeable on the map. Therefore, the scale has little effect on vegetation maps as climatic records. The vegetation of the vast Aralo-Caspian Plains with little relief is shown more or less as was the case on the map of southern Florida by Davis: the lack of relief makes the vegetation map essentially aclimatic in its northwestern part. This changes only when the plains vegetation is compared with that of the adjacent hills and the high mountains beyond. Once again, the legend is not so revealing as that of the Nanga Parbat map. A few times, the term "desert" is used in the legend, there are steppes, meadows, broadleaved deciduous forests, dark coniferous forests, deciduous mesophytic shrubs, etc. There is practically no reference to the climate, and all relations between climate and vegetation are shown by implication as on Tüxen's map. On the other hand, the boldness and extent of the relief result in clearly observable differences in the vegetation which must be due, above all, to climatic variations. In this manner, the vegetation map of Central Asia is clearly recording climatic features, although many legend items relate the vegetation to edaphic conditions. However, climatic facts may be deduced even from some of these. For instance, extensive xerophytic vegetation, located as it is in the heart of the continent, must imply great scarcity of precipitation and a low atmospheric humidity.

Of the three quasi-climatic vegetation maps discussed above, the maps of Central Asia and of the Harz foothills are closer to each other in character than to the map of the Nanga Parbat, because they show the relations between climatic types and the distribution of phytocenoses mostly by implication. In order to appreciate fully what these relations are and how they function, it is necessary either to consult a text or else become familiar with the peculiarities of the local climates. On the Nanga Parbat map, on the other hand, the legend points out some of the crucial aspects of the climate and the resulting vegetation. This, then, leads to the conclusion that the manner of expressing the relationships between vegetation and climate is more significant than the scale in analyzing a vegetation map as a climatic record.

Climatic Vegetation Maps

The climatic vegetation map attempts a systematic coordination of vegetation and climate. This means that throughout the area of the map, this coordination is applied to all types of vegetation and climate. The climatic vegetation maps are so organized that climatic boundaries harmonize with vegetational boundaries. In view of the complexity of climate as an environmental factor on one hand, and the problems presented by the tolerance of species and intracommunity competition on the other, it may seem at first as if any attempts at coordinating climate and vegetation must needs be doomed to failure. Happily, this is not so.

Both climate and vegetation are so complex that authors usually select particular features which can be observed with relative ease. Thus, certain aspects of the physiognomy of plant communities or one or more dominant genera or species can often be singled out without much difficulty. Some aspects of temperature and precipitation are usually selected to describe the climates. The problem lies in choosing features of both the vegetation and the climate which are reasonably representative of the types they are to describe, and which can be coordinated.

Another approach is to consider the phytocenoses as units in their entirety and climatic types as equally comprehensive units. On a vegetation map, it may then be said that climate and vegetation change together. But nothing is said about what particular aspects of vegetation and climate actually do change. It may be temperature here, precipitation there, etc. Likewise, it may be the dominant species of a phytocenose that change or its structure or both.

If a vegetation map is to be a climatic record, then it is necessary that the vegetation can be employed to determine certain climatic differences. The causal relations between the geographical distribution of phytocenoses and various climatic factors must not only be understood, but the mapper must appreciate this relationship as it applies to the mapped area. Thus, the localization of the causal relationships is a matter of concern and its effects must not be underestimated. The effects of insolation on south-facing slopes in different latitudes, as discussed above, is a case in point. If a vegetation map is to be a climatic record, the climate must be interpreted exclusively with the help of the locally occurring phytocenoses. Generalizations are dangerous and can lead to serious errors.

In the following paragraphs, the climatic vegetation map will be discussed with the help of three examples, each of which is quite different from the others. The discussion will begin with the map of the smallest scale and proceed to progressively larger scales.

The first example is the vegetation map of Guatemala at the scale of 1:1,000,000 (HOLDRIDGE, 1959). It presents one of the simplest and clearest methods of correlating vegetation and climate and the key to the method is an integral part of the legend (Figure 20). The reader is thus enabled to study the distribution of vegetation types throughout the country and, simultaneously, appreciate the climatic conditions that prevail in each vegetation type.

HOLDRIDGE draws three sets of parallel lines, inclined to one another at an angle of sixty degrees. One set represents mean annual precipitation in millimeters. All lines are equidistant but the values progress geometrically, thus: 125, 250, 500, 1,000, 2,000, 4,000, and 8,000 millimeters. Another set shows mean annual temperatures in degrees centigrade: 0, 3, 6, 12, and 24° C. Finally, the third set of parallels follows almost inevitably, signifying evapotranspiration values thus: 0.25, 0.50, 1, 2, 4, 8, and 16. The over-all effect is that of a triangular honeycomb in which each hexagon contains a specific type of vegetation because it finds itself at the intersection of given values of temperature, precipitation and evapotranspiration. At its right and left sides, the drawing is flanked by latitudinal zones and altitudinal belts respectively. These zones and belts are so spaced as to harmonize with the main drawing. In this manner every vegetation type is at once coordinated with temperature, precipitation, evapotranspiration, latitude, and altitude.

The drawing is world-wide in its applicability but the map legend lists only those vegetation types which actually occur in Guatemala. The legend terms and those used in the drawing are, of course, the same, for example: "very dry tropical forest," "dry subtropical forest," "humid montane forest," etc. The total range is from hot desert and polar ice sheets to rain forest. HOLDRIDGE's arrangement allows for thirty-eight vegetation types. However, he augments this number by allowing alternate types in a few of the hexagons. Even at such a small scale as that of 1:1,000,000, the vegetation of the world would appear to be more varied than HOLDRIDGE's scheme indicates. Presumably the drawing on the Guatemala map represents the basic scheme and each vegetation type can be divided and subdivided as local circumstances require. At any rate, HOLDRIDGE has devised a climatic scheme, based on quantitative data, into which he has fitted the vegetation of the world empirically.

The second example of a climatic vegetation map is the Perpignan sheet of the vegetation map of France at the scale of 1:200,000 by GAUSSEN (1948). On this map, quite a different approach has been employed, based on the use and manipulation of color. GAUSSEN arranges his colors according to the spectrum and with them describes climatic conditions.

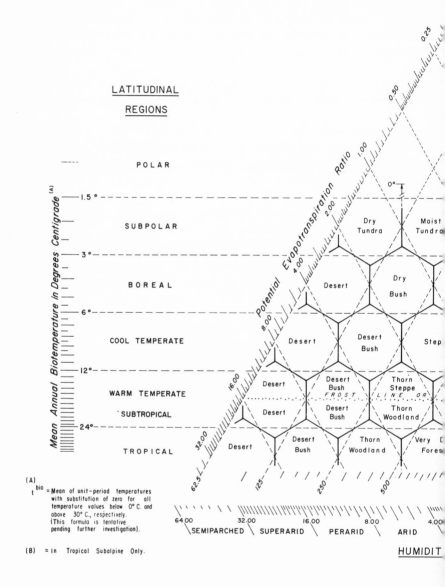

Figure 20. Diagram for classification of world life zones

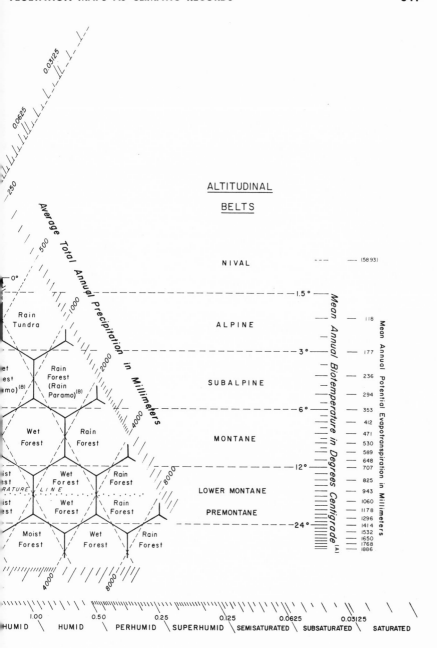

ALTITUDINAL

BELTS

or plant formations. (By permission of L. R. Holdridge.)

The red end of the spectrum corresponds to hot and dry conditions whereas the blue and violet end signifies cold and humid conditions. In an elaborate system, GAUSSEN establishes the degree of dry or humid by the number of dry or humid months in the year, and the character of each month by the number of dry or humid days. All are clearly defined. Unlike HOLDRIDGE, GAUSSEN does not indicate *on his maps* how his system is applied. The uninitiated will therefore miss much of what the map has to offer.

Like HOLDRIDGE, GAUSSEN postulates that given climates go hand in hand with certain types of vegetation. He speaks therefore of plant climates, naming, however, the plants quite specifically. For instance, on the map of Perpignan, a part of the area is shown in blue. Blue is close to the cool and humid end of the spectrum which, in this case (Perpignan), co-incides with a natural forest vegetation of beech (*Fagus silvatica*). GAUS-SEN therefore speaks of a beech climate, characterized by cool summers, cold winters, ample precipitation in all seasons, fog, snow cover in winter, etc. Other climates are described in the same manner.

On this basis, vegetation is shown less effectively than the climate. To elaborate the information on the vegetation, GAUSSEN manipulates his colors ingeniously, as has been shown in Chapter 20.

In addition to the main map, there is a series of smaller-scale inset maps of the same area. Of these, two present the potential natural vegetation and a combination of precipitation and temperatures respectively. These inset maps, therefore, represent an additional feature correlating vegetation and climate in the mapped area. GAUSSEN's genius for organization and his vivid imagination have led him to produce a vegetation map which is so rich in information that it has never been surpassed. The basis of this wealth, however, is GAUSSEN's manner of showing vegetation and climate simultaneously, thus making his vegetation map very much a climatic record as well.

The final example of a climatic vegetation map is the map of Leonberg at a scale of 1:50,000 (ELLENBERG and ZELLER, 1951). This is, of course, a relatively large scale; hence the mapped area is rather small. The climatic recording stations are widely scattered and cannot portray the regional climate in adequate detail. The authors have therefore chosen the phenological method. This enabled them to show the basic climatic types as revealed by the phytocenoses themselves, and the coordination of vegetation and climate has thus become complete. The climatic values are, of course, relative rather than absolute and quantitative because they are based on the seasonal progress of selected ontogenetic phases of certain species instead of instrument readings. On the other hand, the very fact that the reactions of the plants are the points of reference makes the result much more comprehensive than any measurements can hope to be.

The map of Leonberg is therefore a climatic record of unusual interest. The method of preparing it has been described in Chapter 13.

The examples have revealed several methods for recording climates with the help of vegetation but the important fact is that there is indeed a variety of available methods and not just one. Considering the complexity of vegetation and of climate, a choice in methods means that the preparation of vegetation maps as a climatic record can be adapted more readily to given needs. The greater the choice, the finer can be the adaptation. Thus, for instance, there is a choice between arbitrarily fixed quantitative values on one hand, perhaps applicable over large areas, and relative values on the other, such as phenological ones, applicable only in a limited region, but with greater detail and meaning.

Two observations therefore stand out: (1) vegetation maps can be significant climatic records, and (2) a flexible approach permits their applicability to a variety of purposes.

Climatic Classification

One more point requires comment. A consideration of climates has led to some questions regarding their classification. Thus GARNIER (FOSBERG, GARNIER, and KÜCHLER, 1961) takes the point of view that a classification of climates must be based exclusively on climatic criteria and that the classifier must not be influenced by vegetation as was KÖPPEN, for example. This is not only a valid argument but one which is perhaps more logical and in many instances more useful, especially in an era when aeronautics are an integral part of civilization.

There is, however, another consideration, quite as fundamental as the foregoing and favoring vegetational classifications of climates. This is the effect of climate on agriculture, silviculture, range management and related forms of land use. Even though aviation is now a part, if not indeed a symbol of our civilization, agriculture remains man's most basic and essential activity, and there is every indication that this will continue to be so for generations to come. The enormous complexity of the climate and of the reactions of plants to their environment have been shown many times. So far, it has not been possible to unravel these complexities and to express them in adequate form. The fact is that the plants themselves, especially their distribution patterns in a mosaic of phytocenoses, are superior to any other means to gauge the biological potential of an area, and this includes the effects of the local macro- and microclimate. At least for those concerned with land use, the climatic vegetation map remains therefore one of the most realistic climatic records available today.

28

Pedology and Geology

Both the geologists and the soil scientists have long recognized the need for mapping the results of their field explorations. In most regions of the world, the desired data are hidden under a cover of vegetation, and the occasional outcrops may not be sufficiently numerous for mapping, if indeed they are present at all. To be sure of good results, a pedologist must test the soil at regular, closely spaced intervals; the accuracy of a soil map based on such field work is in direct proportion to the density of the grid pattern of these soil tests. Even though the soil should prove uniform in its character throughout the entire area, all tests must be made to ascertain this very uniformity and its boundaries.

Vegetation and Soil Evolution

The quality of the soil depends on the parent material from which it is derived, on the local climate and the vegetation. After due recognition to climate and parent material, the fact that vegetation is so intimately tied to the evolution of the soil makes it almost inevitable that differences in one should be paralleled by differences in the other. For the vegetation not only affects the soil and its formation; in return, it is also strongly affected by the character of the soil and its spatial variations.

Edaphic observations can not only lead to a more accurate delimitation of phytocenoses, but careful mapping of the latter can stimulate edaphic research, leading to a more precise observation of soil profiles, and even to distinguishing soil types which hitherto had not been described. From the viewpoint of the members of a phytocenose, the whole complex of all soil horizons is a unit, and the soil must always be studied in its totality and not just the uppermost horizon.

As long ago as the beginning of this century, LIVINGSTON (1903) observed in Michigan: "That there is a marked relation between the natural vegetation of the state and the nature of the soils has long been known."

In the same study, he publishes a map to demonstrate how remarkably the distribution of soil and vegetation types can coincide. Later, VEATCH (1953) showed the same close parallels in the distribution of soils and vegetation to exist throughout Michigan.

Soil Mapping

Tests conducted by EMBERGER (1955) in conjunction with the French Geological Survey demonstrated that the vegetation can be used as an indicator of soil types (Figure 21). Hence a good vegetation map can often be used to map the soil and, usually, only one test per vegetation unit is necessary. In transitions from one plant community to another, the number of tests needs to be increased in order to safeguard high standards of mapping accuracy. In the case of EMBERGER's experiments there were no exceptions to the rule, and LE HOUÉROU (1955), IONESCU (1956), TÜXEN (1958), and others confirm this close coordination between phytocenoses and soils.

It is obvious, therefore, that mapping the soils of an area with the help of phytocenoses affords the mapper a great saving in time and hence in funds.

Exceptions, nevertheless, do occur. However, even these may have the same type of explanation. For instance, two different plant communities can occur on the same type of soil. A closer inspection may then reveal that it is not so much the soil qualities of each horizon as the varying thickness of the horizons that led to the observed variations in the vegetation. Thus, the vegetation will reveal the finest variations in the site qualities.

GARDNER and BRADSHAW (1954) established close relationships between vegetation and soils in Mendocino County, California, and their work shows how further research into the subject may produce important results. Indeed, the entire mapping program which WIESLANDER developed for California is based on the simultaneous mapping of vegetation and soil; their interrelations became evident on every quadrangle mapped. HILLS (1952) built an elaborate structure of physiognomic, geologic, and edaphic site classes as related to the forest phytocenoses of Ontario. KRAUSE (1950) uses vegetation maps to demonstrate with the help of the floristic composition of some plant communities how convex and concave surfaces have different soils because of the varying forces of erosion and deposition. The vegetation map contributes to the research on these forces by outlining the areas of their activities and effects. In the same study, KRAUSE observes near Fulda, Germany, two important features: (1) which natural phytocenoses and substitute communities can be related to what geological substrata, and (2) that different soil types evolve on a

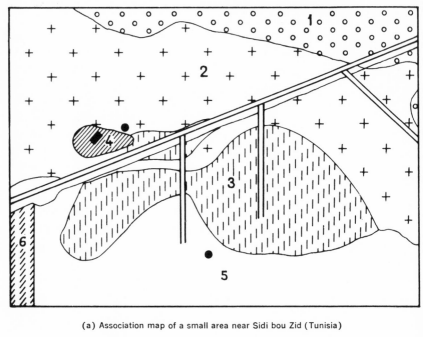

(a) Association map of a small area near Sidi bou Zid (Tunisia)

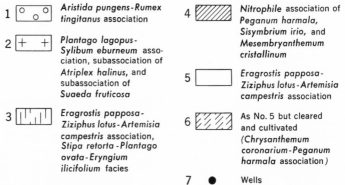

1 — Aristida pungens-Rumex tingitanus association

2 — Plantago lagopus-Sylibum eburneum association, subassociation of Atriplex halinus, and subassociation of Suaeda fruticosa

3 — Eragrostis papposa-Ziziphus lotus-Artemisia campestris association, Stipa retorta-Plantago ovata-Eryngium ilicifolium facies

4 — Nitrophile association of Peganum harmala, Sisymbrium irio, and Mesembryanthemum cristallinum

5 — Eragrostis papposa-Ziziphus lotus-Artemisia campestris association

6 — As No. 5 but cleared and cultivated (Chrysanthemum coronarium-Peganum harmala association)

7 — ● Wells

given geological stratum, e.g. basalt, according to different phytocenoses growing upon them.

This opens up new views on many research possibilities. A comparison of the observations made on a vegetation map does not necessarily prove any theory. But such a vegetation map will nevertheless be an invaluable guide to a researcher who endeavors to establish accurate facts and meas-

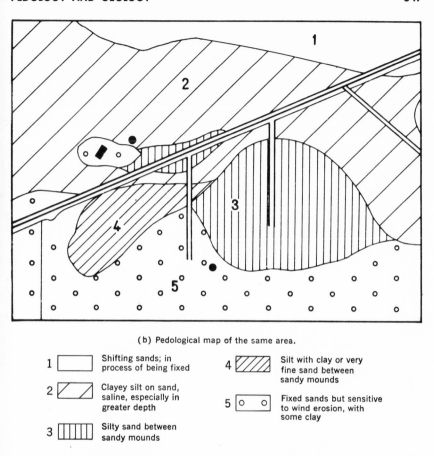

(b) Pedological map of the same area.

1 ☐ Shifting sands; in process of being fixed

2 ▨ Clayey silt on sand, saline, especially in greater depth

3 ⊞ Silty sand between sandy mounds

4 ▨ Silt with clay or very fine sand between sandy mounds

5 ☐o o☐ Fixed sands but sensitive to wind erosion, with some clay

Figure 21. Relationship between the phytocenology (left) and the pedology (above) of an area. (After Emberger, Gaussen, and Rey, 1955.)

urements on the evolution and changes of soils. Most soil changes result from external forces affecting the soil. Nearly always, they go hand in hand with vegetation changes with each influencing the other.

Vegetation and Substratum

WELLS (1962) found near San Luis Obispo, California, that physiognomic vegetation types cannot readily be related to the geologic or edaphic substratum: "An investigation of a large variety of substrata shows that grassland, shrubland and forest often coexist as discrete types in narrowly circumscribed areas on the same substratum. . . . In general, most of the major physiognomic types are abundantly, but not equally, represented on most depths of soil and directions of slope on all geological substrata." But later he finds: "If the vegetation is regarded from the floristic standpoint, then the nature of the geological substratum has a pronounced effect, at least in several cases. Perhaps the most striking examples are in the genera *Arctostaphylos* and *Ceanothus*; most of the numerous species which occur locally are confined to one, or a few, types of substratum. Other striking examples of segregation are seen in the conifers, e.g. *Cupressus sargentii* occurs only on serpentine, where it forms picturesque forests. On the other hand, serpentine oak (*Quercus durata*) and serpentine manzanita (*Arctostaphylos obispoensis*) were found also on diabase."

Other Pedological Uses of Vegetation Maps

There are also quite different aspects of pedological research which may greatly benefit from the use of vegetation maps. For instance, the tightly woven interrelations between the vegetation and its sites have been pointed out many times. It is therefore easy to see that pedologists concerned with the evolution and distribution of different types of humus can greatly benefit from vegetation maps, especially from those prepared at large scales. LAVERGNE (1955) has pioneered in this field. The vast amount of research yet to be done here has barely been recognized, yet, the results of such investigations may be of far-reaching importance in both basic and applied science.

WESTHOFF (1954) points out that from a scientific point of view, a disagreement between vegetation maps and soil maps is more interesting than an agreement. He finds such disagreements on very immature soils in regions of sand dunes near the ocean, in saline ooze and the freshwater sections of tidal delta regions. In all such areas the distribution of plant communities may show little or no analogy with the soils and this is not astonishing because the differentiation of the vegetation is here primarily the result of biotic, microclimatic and hydrological factors. This allows a deeper insight into the effects of non-edaphic site qualities and a separation of the causal significance of the edaphic from the non-edaphic factors.

Phytocenose-Soil Type Correlations

For the preparation of large-scale soil maps or geological maps, or for prospecting and many other activities to which pedologists and geologists must devote much time, a vegetation map is a guide that can greatly simplify the field work. For "it is evident that there will be a broad change in the soil with every change in the regional vegetation" (HILLS, 1944).

Actually, the degree of analogy between vegetation and soil maps depends to a considerable degree on the criteria used in identifying the soil types.

Soils are very complex. The physical, chemical, and biological features of soils are so numerous that phytocenologists must understand the relations between a soil type and phytocenose or else their conclusions may have little or no value. It is, of course, true that phytocenoses are closely related to their site, more specifically, to those aspects of the site which affect plant growth. The close relationship between phytocenoses and soils is well documented where individual concrete stands are concerned. The relationship is much less close where the distribution of abstract types of phytocenoses is compared with that of abstract soil types.

Soils and sites are by no means identical. The site includes climate, topography, water, and biota in addition to the soil. ELLENBERG (1958) pointed out that, in a sense, soil is not a site factor. The real site factors are said to be heat, light, water, the supply of nutrients and trace elements, as well as certain physical and chemical forms of damage. It does not follow necessarily, therefore, that the distribution of phytocenoses and soil types are strictly parallel. The coincidence of phytocenoses and soil types is of practical value only if the soil features which are considered to be typical have a bearing on the practical situation and on the problems at hand.

The degree of coincidence between phytocenoses and soil types depends on the criteria used to identify the soils, and the coincidence is often greater where phytocenologists rather than pedologists established the types. In addition, the nature of the horizons affects the vegetation. As the evolution of a soil type affects the formation of horizons without necessarily paralleling the evolution of the vegetation, it follows that soil and vegetation need not always coincide, even though they often do. It is for this reason that extensive programs of vegetation mapping are often carried on simultaneously with soil mapping, as for instance in California, The Netherlands, France, etc.

MEISEL (1958) compared vegetation maps with soil maps of the same area and used the coincidences or the lack of them as a basis for his research. He observed that a soil map by itself does not reveal the distribution of vegetation types. It shows soils, i.e., it shows a great variety of soil qualities. It does not show which of these qualities and which degree of intensity of these qualities determines the continuity or a change in the vegetation. Only detailed comparisons with vegetation maps can clarify such problems. Even then, a coincidence can be explained only if based on features that are shown on the map. For instance, two different phytocenoses occurred on the same soil type indicating a difference not shown on the soils map. In this case, MEISEL found it was not so much the chemical makeup of the soil but a difference in the fluctuations of the water table.

APINIS (1961) pointed out that soil types are often defined by quantitative measurements of their features. This ignores the microbial soil fauna and flora which can have a decisive influence on the phytocenoses. Where the soil biota are not included in the description of the soil type it happens that the distribution of soils and plant communities can not be correlated easily.

Vegetation and Geology

While the relations between vegetation and soil and other site qualities can readily be demonstrated, the ties to topography are not always so obvious. Of course, the contrasts between high and low altitudes, or between north and south facing slopes are nothing new. But there are more delicate variations in the character of the landforms which can become evident with the help of vegetation maps. The following example is taken from MENSCHING (1950) who made his observations in the valley of the Weser River in northwestern Germany.

The Weser valley, in the examined area, consists of a broad flood plain. This flood plain is composed of material which dates back to Pleistocene times, but in part it is much more recent. Normally, the recent material, deposited by annual floods in historic times, rests on the material deposited here during the later glacial periods. Occasionally, the recent material does not cover the entire flood plain, and the older glacial material lies at the surface as if it were looking through windows in the recent material. It would be tedious and very time consuming, and sometimes quite difficult to locate these windows and to determine their extent. But the vegetation comes to the rescue. The plant communities on the two types of substratum are not at all alike because the glacial material consists of coarse gravel whereas the recent material is composed of fine-grained loam which the Weser brings primarily from loess regions. The vegetation map, in this case, not only shows important edaphic variations in the landscape but it helps materially in solving problems in historical geology as well.

In the United States, BRAUN (1950) established relations between physiography and vegetation. In her book on the deciduous forests of eastern North America, the map of the physiographic provinces shows the same boundaries as the map of the vegetation. The area is vast and BRAUN may not always be convincing, but the numerous parallels between physiography and vegetation certainly are so striking as to invite further investigations.

In Alabama, HARPER (1943) used geological data as a basis for a vegetation map of his state and so showed the close correlations between the geological and phytocenological features of the region. However, his map scale is small (1:4,000,000) and hence highly generalized. In contrast, DAVIS (1943) used a much larger scale (1:400,000) to relate the character and distribution of the vegetation in southern Florida to geology, soils, and groundwater. His detailed map was a great success and has been quoted many times.

Vegetation maps and geological maps often disagree because the latter show the age rather than the quality of the rocks. A lithological map is much more revealing to phytocenologists, for it makes a great deal of difference to plant communities whether the substratum is limestone or shale, but whether such materials are of triassic or cretaceous age is largely irrelevant. Many a graduate student of geology would welcome a project like preparing a detailed lithological map of his county at a scale of 1:50,000 and thereby pave the way for much collaboration in research among geologists and phytocenologists.

A final example for the usefulness of vegetation maps in geology may be found in the growing interest in vegetation as an indicator of commercially valuable minerals. Thus CANNON (1960) writes: "Botanical methods of prospecting for uranium on the Colorado Plateau have been developed by the U.S. Geological Survey. Detailed investigation has shown that a relation exists between the distribution of mineralized ground and of specific herbaceous plants. The distribution of these plants is controlled by the presence of selenium, sulfur, and other trace elements available in the environment of the uranium deposit. Investigation also has shown that the uranium content of trees rooted in ore is significantly higher than that of trees rooted in barren ground. On the flat-lying sediments at lower altitudes of the Colorado Plateau there is a definite correlation between major plant zones and stratigraphic units. Chemical differences that occur in a mineralized area within a formation produce, on the other hand, recognizable changes in the plant societies, which may be useful as indicators in prospecting. Information concerning the availability of ions in an ore environment and the absorption of ions by plant species is important in the development of botanical prospecting techniques."

Anthropogenic Changes

A different aspect of the vegetation-soil relations derives from man's interference in the landscape. Assume that the lower half of a gently sloping forested area is cleared and planted to grains and row crops. The effect will become apparent in spite of the slight gradient because, on the fields, the exposed top soil will be removed by wind and water faster than in the forest. It may take but a few human generations before the ploughed and cultivated soil is no longer the same as in the adjacent forest. The process is irreversible. The potential natural vegetation of today will no longer be uniform for there are two sites now where there used to be only one. The differences may be minor. In northeastern Kansas, for instance, the potential natural vegetation will still be oak-hickory forest or bluestem prairie (KÜCHLER, 1964). But the finer divisions and subdivisions in the floristic composition of the lowest synusias will reveal the differences unfailingly.

The numerous and varied relations between phytocenoses and their substrata certainly offer a researcher rich rewards. Many observations on these relations, especially in agriculture and forestry, have resulted in a growing use of vegetation maps. But in fact, there is so far only a modest beginning, and the future holds great promise for those who will explore these relations more fully.

29

Agriculture

In the United States, much has been said in recent years about the agricultural surplus. This leads to the impression that (1) our agriculture now has reached such a state of perfection that we can easily produce more than we need and (2) there is little need for further improvement. It can therefore be asked legitimately, What need is there for spending large sums on further agricultural research?

On the surface, the two impressions seem indeed valid but they represent only one aspect in the complex agricultural life of the world today. Our abundance is sadly balanced by hunger, malnutrition and deficiencies in so many parts of the globe that more than half of mankind is actually suffering. Furthermore, the number of people in the world is increasing at such a rate that overproduction in one area is largely meaningless in the world as a whole.

Viewed from another angle, agriculture has changed during recent years in many parts of the world. Whereas farming used to be a way of life it is now assuming more and more the character of an industry. An industry must be viable in a competitive market or else it must obtain special considerations from the government, such as price supports, tariff regulations, etc. Where these conditions are not met, the industry will fail and cease.

The revolutionary character of our era implies instability and a constant need for adjustment; but as the world has changed from a number of more or less self-sufficient regions into an ever more tightly knit unit, events anywhere on the globe, be they physical, economic, political or sociological, affect agriculture at home. The result of this development is that now, more than ever, there is a need to assess the character of the land correctly, discover more accurately what its real potential is, avoid wasteful means of production, adjust to market requirements, study means to sustain high yields indefinitely, and improve the productivity of the land rather than mine the soil or permit erosion to carry it away.

Good agricultural land, i.e., land with a high potential for the production of crops and livestock, is a precious commodity, and its value will rise as the demand for food and industrial crops grows and more valuable farmland falls prey to urbanization. For instance, Santa Clara County in California, once one of the most productive agricultural counties in the nation, has become much industrialized, and many of the industries, towns, and highways are sprawling over what used to be some of the very best farmlands.

Modern technology is therefore not only a boon to agriculture; it is also a threat. It combines with the high cost of machinery, keen competition in the world market, government regulations and, of course, the traditional hazards of the weather to force the farmer into a position in which only the most rational and efficient land use and means of production can keep him solvent and within reasonable limits of economic stability.

The Farmer's Knowledge of His Land

One of the basic conditions for this is an intimate knowledge of the land and its potential. The farmer, of course, knows his land better than any one else, but the land must now be viewed in the light of modern conditions in a complex technological world. A study of the vegetation is one way to become aware of variations and differences in the character and quality of the sites on which the crops are produced, differences that can affect the yields directly.

As the revolutionary changes of our times exert their increasing pressures on the farmer from all sides, he becomes more intricately enmeshed in a technological economy over which he has no control, and the various facets of which he finds difficult to comprehend. Increasingly, he comes to rely on outsiders, on experts in specialized fields, scientists at agricultural experiment stations, chemists and geneticists, technicians and government agents. In addition, he is harrassed by hordes of representatives from commercial concerns who explain why he can no longer afford to do without their goods, and these goods come in a bewildering variety of machinery, fertilizers, herbicides, pesticides, crop insurance, and feeds with chlortetracycline, sulfamethazine, and a host of equally baffling admixtures.

The one stabilizing factor in the farmer's life is his land, the biotopes on which he produces his crops. In the last analysis, this is the most critical factor in this whole business of farming. The land is there, season after season, awaiting his treatment and his care.

All types of actual vegetation, both natural and anthropogenic, must fit into their respective biotopes in order to survive. Crop plants have an advantage over wild plants: they have man to help them fight competition which usually spells the difference between life and death. Most crop plants would be crushed by their native competitors in a remarkably short time. With man's help, however, the only remaining question is whether the site qualities correspond to the exigencies of the crop plants. If this is so, such crop plants are in harmony with their environment. They can be expected to produce good yields and hence be economically sound, market conditions permitting. Crops of this kind are ecologically adjusted to their sites and there is no need to alter the environment. The application of fertilizer should not be taken as an alteration of the environment, it is rather a replacement of substances removed.

Modifying the Environment

Man had discovered long ago that many crop plants would be economically justifiable in an unsuited environment if it could be modified to overcome its disadvantages. Thus steep slopes can be terraced, wet lands can be drained, dry lands can be irrigated, periodically flooded areas can be protected with dikes, etc. Such modifications are worthwhile if their cost and undesirable side effects do not outweigh the resulting beneficial effects. In such a landscape, therefore, given crop plants are potentially in harmony with the environment. They become economically feasible only after man establishes this harmony between the crop plants and their sites by modifying the latter. For completeness' sake, it must be mentioned that there are areas unsuited to given crop plants and in which melioration is not feasible because it would be economically unsound. However, a division of agricultural land into suitable, potentially suitable and unsuitable areas is not fixed and a progressing technology may bring about shifts in the future as, indeed, it has in the past.

The vegetation mapper has become deeply involved in agricultural problems and his contributions can be of considerable value. His maps reveal first of all what plant communities exist, their location and their extent. In addition, vegetation maps reveal conditions and site qualities. Finally, on the basis of the foregoing, they often permit conclusions on the possibilities for melioration.

As a matter of convenience, the vegetation mapper usually divides all agricultural land into two types: (1) the areas with messicol vegetation, i.e., cropland, including cultivated and fallow fields, orchards, vineyards, market gardens, etc., and (2) the various kinds of grasslands and ranges, i.e., all types of pastures.

Optimum Land Use

Thanks to progress, the farmer can now change land unsuited to crop production into suitable land, and he can increase the yields to levels undreamed of even as little as one generation ago. But the biotopes are the same: river bottoms, uplands, level land and slopes, northern and southern exposures, clay soils and sand. The farmer may be using all manner of modern devices but the biotopes are the same and the farmer must continue to take them into account, now more than ever. To the gross contrasts between biotopes are added the fine variations and nuances and all must be considered in managing the land. The more intensive farming becomes, the more the farmer must be aware of the features of his land, even the very delicate ones.

The vegetation mapper cannot tell the farmer how to farm, but he can tell him what there is, where it is, and the extent of it. He can tell him which sites may be considered alike and hence likely to succeed (or fail) uniformly throughout the combined areas of these sites. The farmer and his agronomical advisers can then decide what to do under the given circumstances. In the vast plains of the central United States, individual farmers cultivate many hundreds and even thousands of acres. Extensive cultivation ignores the features of the landscape and the farmer will show little inclination for a refinement of his methods. The relatively cheap mechanical production may imply low yields but a narrow profit margin is acceptable if only the farmer controls a sufficient number of acres. This is a wasteful manner of farming and there is a question whether even an "opulent society" can afford to tolerate waste.

Intensive farming implies a much finer coordination between the farmer and his land. Detailed information on the character of each biotope on the farm is useful and more likely to be applied. On intensively cultivated fields, planted to annual crops like grains, soy beans, cotton, vegetables, flax, etc., the crops have replaced the natural vegetation and such competitors as weeds are removed by proper methods of cultivation. Even so, weeds may be plentiful and permit the vegetation mapper to delimit areas of different character with the help of weed communities. All too often, the value of weeds is overlooked. Like all other plants, weeds do not grow just anywhere, and they, too, occur in definite combinations. These weed communities may be the best indicators of the conditions of the cultivated soil, revealing areas of equal potential yield, whether of crops already planted or to be planted. Weed communities must be observed quite completely because many weeds are ubiquitous, having wide ranges of tolerance. The mapping of weed communities is increasingly difficult as more efficient herbicides keep the fields clean. The rotation of crops adds to the control of weeds. For instance, a field in northeastern Kansas, planted to milo for a number of years, became infested with Johnson grass (*Sorghum halepense*). This noxious weed was eradicated within three years by changing from milo to winter wheat and repeated cultivation after the wheat harvest.

The usefulness of vegetation maps in agriculture becomes more obvious where perennial crops are produced, as in orchards, vineyards, pastures, etc. The masterly contribution by ELLENBERG and ZELLER (1951) has already been discussed in Chapter 23; it is devoted above all to orchardists and represents one of the most successful techniques in relating vegetation mapping to agricultural pursuits. One of the stated goals of this work was to assure the farmer the greatest possible sustained yields, and hence income, on the basis of a rational ecological use of all available biotopes. It has remained unsurpassed among the scientific publications of its kind.

In tropical regions, tree and shrub plantations (coconuts, coffee, oil palms, rubber, etc.) parallel the orchards (apples, cherries, apricots, etc.) of the middle latitudes. Orcharding is usually considered an intensive form of agriculture but the areas involved in individual establishments may be very large in all latitudes; the giant fig and peach orchards of up to 16,000 hectares (40,000 acres) in the Central Valley of California are a case in point.

Range Management

The distribution in the landscape and the yields of pastures and meadows reflect a close relationship to biotopes more readily than cultivated fields do. The composition of ranges is not usually determined by man; it is more generally the result of natural selection in which only those species survive that can compete successfully on the given biotopes and at the same time withstand the harsh treatment by man and beast. Grazing and trampling, burning, mowing and sometimes fertilizing may all be practiced individually or in combination, but in the course of years the ranges become adjusted to such conditions and can be remarkably stable. Vegetation mappers often find that they must map range lands at large scales because the herbaceous vegetation responds readily to minor variations in site qualities (cf. Chapter 16). Small-scale maps of grasslands can only be very generalized. Until fairly recently, the vast ranges of the western United States, Argentina, Australia, Africa, and the Soviet Union (to name but a few) were relatively natural, having evolved through very long periods. Intensified use, especially during the last hundred years has profoundly affected these grasslands, and all too often the change has been for the worse. The pastures were overgrazed, undesirable species immigrated and spread at the expense of desirable ones, some of the top soil was carried away by wind and water, and altogether the value of the great ranges declined. Today scientific investigations can reveal several important facts. It is now possible to establish within reasonable limits the potential natural vegetation of an area. The requirements and tolerances of species can be determined, as well as their nutritive value. It is therefore possible to observe quite accurately the degree to which a range has been damaged.

A vegetation map can therefore reveal the carrying capacity of different parts of the range according to the conditions and quality of the component species. It can also help a great deal in the rehabilitation of run-down ranges and maintenance of a high level of production by showing the character of the sites, what species to employ in reseeding the range, what plant communities to promote in order to control undesirable species, and to assure a maximum water supply. This last point is particularly important in most of the great grasslands of the world and the water relations of the plant communities stimulate some of the most significant and rewarding studies. These include such topics as precipitation and run-off, water holding capacity of the soil, quality, fluctuation and movements of the ground water, and the calibration of phytocenoses with regard to these water features.

The Phytocenology of Grasslands

Man can help himself appreciably by promoting the economically most valuable grasses of the available biotopes. If he plants other grasses, they may at first succeed very well but eventually they are apt to decline. Their competition retards the development of the better adjusted grasses and the yields may therefore be low for years. SCHMITHÜSEN (1942) reports an experiment in which 4 different mixtures of grass seeds corresponded to four specific meadow types. All four mixtures were sown on the biotopes of two of these meadow types. In each instance, the seed mixture that corresponded to the biotope was easily the most productive. The others were not only less productive but in the course of years their floristic composition evolved toward the type that fitted the biotope. Much research has been done in Europe concerning the phytocenology of grasslands (hay meadows, pastures, etc.). A few examples will be illustrative.

The state government of (then) Baden in southwestern Germany had all grasslands of the Upper Rhine Plain located in that state mapped phytocenologically. The object of so vast an undertaking was to determine the effects of canal construction in Alsace, west of the Rhine, on the quality and yields of the grasslands in Baden east of the Rhine. The grasslands were mapped on numerous topographic sheets at 1:25,000. From these, a new vegetation map at 1:100,000 was then compiled which showed the biotopes of the grassland area with their respective phytocenoses. The map revealed that the latter were not scattered helter skelter but that certain plant communities dominated in certain landscapes, being absent elsewhere. The vegetation map served as a basis for further investigations which required hydrological, geological and meteorological data. The results not only fulfilled the expectations but, in addition, permitted a better insight into the water balance of the region, the intake and loss of water and the forces bearing on these (KRAUSE, 1954a).

In the Black Forest, KRAUSE (1954b) used vegetation maps of grasslands near timberline for a detailed ecological analysis and successfully related it to local land-use problems. TÜXEN and PREISING (1951), ELLENBERG (1952), and others worked along similar lines in northern Germany.

A novel use of vegetation maps was introduced in the Crau region of southern France where hay of a particular type and quality is highly esteemed and which therefore commands a high price. Gradually, hay from other regions and of inferior quality was sold under the name of the better hay. The government was asked to regulate the matter and the result was a vegetation map which indicated the floristic composition of the meadows. One could then see at a glance where and only where the superior hay could be produced. The use of the name of the better hay is now restricted to the proper areas (MOLINIER, 1951).

KÖNEKAMP and WEISE (1952), in their study of grasslands, asked themselves what kind of information they would like to obtain from vegetation maps. They formulated the following five questions, to which they sought the answers on their maps: (1) Where is it more economical to change grasslands into (a) cultivated fields or (b) forests? (2) Where is it most economical to maintain grasslands even though other land use is feasible? (3) How far may drainage and melioration projects go in lowering the water table? (4) Can yields be raised through special procedures and what is the yield potential of grasslands? (5) What procedures should be followed?

They submitted their detailed vegetation map of a meadow to an agronomist who, upon analyzing it, observed, concluded, and recommended as follows:

1. At present the meadow yields only 0.66 tons of hay per acre annually.
2. The application of fertilizer will lead to a slow improvement of the quality of the hay. The increase in yield will be unsatisfactory and is unlikely to exceed 1.3 tons of hay per acre.
3. The application of fertilizer combined with controlled grazing will lead to a slow improvement but drought damage during the summer becomes a serious hazard.
4. It will be more economical to plough up the meadow and plant it to alfalfa, which should yield approximately 2.6 tons per acre.

KNAPP (1949) demonstrates various aspects of phytocenological interpretation with an example of a meadow and its floristic composition.

Table 26 lists the species of which the meadow is composed and their coverage expressed in percentage of the area.

Table 26 *

	Coverage (%)
Grasses and Grasslike Plants:	
Poa pratensis ssp. angustifolia	60
Arrhenatherum elatius	15
Dactylis glomerata	8
Agropyron repens	3
Festuca rubra var. genuina	2
Avena pubescens	2
Luzula campestris	+
Clover Species and Related Plants:	
Trifolium pratense	3
Lotus corniculatus	1
Vicia sepium	1
Lathyrus pratensis	+
Medicago lupulina	+
Vicia cracca	+
Other Forbs:	
Achillea millefolium	1
Pastinaca sativa	1
Rumex acetosa	+
Leontodon hispidus	+
Daucus carota	+
Campanula patula	+
Veronica chamaedrys	+
Ranunculus acer	+
Galium mollugo	+
Silaus pratensis	+
Plantago media	+
Prunella vulgaris	+
Cerastium caespitosum	+
Saxifraga granulata	+
Salvia pratensis	+
Taraxacum officinale	+
Viola hirta	+
Plantago lanceolata	+
Euphorbia esula ssp. pinifolia	+
Scabiosa ochroleuca	r
Galium verum	r
Melandrium album	r
Geranium pratense	r
Crepis biennis	r
Ranunculus bulbosus	r

* After KNAPP (1949).

A trained phytocenologist can glean from this table in what type of climate this meadow grows, and if he was trained in Germany, he can even deduce the particular German region where this meadow must occur.

The presence of *Daucus carota*, *Pastinaca sativa*, *Silaus pratensis*, and *Salvia pratensis* shows that in central Europe this meadow cannot be in the mountains. It must be in an area where the climate is characterized by higher temperatures (average annual temperature over 7° C) and a longer growing season (lilac must bloom not later than the end of May). The presence of *Campanula patula* and *Salvia pratensis* excludes the north-western part of Europe with its marine climate and cool moist summers. The absence of *Bromus erectus* makes it unlikely that the meadow is in southern or southwestern central Europe. There remain only the plains of eastern central Europe in which this meadow can occur. The presence of *Scabiosa ochroleuca* indicates that within these plains the meadow must be in a relatively dry area where the mean annual precipitation does not exceed 550 millimeters, because only there does *Scabiosa ochroleuca* have enough power to expand and maintain itself in such a meadow. Within Germany, the only possible areas are the region around Magdeburg and the adjacent parts towards the Southeast, east of the Harz mountains.

Concerning the management of this meadow, the presence of *Arrhenatherum elatius, Daucus carota, Pastinaca sativa, Crepis biennis,* and *Geranium pratense* shows that this meadow is mowed consistently. The complete absence of species that are characteristic for pastures confirms this and shows that grazing is not practiced.

The yield of hay should be some 4,000–4,500 kilograms per hectare. The quality of the hay is relatively high although the prevalence of *Poa pratensis* makes it a little hard. The proportion of proper meadow weeds is remarkably low and forage grasses predominate. Next in line are clover types and forage forbs. It is decisive for the quality of the hay that the first crop of the year is cut early because *Poa pratensis* sprouts very early in the season and develops its inflorescences quickly and soon afterwards turns hard. For the second most common grass, the *Arrhenatherum elatius*, an early harvest is advantageous, too.

The floristic composition of the meadow indicates that the site is relatively dry. There are no plants that indicate a water supply adequate for the best hay yields. On the other hand, the insufficient moisture is shown by the presence of *Salvia pratensis, Viola hirta, Scabiosa ochroleuca, Galium verum,* and *Ranunculus bulbosus.* For this reason, conditions are more favorable for cultivated crops which could produce much larger profits. There are no plants indicating that the soil is shallow or stony to hinder ploughing and cultivating.

If, for whatever reason, the meadow is to be continued, higher yields can be attained only by irrigation or, at least to some degrees, by the application of organic fertilizer (compost, manure) which promotes the water holding capacity of the soil.

Finally, the presence of *Luzula campestris* and *Saxifraga granulata* indicates a slight shortage of lime.

This analysis illustrates how the phytocenologist can interpret the plant communities, shedding light on the critical site qualities and how agronomists and farmers can employ this information in their search for a more efficient land use and better yields.

The interpretation of the many plant communities and their pattern, as revealed on the vegetation map, gains in depth and comprehensiveness as more knowledge accumulates.   But even when the quality and quantity of the available information are highly satisfactory, the interpreter of the vegetation map must be careful to use this knowledge only in regions where it applies.

30

Forestry

Much has been said in recent years about the significance of site qualities and site classifications as applied to forestry. In fact, forestry is like agriculture where site qualities are of equal importance. Like agronomy, modern silviculture is fast becoming an applied science and more specifically, applied ecology. Basic research is needed in silviculture just as in all sciences, and according to ALLEN (1963), forester of the Weyerhaeuser Company, research in forestry has seriously lagged compared with that in agriculture but a turning point seems to have been reached.

All-inclusive Vegetation Mapping

Only a comprehensive recording and mapping of *all* synusias by life forms and taxa will permit an adequate recognition of phytocenoses. This implies specifically that foresters must map not only trees but also what is underneath: the shrubs and forbs, including even the mosses, etc. Foresters are, of course, primarily interested in trees, but tree species often have broad ecological tolerances and will occur on various biotopes. It happens therefore quite regularly that the finer distinctions between site qualities are shown much more effectively by the herbaceous synusias. Such complete mapping applies not only to more or less natural forests but also to semi-natural ones and even to plantation forests.

The vegetation mapper maps first the actual vegetation. This is the logical and necessary first step. There follows then the preparation of maps showing the potential natural vegetation, and from the point of view of the silviculturist, it is these latter that best serve as the basic documents for his manysided activities. The maps of the potential natural vegetation are his points of reference. The reason why these maps are of such fundamental value for the silviculturist is that they reveal what the forest on a given site could and should be like.

THILL (1961) lists four items as being basic for rational silviculture.

363

(1) Recognition of phytocenoses; this includes actual and potential natural vegetation; (2) the site qualities as related to the established phytocenoses; (3) tree reproduction and forest regeneration as related to points 1 and 2; (4) productivity and yields as related to points 1, 2, and 3. The vegetation maps are the basic expression of point 1 and thus become the very foundation of the entire structure of silviculture and forest economics.

One of the basic differences between forestry and any other form of land use is the time involved to produce a crop. Grasslands and cultivated fields permit a harvest a few months after sowing or planting and the much slower orchards and vineyards after a few years. But in the case of forestry it is not unusual to deal with one, two, or even three human generations before a crop has matured to its greatest value.

This places the forester in a difficult position. He must know just how to manage his forests, select his trees (or tree seeds), utilize whatever habitats are at his disposal, and plan for a harvest 30–80 years from planting time. A mistake may not be recognized until decades have passed and the resulting losses can be severe. No quick correction is possible, for any change of direction again takes long periods before producing the desired results.

The forester is therefore extremely interested in the character of his area and he must know climate and soil in detail and as comprehensively as possible. As the environment cannot be grasped in all its facets, it is both simpler and more useful to start with the actual vegetation. Plant communities portray faithfully whatever benefits an environment may offer, as well as its limitations. Large-scale vegetation maps permit a clear mapping of trees, and also of the undergrowth and even the ground cover, and are the surest device for understanding the nature of the local environmental conditions. With such vegetation maps at hand the forester can avoid many mistakes, and at the same time manage the forest for a sustained maximum yield.

Selection of Crops and Management Methods

One of the silviculturist's important activities that can be based on the interpretation of vegetation maps is the selection of tree species, even if these are not native to his area. If a given tree species is to be promoted because of the demand for its wood, then the first step should be to consult a vegetation map. The purpose of this is to determine what areas are available and suitable for this particular species, their extent and accessibility.

The most desirable forest stand not only produces a maximum amount of wood but the wood must have good quality, and the forest must remain productive through decades and, indeed, more or less indefinitely. It is therefore important that the forest consist of tree species which are best adapted to the given site and the forester must select only those species for which this site furnishes ecologically optimal growth conditions. Some tree species may be damaging the soil, especially if the trees are not native to the region or are planted in pure stands. As soon as the herbaceous ground cover indicates such a danger, a new map should be prepared to establish the extent of the area affected.

According to SCHMITHÜSEN (1942), accurate ecological studies of various sites have shown that the introduction of exotic tree species into a given phytocenose can harm the latter by adversely affecting the soil, or in some other fashion. For instance, in northwestern Europe, the beech (*Fagus silvatica*) was planted on sites where it was not native. Its foliage turned strongly acid and formed an undesirable raw humus. In nearby areas where the beech belonged, this either did not happen at all or only to a negligible extent. It is even better known that the spruce (*Picea excelsa*), when planted where it is not native, may at first produce a high yield per acre. At the same time, it can ruin the soil by the formation of raw humus, by podsolization, or compaction and gleization. In addition, there are many observations to demonstrate that tree species exotic to a given biotope are more susceptible to pests and diseases than the native species or than the introduced species are in their home region. Large-scale vegetation maps can reveal sites that can be classified according to their capabilities and their potential productivity. Silviculture adapted to the site potentials is apt to succeed, whereas the danger of failure increases the less the silvicultural methods and the species involved are adjusted to the sites. This makes the wood unduly expensive. For instance, considerable funds may be needed to suppress broadleaved tree species where their biotopes are planted to pines as in parts of New England or the southeastern United States.

The idea of mapping the vegetation of an area periodically, perhaps every ten or twenty years, is particularly valuable where the forest is not closely related to the climax communities. For the proper recognition of a successive stage in the development of the forest has an important bearing on forest management.

This, in turn, leads to the afforestation of deforested land where the introduction of species of the native climax has repeatedly led to failure. Sometimes it seems necessary to get one of the earlier successional stages established first and, in the protection of this, proceed to plant the species that are ultimately to make up the forest composition. In the Karst Mountains of northwest Yugoslavia, it has been found necessary, in a number of instances, to sow grass on the denuded areas and thus provide first a more or less continuous plant cover before pioneer shrubs and trees can be established successfully (WRABER, 1963).

A vegetation map will also reveal information concerning the forestation of non-stocked areas and the reforestation of cut-over sections. In this case, it is particularly important to know the implications of the vegetation and especially its history. AICHINGER (1954) gives two examples to illustrate this point.

A clear-cut area had become occupied by the *Epilobium angustifolium-Senecio silvaticus* association (Tx. 1937). The unsuspecting forester who sees only the present community might easily select the wrong tree species for afforestation because it so happens that this particular association gets established on clear-cut areas of at least three different forest types. In analysis of the vegetation, the previous community should therefore be given too, to guide the forester in his next steps. Employing AICHINGER's method, the description of the *Epilobium* community must be a phase of any one of three seres:

1. Querceto-Betuletum ⤓ *Epilobium angustifolium–Senecio silvaticus* Ass. Tx. 1937;*
2. Piceetum hercynicum ⤓ *Epilobium angustifolium–Senecio silvaticus* Ass. Tx. 1937;
3. Fagetum boreoatlanticum luzuletosum ⤓ *Epilobium angustifolium–Senecio silvaticus* Ass. Tax. 1937.

As the same *Epilobium* community can follow various predecessors, it is important for the forester to know its origin in his particular area so as not to be misled in his efforts at reforestation.

The other one of AICHINGER's examples refers to two heaths which evolved from different forest origins: (1) Pinetum mugi myrtillosum turfosum ⤓ Vaccinietum myrtilli ↓ Nardetum strictae turfosum ↗ Callunetum, and (2) Laricetum deciduae silicicolum myrtillosum ⤓ Vaccinietum myrtilli ↓ Nardetum strictae ↗ Callunetum. Obviously, the two heaths require different management but in this instance a four-step succession must be recognized before the difference between the two sites is adequately indicated by the vegetation.

The significance and usefulness of vegetation maps in reforestation in denuded karst and limestone mountains was discussed by WRABER (1963). Detailed studies showed that the protection of the countryside against floods and erosion can be a more important function of reforestation than the production of immediate economic returns by lumbering and grazing etc. Foresters and agronomists are sometimes slow in accepting this point of view. The studies further revealed that forests must be of adequate size to fulfill their functions and that some agricultural land may have to be included in the areas to be reforested.

* See Chapter 17, p. 214, for an explanation of AICHINGER's arrow symbols.

WESTVELD (1954), with long silvicultural experience in New England, concludes with the Europeans that the ground cover under the trees is of particular value to foresters: "A ground-vegetation type map is the practical equivalent of a type management map. Therein lies its real value, for ground-vegetation types can be translated directly into site potentialities.

"Not only do vegetation types provide the index to timber yield potentials, but they also provide a sound basis for proper orientation of silvicultural goals. Knowing where the most favorable site types occur for the growth of specific tree species is one of the principal requisites of profitable timber production.

"For example, the ground vegetation type equivalent to the red spruce–yellow birch type is *Oxalis-Cornus*. Even should the present tree cover, owing to past cutting practices, consist mainly of hardwoods, the presence of *Oxalis acetosella* and *Cornus canadensis*, key indicators of soft wood sites when they occur in combination, warns the forester against managing primarily for hardwoods. Here silviculture should be aimed at reestablishing the normal softwood representation."

An Index to Timber Yield

WESTVELD's observation of the relation between timber yield potentials and site qualities as indicated by the herbaceous synusia on the forest floor is well illustrated by an example given by KNAPP (1949).

The task is to relate the timber yield of oaks as expressed in the height of the mature trees to the plant communities in which the oaks occur. In a large and uniformly managed oak-mixed forest, 20 quadrats of 25 square meters each are selected and the floristic composition of the vegetation recorded. The height of the oak trees in each quadrat is measured and the results of the quadrat investigations are given in a table; the quadrats are arranged consecutively so as to show an increasing height of the trees from left to right (Table 27).

The species associated with the oaks can be arranged into four groups. In the examined area the species of group I show no relation to the height of the oaks. A number of species in this group has been omitted from this table. Those of group II occur on sites where the annual increment of oaks is the least. The first species of this group are limited to the most unfavorable sites; they are followed by others which penetrate into progressively more favorable sites. The two species in group III are absent from the poorest sites as well as from the best one. The species of group IV, too, are missing on the poorer sites. The further down they appear in the table, the more are they limited to sites where the oaks grow best.

As a result of this study it is possible to estimate the height of the

Table 27. Height of Trees (*Quercus robur*) correlated

Height of Oaks in m:	17,5	18,5	19,0	19,5	21,0	21,5	21,5
I. Stellaria holostea	r	+	+	+	+	+	+
Fagus silvatica	+	r	+	+	+	+	+
Vicia sepium	+	r	+	+	+	|	+
Quercus robur	+	+	r	+	r	+	+
Poa nemoralis	+	|	+	+	+	+	+
Lonicera xylosteum	r	+	.	+	+	.	+
Carpinus betulus	.	+	r	r	.	r	r
Potentilla sterilis	.	+	+	.	r	+	+
Catharinaea undulata	|	+	+	+	r	+	.
II. Veronica officinalis	+	.	.	.	.	.	.
Hieracium boreale	r	.	.	.	.	.	.
Rhytidiadelphus triquetrus	+	+	.	.	.	.	.
Hieracium murorum	+	+	.	.	.	.	.
Hylocomium proliferum	+	+	|	r	.	.	.
Dicranum scoparium	+	+	+	+	.	.	.
Festuca ovina	2	|	2	|	r	.	.
Campanula persicifolia	+	+	+	+	+	.	.
Polytrichum attenuatum	+	+	+	+	r	r	+
Brachypodium pinnatum	|	|	+	2	2	2	2
Carex montana	|	|	2	2	|	|	|
III. Luzula pilosa	.	.	.	+	r	+	+
Carex umbrosa	.	.	.	.	+	+	|
IV. Milium effusum	.	.	.	.	.	+	+
Asperula odorata	.	.	.	.	.	.	.
Viola silvatica	.	.	.	.	.	.	.
Carex silvatica	.	.	.	.	.	.	.
Festuca gigantea	.	.	.	.	.	.	.
Carex remota	.	.	.	.	.	.	.
Daphne mezereum	.	.	.	.	.	.	.
Ranunculus ficaria	.	.	.	.	.	.	.

* After KNAPP (1949).

mature oaks quite accurately on the basis of the floristic composition of the individual herbaceous communities. If, for instance, in one such community, *Viola silvatica, Asperula odorata, Milium effusum, Carex montana,* and *Brachypodium pinnatum* are important, the height of the oaks will be 23–24 meters. Comparisons between estimates and measurements of the height of oaks gave the following results:

Estimated	Measured
18–18.5 m	18.5 m
22 m	22.0 m
25–27 m	25.5 m

Such indicator communities can obviously be calibrated accurately with regard to a given feature. Once this is done, they reveal the silvicultural potential even under different types of management. When the results of with Herbaceous Ground Cover in 20 Sample Plots°

22.0	22.0	23.0	23.5	24.0	24.5	25.0	26.0	26.0	26.0	26.5	27.0	29.0
r	+	l	+	+	+	+	l	+	+	+	+	+
+	+	+	l	+	`+	+	+	+	+	+	+	+
+	+	+	+	+	+	+	+	r	+	r	r	+
+	r	+	+	+	+	+	r	+	+	r	+	+
+	+	+	l	+	+	+	.	+	.	+	+	+
+	+	+	+	+	.	+	r	+	+	r	+	+
.	.	r	+	+	r	+	r	+	+	r	+	r
+	+	.	r	+	l	+	.	+	+	+	+	.
r	.	+	.	.	+	+	+	.	.	+	+	+
.	.	.	.	.	.	.	.	.	.	.	.	.
.	.	.	.	.	.	.	.	.	.	.	.	.
.	.	.	.	.	.	.	.	.	.	.	.	.
.	.	.	.	.	.	.	.	.	.	.	.	.
.	.	.	.	.	.	.	.	.	.	.	.	.
.	.	.	.	.	.	.	.	.	.	.	.	.
.	.	.	.	.	.	.	.	.	.	.	.	.
.	.	.	.	.	.	.	.	.	.	.	.	.
+	r	.	.	.	.	.	.	.	.	.	.	.
l	+	l	2	l	.	.	.	.	.	.	.	.
+	+	l	2	.	+	.	.	.	.	.	.	.
+	+	+	+	r	.	.	l	+	+	l	l	.
.	r	.	+	l	+	+	l	l	+	l	+	.
+	+	+	+	+	+	l	l	l	l	l	l	+
l	l	+	.	+	l	l	l	l	l	l	l	l
+	l	.	r	+	r	l	+	r	+	+	+	+
.	.	.	.	.	.	l	l	l	r	+	l	+
.	.	.	.	.	.	+	.	+	r	+	+	+
.	.	.	.	.	.	.	+	r	r	r	r	+
.	.	.	.	.	.	.	.	.	.	.	.	+
.	.	.	.	.	.	.	.	.	.	.	.	+

many such studies become available, the relation between the floristic composition of the plant communities and the economic possibilities can be determined.

Of course, there are exceptions to the rule. If, for instance, the upper and lower layers of the substratum are quite unlike, and the upper layer is so thick as to reach beyond the roots of the forbs, then a herbaceous vegetation reflects only the upper horizons and the usefulness of the land for tree growth can not be gleaned from the lowest synusias.

An Essential, Versatile Silvicultural Tool

A leading forester of Oregon, working for the Weyerhaeuser Timber Company, considers the vegetation maps of the company's holdings one of the best investments the company ever made.* He found that a vegetation map is to the forester what a house plan is for a builder, permitting a detailed analysis of every part of the forest. He also observed that vegetation maps eliminate guess work and save large expenditures by showing location, extent and outline of areas involving pest control, volume estimates, thinning, fire control, etc., and discovered that a vegetation map serves many purposes unsuspected before it was available. MRAZ and SAMEK (1963) confirm that vegetation maps are economical even when their preparation is expensive.

In many parts of Europe vegetation maps have become essential tools in forestry and in California a state forester concluded that silviculture without vegetation maps has become unthinkable.

Where forestry is practiced as an intensive form of land use, the need for detail on vegetation maps can be considerable. For instance, TRAUT-MANN (1963) mapped forests in detail and found it useful to divide the subassociation Querco-Carpinetum athyrietosum into several dozen (!) subdivisions in order to adequately serve the needs of the silviculturists. He mapped at scales of 1:5,000 and somewhat smaller. THILL (1961) reports that the Centre de cartographie phytosociologique is mapping the vegetation of Belgium at a scale of 1:20,000. This, he says, is the scale adopted for the entire nation but it is sometimes too small to reveal all desirable details. Those interested are therefore free to inspect the unpublished manuscript maps on file, which are prepared at 1:10,000 and even at 1:2,500. According to HORVAT (1963), the Hungarian Forest Service maps the forests within its jurisdiction at 1:10,000.

Tropical Forests

New problems are added when the vegetation mapper must work in the humid tropics.

In many tropical countries, an interest in the character and meaning of the vegetation has been awakened because the increasing populations and the growing demands for tropical raw materials require a more rational land use. In the past, slowly growing or stagnant population figures permitted an indifference toward vegetation which extended from the various government agencies even into the rank and file of the scientists. The changes we are witnessing today all over the tropical world are dramatic, and scientists from non-tropical countries have a real share of the responsibility for the direction these changes are taking. It is true, of course, that a considerable number of excellent men have been studying the tropical vegetation for some time and in some detail. In spite of considerable

---

* Thomas J. Orr, during a field trip with the author on July 20, 1956.

achievements, however, much remains to be done. Indeed, in many regions little more is known than the barest distinctions between forests and savannas if, in fact, any information is available at all.

Vegetation maps are now obtainable for all parts of the world. However, most maps are on a very small scale and therefore imply a degree of generalization which makes them useless for most forestry purposes. An extensive mapping program of all tropical vegetation would be most useful and such maps can be prepared at a scale of 1:1,000,000 or larger. GAUSSEN (1949) and KÜCHLER (1952) have discussed the possibility of mapping the vegetation of the world including the humid tropics at this scale. HUMBERT (1961) finds that the vegetation of Madagascar can be mapped at 1:1,000,000 and in India four vegetation maps have been published at this same scale (LEGRIS, 1962). To use the scale of 1:1,000,000 does not exclude vegetation maps at a larger scale. For instance, various sections of the Congo region have been mapped in considerable detail (DEVRED, 1960) and valuable vegetation maps are available at various scales for sections of Peru, Indonesia, West Africa, India, and elsewhere. But the amount to be done remains vast because so much of the tropical vegetation has never been mapped at all and the existing small-scale maps are based on travellers' reports rather than on actual mapping. Where vegetation maps do exist, their scale is often too small to reveal the desirable detail. Such maps are therefore useful primarily as guides for future and more accurate mapping. But the fact that good maps at small scales exist should not discourage future mapping. On the contrary, their very existence usually points to a real need for vegetation maps in these areas.

Indeed, this need is now very great in most tropical regions. Various national and international governmental and private agencies are making funds available for so-called developing areas, and whatever problems of land use are involved, the preparation of vegetation maps should be given a high priority. However, if this were to be done, an important question would arise immediately.

The forests of the humid tropics are characterized by a bewildering number of life forms and taxa. A large share of the latter remains unidentified. This creates real problems for the vegetation mapper and is one of the reasons why vegetation maps of tropical areas are either so highly generalized or unavailable. Mapping the forests in humid tropical areas is further complicated by inaccessibility. Progress must often be on foot, which is extremely time-consuming and limits the mapper to his most immediate environment. In addition, base maps are often unavailable or unreliable. Aerial photographs assume therefore a particular significance and BENNETT (1963) has discussed the advantages of light aircraft in mapping tropical forests. But aerial photographs cannot replace studies on the ground.

The chief purpose of a broad approach is above all to permit the actual mapping of vegetation, especially where highly organized systems cannot be readily applied. What is particularly important here is to have the vegetation mapped at all. Once the different types are outlined on a map at 1:1,000,000 or larger, the more important ones can be singled out for further study. In this manner, our knowledge of the tropical vegetation is gradually deepened, slowly perhaps, but nevertheless surely.

A splendid example of utilizing every possible means at hand to map the vegetation of a country in the humid tropics was given by WYATT-SMITH (1962) in Malaya. It is not in any sense a conventional map, as it does not follow any of the traditional methods. Admittedly, it is a provisional map, but it is valuable for two reasons: it is a splendid beginning for an eventual vegetation map as needed for the development of the country and it reveals as no other map what problems await a vegetation mapper in equatorial regions and how to attack them. For this latter reason, the vegetation map of Malaya has already become a classic.

Vegetation mappers from the temperate middle latitudes are reminded that tropical vegetation is usually more complex in behavior than the vegetation in cooler climates. This implies that some terms, coined in the middle latitudes, may not always fit tropical conditions well, as for example the term "deciduous."

The contrast between "evergreen" and "deciduous" seems clear: the former means that plants bear green leaves throughout the year, and the latter means that they do not. For instance, in the beech-maple forests of Ohio, all trees will lose their leaves at about the same time and remain bare until, at the appropriate time in the spring, they all produce their new foliage. All members of a species act in unison: all have their leaves or none have their leaves. This may be called the "classical" form of deciduousness.

In the tropics, it is entirely normal that plants do not exhibit a common rhythm, as do plants in the higher latitudes. For instance, in northern Thailand, three specimens of *Dipterocarpus tuberculatus* were observed simultaneously, one with last year's foliage, one bare, and one with new foliage fully developed. In the same area, *Dipterocarpus obtusifolius* was evergreen throughout the year, although it is usually deciduous. On the other hand, the teak tree (*Tectona grandis*) is deciduous in northern Thailand but evergreen near Bangkok, implying different behavior in different regions; such regions merge gradually and have no clear boundaries.

Another feature of tropical deciduousness is the difficulty of relating it to seasons. In the higher latitudes, the onset of the cold season with its shorter days induces deciduous plants to drop their leaves. In the low latitudes, such an adverse period is usually represented by the dry season. The length of day varies little, especially in equatorial regions. The drought, on the other hand, may be forbidding, and it is easy to see that survival seems best assured by remaining leafless until the return of the rain ends the danger of desiccation. Yet, numerous plants will unfold their young leaves at the height of the dry season, when heat and aridity are most intense.

Unless the vegetation mapper spends the entire year in the tropical region to be mapped, he may be unable to judge whether the phytocenoses are deciduous or not, even though he is working during the dry season. This certainly differs from conditions in the middle latitudes where, during the fall, winter, and early spring, one look may tell the observer the whole story.

In an effort to clarify the situation (at least for the record), it is proposed that the term "deciduous" be reserved for its "classical" form as described above. It is further suggested that the term "tropophyllous" be used for the irregular, indefinite, and unreliable forms of deciduousness as encountered in so many parts of the tropics. Such a distinction should often prove useful.

The term "tropophyllous" is not new and is usually employed as a synonym for "deciduous." It is derived from the Greek word *tropos* (turn) and *phyllon* (leaf). As here proposed, tropophyllous refers to plants that may, and usually do, lose their leaves during some period of each year without specifying the exact time or duration of this period. Tropophyllous plants may shed their leaves on an individual basis rather than as members of a species. The term "tropophyllous" can be applied to individual plants, to taxa, and to phytocenoses composed wholly or in part of such plants. Tropophyllous vegetation is very common in the tropics but does not occur in the higher latitudes.

Plant communities consisting of both evergreen and tropophyllous plants are found in all but the driest parts of the tropics but are best developed in regions with a short dry season. Such phytocenoses are best referred to as being semi-evergreen, not semi-deciduous.

The vegetation mapper produces evidence for site qualities; they become apparent on the vegetation map. But it is for the silviculturist to decide how to utilize these sites and what particular species, varieties, and ecotypes of forest trees to plant on these sites. This is not the task of the mapper. The latter can establish the phytocenoses, their extent and distribution. He can relate them to a complex interrelated and interacting set of environmental factors, although in this he will often find the collaboration of pedologists helpful, even necessary. But it is the silviculturist who knows the needs, requirements, and tolerances of the trees, and only he can determine the most appropriate and economical use of a given site at a given time.

31

Land Management and Planning

Vegetation maps are very useful tools in managing and planning the utilization of the land. The economic development of an area implies that present methods of exploiting the plant resources of a region can and must be improved to assure a greater yield and, indeed, one that can be sustained through the years. Therefore the economist needs information on climate and soil, on the natural vegetation, and on present land use. The economist has come to rely on statistics, but these do not reveal areal patterns. On the other hand, a vegetation map does just that and can express statistical material as well.

The use of vegetation maps in planning is predicated on the thesis that the vegetation is the most complete and comprehensive expression of site conditions and site qualities and a comprehensive inventory of these. Modern phytocenology has done more than to reveal the character and the geographical distribution of plant communities. It is gaining an increasingly deep insight into the living conditions of phytocenoses, and their requirements of and reactions to their sites, i.e., climate, soil, and land use. Once the exigencies of a phytocenose are understood, it is possible to conclude from its presence what the climatic, microclimatic, and edaphic conditions of its site must be. This information, in turn, reveals the potential land use. Much research is yet to be done if vegetation maps are to be exploited to the fullest, but it is already possible to use phytocenoses for measuring productivity, as for instance in the case of pastures, hay meadows, and various forest types.

Potential Natural Vegetation as a Guide to Planning

The value of vegetation maps to the planner is increased by the fact that such maps reveal not only the static features of the vegetation but

374

the dynamic ones as well. As in other fields where the interest is focused on the nature of the land and its potential, vegetation maps of existing plant communities made for planning are employed to establish first of all a map of the potential natural vegetation. This consists of the natural phytocenoses toward which the plant communities always tend to evolve. A map of the actual vegetation and the potential natural vegetation represents therefore a double inventory: i.e., an inventory of what actually exists at the time of mapping and an inventory of what might be or what lies within the realm of possibility (the potential natural vegetation or the substitute communities based on it by the planner).

On a map of the potential natural vegetation, the mapper has reduced the complexity of the cultural landscape and instead reveals the basic features of the natural order of the landscape, i.e., the distribution pattern of its biotopes. Such a map shows at a glance the sites of relatively uniform character and their potential development and exploitation. For it may be concluded that, if different sites have the same phytocenoses of the potential natural vegetation, the biotic and abiotic relations of these sites must also be the same, and hence also their biological potential for land use. The vegetation map reveals through these natural sites or biotopes the location and the extent of areas with an equal biological potential. In other words, vegetation maps can reveal areas with the same potential for production and for yields and given programs may be expected to succeed or to fail throughout the entire extent of such isopotential areas. Data on isopotential areas are clearly among the most valuable types of information that planners can use in their endeavor to raise the productivity of a region to its optimum and to maintain and stabilize it there.

Cost of Planless and Poorly Planned Land Use

Planning as we know it today is relatively new. The so-called "lumber barons" and "cattle barons" of the nineteenth century were quite ignorant of it. Their slogans, "Get rich quick" and "Get rich and get out," were based on a nakedly materialistic philosophy with no other goal than the immediate production of large profits. It disregards the physical and biological laws that produced their wealth in the first place and fails to appreciate the broader and ever so intricate interrelations of all biotic and abiotic features of the landscape. But there are limits to land use. Working within these limits, and ever mindful of the character and personality of the landscape, man can indeed render the land most productive and keep it so. But if he exceeds these bounds, disaster is sure to follow. By now, we have ample experience with overgrazed pastures, wrecked forests, floods, dust storms, gullying, sheet erosion and similar calamities. During the past thirty years, a vast number of publications has revealed only

too clearly how one site after another was destroyed or damaged by people who ignored the natural laws of the land. It is now equally well
known that the reconstruction of a damaged site is not only very expensive; it may cost sums far in excess of the realized profits.

Furthermore, past planners frequently failed to see that amelioration
projects in one area may produce harmful effects elsewhere. This is common as a result of deforestation where increased runoff leads to the destruction of valuable land by forcing the rivers to rise over their banks,
covering the fields with sand and gravel and causing hundreds and thousands of people to abandon their homes to destructive floods. The natural order of the landscape cannot be ignored with impunity, and in planning the most appropriate use of our country, this order must be
appreciated and considered.

The intelligent use of the land for optimum results requires a detailed
knowledge of what and how much the land can produce under given circumstances, i.e., a knowledge of its biological potential. It requires furthermore that the land use be managed so as to insure continuity of high
yields. Not only is it necessary to conserve existing resources of soil,
water, and vegetation but also to analyze the condition of each with an
eye on amelioration. Groundwater may be abundant and permit irrigation or a greater carrying capacity of pastures. Forest land may be made
to produce a higher income for its owner if changed into cultivated fields,
but the reverse may be true too, as shown in many parts of the South.

Land Allocation and Consolidation

ELLENBERG's (1937) studies in northwestern Germany revealed that the
potential natural vegetation types closely coincided with types of settlements, land use, house types, and density of population. The introduction of mineral fertilizers and scientific agriculture has sometimes blurred
the limits of such types, and sometimes even brought them into sharper
focus. BUCHWALD (1951) describes cases where vegetation maps are successfully employed in town and country planning, in regional land-use
planning, in testing grasslands with regard to their adaptability to agriculture, horticulture, orcharding, and silviculture, and even in locating or
relocating settlements in the moor and heath regions of postwar settlements and in the reconstruction of cities (e.g., Paderborn).

Planning is not equivalent to zoning. Certainly, there are occasions
when agricultural land must be permitted to become suburban land or to
be changed into industrial sites. But the expansion of housing projects
and industries must not unduly and indiscriminately encroach on the most
productive agricultural land. This lesson has not been learned well in
the United States where even the best soils and the most productive areas

can be zoned as industrial sites, taxing the farmers out of existence. Much sound planning will be needed to prevent such calamities in the future (cf. YOUNG and GRIFFIN, 1957).

In many parts of the world, inheritance practices and other factors have had the effect of breaking up efficiently operated farms into smaller units. In the course of time, these units become still smaller and more and more scattered through the landscape; the farmer must then spend an inordinate amount of his time on getting to his fields or from one field to another. In a number of countries, notably in Europe, government planners have been working toward a consolidation of farm holdings in order to increase efficiency, introduce or increase mechanization, and quite generally put the operation of farms on a more rational basis.

Farmers usually agree with the logic of this viewpoint, but many have shown great reluctance to actually participate in a consolidation scheme. They fear that the land they surrender may be more productive than the land they receive in return. Obviously, the consolidation must be designed so as to improve the farmer's position or at least not to weaken it.

The farmers' doubts may be dispelled by using a vegetation map which reveals the biological potential of the various sites involved. As the phytocenoses shown on vegetation maps can be calibrated to reveal production and yield potentials, it becomes feasible to evaluate sites accurately and objectively and to see which areas may be exchanged on an even basis, and where a farmer needs more acreage (or less) to maintain at least his previous production. The benefits of consolidation then add to the farmer's economic position and win his support for the plan.

Water Resources and Flood Control

Public and private agencies concerned with the construction of dams, canals, reservoirs, and irrigation or drainage projects frequently pay enormous indemnities to landowners on whose land the level of the water table has changed as a result of these activities. In such instances, careful planning calls for vegetation maps, to be prepared before the projects are started and again several years after their completion. The vegetation maps will reveal the character and exact extent of the change. Sometimes the supposed damage does not exist, or it is limited to small areas. In some cases there may even be an improvement, with greater yields than before. ELLENBERG (1952) illustrates this problem graphically: the Aller, a tributary of the Weser River, was regulated by making one cut across a loop and by erecting four barrages. Vegetation maps prepared before and after the regulation of the river revealed the changes in the depth of the water table and the subsequent deterioration or improvement of the pastures and hay meadows. Then, in the same valley, another barrage was built but, surprisingly, the resulting changes in the depth of the water table could not be traced on the vegetation maps. Investigations revealed that, both before and after construction, the water table was so deep that it always remained out of reach of the shallow-rooted grassland communities. All indemnity claims could therefore be dismissed! In a similar case near Braunschweig, the use of vegetation maps saved the government indemnity payments amounting to approximately $240,000 (BUCHWALD, 1951). Vegetation maps are therefore valuable tools in determining a fair compensation for possible damage to fields and meadows resulting from public works, and more than pay for themselves.

BUCHWALD(1953) concerned himself with a general plan for the regulation and use of the water of the Argen River and its tributaries in the northern foothills of the Alps. The plan affected the entire watershed of the Argen and implied appreciable changes. He therefore focused his attention on

1. areas in which the water table would be lowered
2. areas in which the water table would be raised
3. areas to be flooded
4. areas to be irrigated

In developing the general basis for planning the regional control of the water, he observed the role of the vegetation is that of a water consumer and that of a regulator of runoff. This forced him to include detailed vegetation studies in the regional planning of water control if the latter was to be effective. For instance, the vegetation maps revealed accurately how all grasslands in the area could be classified according to the water-holding capacity and the perviousness of the soil. The phytocenoses obviously reacted clearly to this feature.

There are instances in which the construction of dams, of drainage canals, etc., can do more harm than good, because the damage done to the affected land may be greater than the anticipated benefits of the project. A vegetation map permits a clear and detailed analysis of the conditions as they prevail before the project is undertaken. An experienced analyst can often predict conditions that will arise after the completion of the project if good vegetation maps are available to him. Thus serious harm can be avoided; possibly the entire project is abandoned.

Countries which are located in regions with mountains of alpine character are often subject to great calamities caused by floods from suddenly melting snows and glaciers or by avalanches. In the densely populated Alps, the losses are invariably high, and huge sums have already been spent in attempting to prevent the recurrence of such disasters. The extraordinary snow masses which accumulated during the winter of 1950–1951, and the record loss of life and property that resulted from the unusual number of avalanches, point out only too forcefully that attempts at prevention had been only a partial success at best. But even before this disastrous winter, people had come to realize more and more that the proper management of vegetation is a far more effective agent in subduing snow and streams than any other means. Now the Austrian government, through the Bureau for the Control of Streams and Avalanches (Wildbach- und Lawinenverbauamt) of its Forest Service, has commissioned properly qualified experts to prepare vegetation maps of the entire province of Tirol on the scale of 1:25,000!

Planning with Insufficient Data

Another example may illustrate how a lack of vegetation maps can lead to great financial losses through faulty planning. *Suaeda fruticosa* dominates the vegetation of a part of southern France. This perennial indicates a slight salinity of the soil; nevertheless, light cultivation is carried on profitably. It was found that the same species dominates the vegetation of parts of Algeria and this was taken to mean that there, too, the land is suitable for light cultivation. As a result, elaborate plans for large-scale settlement were prepared and pushed forward to the point of laying out streets, building houses for settlers, and constructing public utilities. The failure of repeated attempts at settlement cost the government as well as private individuals a fortune. Afterwards, vegetation maps of both areas were prepared and they revealed that the vegetation of one area was quite different from that of the other, and that the dominant *Suaeda fruticosa* was one of the few species that occurred in both. It also happened that this species has wide ecological tolerances and was therefore unsuited to serve as an indicator. It was a powerful proof that environmental features including soils should not be evaluated by the presence or absence of one particular species but always and exclusively by the character of the entire phytocenose. It also emphasized the need for preparing vegetation maps in the earliest planning stages rather than much later or not at all.

Specialized Vegetation Maps

LONG (1959) reports that the Centre d'études phytosociologiques et écologiques (formerly the Service de la carte des groupements végétaux de la France) at Montpellier prepares vegetation maps of France and overseas for various national or local government agencies which are responsible for the solution of regional or local planning problems. Vegetation maps are also required by private organizations or individuals interested in the possibilities of improving their land-use practices in order to increase the yields of some given crops or pastures or similarly narrow goals. A recent example is the mapping of the vegetation in the Sologne in central France at the large scale of 1:5,000 (GODRON and LE HOUÉROU). The categories of the vegetation are presented in the form of ecological units. The mappers first established the phytocenoses and then expressed them in terms of a series characterized by decreasing xericity. Other environmental factors can be applied in the same manner, i.e., correlated with the floristically determined plant communities.

Once such a vegetation map had been completed, a number of specialized maps was derived from it to show particular features of the region, more specifically the aptitude of the land for (1) the production of crops, (2) pastures and hay meadows, (3) silviculture, and (4) drainage as related to higher yields. The last of these proved to be of special significance in the Sologne, where excess water is often a problem.

The preparation of these specialized maps was made possible by the original vegetation map and its interpretation with regard to the interrelations between the phytocenoses, the edaphic conditions, and the productivity standards of the sites. Similar work was done successfully in Tunisia (LONG, 1954; LE HOUÉROU, 1958) and Morocco (IONESCU, 1958).

In the United States, too, planning agencies have shown their awareness of the usefulness of vegetation maps. Some of the best-known examples are those of river basins, e.g., the drainage areas of the Colorado, the Pecos River, the Powder River, the Tennessee, the Rio Grande, the Red, White, and Arkansas Rivers, and others. Some of these basin maps are of relatively small scale because of the vastness of the areas involved. Thus, GARDNER (1961) mapped the vegetation of the Walnut Gulch Experimental Watershed at the scale of 1:350,000. However, the flexible approach to scales is the only useful one. For instance, EMBERGER and LONG (1962) adapt their vegetation maps to the exigencies of planning and use scales ranging from 1:2,500 to 1:250,000.

Planning in Underdeveloped Nations

In many new countries whose economy is only now evolving, vegetation maps are among the planner's most prized tools. LEBRUN and DEVRED discuss the use of such maps in the (formerly Belgian) Congo and report that vegetation maps are made at large scales (1:25,000–1:100,000) and small scales (1:100,000–1:1,000,000). A considerable number of such maps have already been published.

The purpose of the small-scale maps is to serve research, to define and delimit the areas where the vegetation can guide land-use planning, to reveal the general relations between the vegetation and the natural and anthropic features of the environment, and to formulate projects for the exploitation of the plant resources. The maps serve also as a basis for the introduction of crop species from other parts of the world, as they show the ecoclimatic analogies between the countries of origin and the various regions of the Congo. Finally, these maps are the best means to show and, indeed, to define the climax vegetation zones of the country. Following the recommendations of KÜCHLER (1954b), the terminology used in the map legends is kept simple and clear so that non-phytocenologists can use these maps to full advantage.

The large-scale maps are prepared in areas selected on the small scale maps and serve as a basis for detailed planning. This is concerned with the production of industrial and food crops, tree and shrub plantations of oil palms, rubber, coffee, etc., the management of natural, improved or artificial pastures, forestry, the location of villages, social, commercial, and industrial centers, agricultural experiment stations, the study of water resources, the stabilization and rationalization of agriculture and erosion control. Even around urban centers, as for instance the fast-growing mining city of Elisabethville, large-scale vegetation maps are useful in selecting sites for parks, a suburban belt of market gardens and intensive livestock production, mixed residential and agricultural areas for the families of industrial or retired laborers, for forests devoted to the production of firewood, charcoal, etc. (LEBRUN, 1961).

The vegetation maps of the Congo have been an unqualified success. Planners in other countries of the humid tropics may therefore want to avail themselves of the rich store of knowledge and experience of Belgian phytocenologists.

Natural Vegetation as a Controlling Agent

Recently, planners have learned to appreciate the stability of the natural vegetation, be it real or potential. Efforts are therefore being made to establish it wherever permanence is an asset in protecting the landscape against erosion, as for instance on right-of-ways of highways, railroads, and power lines, on dams and dikes, on stream and river banks and ocean shores. Another example of growing significance is the management of water supplies for urban use and the production of hydroelectric power. The stabilization of water supplies is much enhanced by a judiciously managed natural vegetation, and the vegetation map is surely a most valuable guide for the planner interested in establishing such permanent phytocenoses.

Ideally, the planner's results consist of the most rational land use possible within the frame work of the ecological, agricultural, and economic conditions of the region and of the period. In his efforts to achieve such results, the planner will often find the vegetation map one of his most versatile tools. He must prize vegetation maps for their static and dynamic qualities and their many-sided exploitability, including information on the possibilities and limits of more intensive forms of land use. It will save the planner innumerable and time-consuming trips into the field and appreciably reduce his expenses. At the same time, the planner can look forward to results which statistics of soil and climate can never promise.

32

Education

Perhaps there is no more important activity than to train our youth to lead lives full of service cheerfully given, rich in contributions to the welfare of our fellow man. Our technological civilization makes ever-greater demands on the character and skill of modern man, and the quality of his training becomes a crucial issue, perhaps more so than ever in the long history of mankind.

An increasing number of fields of learning are now employing maps. This does not imply that vegetation maps find a use in all these fields. However, the possibilities of applying them are much wider than has been suspected in the past.

For example, a vegetation map can be useful to the historian because it reveals the conditions of the landscape which exercise an influence on the development of its settlements, its productivity, and hence its significance relative to that of other areas (SCHWICKERATH, 1954; ELLENBERG, 1937; J. TÜXEN, 1963). A professor of Russian history happened to come across a vegetation map of the Ukraine. When the details and their significance had been explained to him, he delightedly discovered that here lay one explanation for the land distribution among the Russian nobles by the Crown.

In some instances, as in the case of botany, geography, and pedology, it is obvious that vegetation maps lend themselves well as instructional devices. Geographers, for example, have long realized that no feature of the landscape reveals so much so readily about the character of a region as does the vegetation. It permits the division of the landscape into ecological sections which are among the most significant units of any areal study. To map the vegetation is therefore an extremely useful activity for geographers, not only because of the resulting maps that may reasonably be expected, but also because of the effective training which it affords to students. Geographers will never be able to pay their debt of gratitude to HENRI GAUSSEN, who taught them in his maps of France at 1:200,000 how to develop the vegetation map into a veritable regional geography.

In 1949, the Association of American Geographers held a symposium on "what graduate students should study." The three participants were generally recognized leaders of American geography; independently, each one emphasized that the study of vegetation was one of the essential aspects of geography, and that graduate students should become acquainted with it. It is obvious, then, that for geographers vegetation maps have become basic tools.

Vegetation maps of National Parks and all types of areas where human interference in the landscape has been reduced to a minimum are of special educational interest. The analysis of vegetation maps of such reserves reveals the nature of the landscape; it teaches us how the environment acts on the vegetation and the reaction of the latter. Protected areas may be likened to laboratories in which Nature performs all experiments and demonstrations. Their benefits to forestry, agriculture, and land management have barely begun to be realized.

From an educational point of view, a vegetation map must be instructive to serve its purpose. The little map by KRAUSE (1952) of Europe and western Siberia may be selected as an example. The author tries to present his "mosaic of plant communities" in the form of regional complexes and shows how in each region a considerable variety of vegetation types is possible, but how they are nevertheless the necessary result of the regional macro-environment in which one or more particular features set the stage. For instance, the local and microclimates are particularly significant in regions of bold relief, whereas the depth of the water table is the critical factor in the North Sea marshes. KRAUSE warns against hasty classification of vegetation types and reminds prospective classifiers of the particularities in the evolution of the vegetational complexes as they vary from case to case. It is also most instructive to compare KRAUSE's map with SCHMID's (1949) map of the Mediterranean Region and his work on vegetation belts, or with some other vegetation map of the same area.

Textbook Supplements

It seems that the critical study of analogies and discrepancies often leads to interesting discoveries and revelations concerning the geographical distribution of vegetation types. Graduate students at universities who wish to become acquainted with the principles of phytocenology should be taught to use vegetation maps throughout their studies. Vegetation maps not only help the student immensely as a visual aid in his endeavor to absorb the information in his textbook, but they constantly stimulate his imagination. With a large-scale map in hand, the student should wander through the landscape and learn to observe and interpret. Nothing helps him so much in advancing his knowledge as to be face to face with the objects of his science and to employ the tools that his predecessors developed for him.

This is not to say that all students of vegetation must always use large-scale maps. Indeed, the less advanced student, the beginner, will appreciate small-scale maps because their simplicity makes them more readily appreciated. Small-scale vegetation maps, be they like KRAUSE's above-mentioned map, vegetation maps in atlases, or of the wall map type as used in schools, all have one important feature in common: they reveal the broad relations of vegetation types to topographic and climatic regions and make the student aware of the basic principles in the plant-site relationships. When these have been grasped, distinctions can be made between natural and cultural vegetation, and the study can progress to maps of larger scales with their finer detail. But such progress should be gradual and not in one step from very small scales to very large ones. The following maps form a stimulating sequence:

1. SHANTZ AND ZON: U.S.A. 1:8,000,000
2. KÜCHLER: U.S.A. 1:3,168,000
3. HUECK: Venezuela. 1:2,000,000
4. DEVRED: Kwango. 1:1,000,000
5. GAUSSEN-VERNET: Tunis-Sfax. 1:1,000,000
6. DUCK-FLETCHER: Oklahoma. 1:500,000
7. DAVIS: southern Florida. 1:400,000
8. FOREST SERVICE: Northwest Washington. 1:250,000
9. GAUSSEN: Perpignan. 1:200,000
10. SCHMID: Switzerland. 1:200,000
11. WIESLANDER: California. 1:125,000 or 62,500
12. GAMS: Follatères. 1:50,000
13. ELLENBERG-ZELLER: Leonberg. 1:50,000
14. MOLINIER: Aix. 1:20,000
15. SEIBERT: Schlitz. 1:15,000
16. TÜXEN: Baltrum. 1:10,000
17. WALTHER: Elbe Valley. 1:5,000

Such a sequence includes a variety of approaches to the study of vegetation and makes the student aware of some of the complexities of phytocenology. It also introduces him to the principles underlying intelligent land use and opens up many vistas. Quite particularly, however, the student's imagination is stimulated and he discovers new worlds to conquer.

Teaching Tools

MOLINIER (1957) summarizes the advantages accruing to an instructor who has vegetation maps of his area at his disposal: (1) In courses of biology, botany, and zoology, the instructor can "demonstrate" on the vegetation map the biogeocenoses, i.e., the phytocenoses with their associated animal life in their ecological setting in the landscape. (2) The instructor can plan his field trips with students, select appropriate phytocenoses, prepare his demonstrations. He may choose communities like different types of forest, grasslands, grain fields with their associated weed communities, a river or stream bank, a sea shore (beach or rocky), a pond, etc. He can see on his map what phytocenoses are available in his area and where they are located. If the map is accompanied by a text, he can obtain the names of the more important species and the dynamic aspects of the vegetation. (3) In the field, and with map in hand, the instructor can explain the vegetation to his students, and thanks to the map and his preparation, can speak precisely and with authority, thus benefiting his students greatly.

REY (1957b) is also concerned with pedagogical problems and shows how the map of France at 1:200,000 may be employed to advantage.

Post-Academic Education

TOMASELLI (1961) observes that not only high school and college students need to be educated but others as well. For instance, in Italy he observes a lack of appreciation of vegetation maps among foresters, due at least in part to a lack of information or appropriate training.

TOMASELLI's observations need not have been limited to Italy; it is precisely for this reason that some individuals or institutions have begun to correct this condition. Many years ago WIESLANDER in California developed short "demonstration courses" of one to five days for the benefit of foresters, pedologists, farmers, ranchers, planners, etc. He took them and his maps to the field and taught them and showed them how the vegetation maps could serve them.

The Federal Bureau for Vegetation Mapping Courses

TÜXEN, at the Federal Bureau of Vegetation Mapping, instituted courses of three days' duration. Like WIESLANDER's demonstration courses, these short courses are devoted primarily to students anxious to learn more about phytocenology, teachers who want to utilize this field in their classes, representatives of related sciences who seek to strengthen their research, agronomists, silviculturists, and others. WALTHER (1963) describes these courses as follows:

The courses are focused on vegetation mapping because (1) it is a typical method of research in phytocenology; (2) every vegetation map is the result of a research project in the course of which aspects of morphological, systematic, ecological, syndynamic, and syngenetic phytocenology are used; (3) the vegetation map is the very foundation of the application of phytocenology in numerous related basic and applied sciences; the latter include agronomy and silviculture. Such a short course can only serve as an introduction to the relevant methods. The length of an adequate course in vegetation mapping should be at least one growing season.

The courses cover only the techniques of mapping the actual vegetation. Maps of the actual vegetation are in any case a prerequisite for the mapping of the potential natural vegetation and the latter requires much more experience than these short courses could possibly offer.

Experience has shown that in vegetation mapping, as in all scientific research, the soundest method implies a progress from analysis to synthesis. The course leads therefore from stand examinations in the field to the preparation and completion of a vegetation map. The method is convincing for beginners as well as sceptics.

Tables 28 and 29 summarize the methods employed to introduce the participants to vegetation mapping and phytocenological analysis. The tables reveal how the course work alternates between lectures and exercises in classroom and laboratory on one hand and field demonstrations and actual mapping on the other.

Table 28. Making a Vegetation Map (Actual Vegetation)

<u>In the Field:</u>   <u>In the Laboratory:</u>

Collecting Data

selection of stand samples
collecting data

Preparation of Tables
    raw table
    extract table
    differentiated (final) table

Mapping the Vegetation
    instruction in mapping
mapping in the field
checking field map

Exploitation
    explanation of field map for scientific and
      economic purposes
    design of specialty maps
    generalization of vegetation-type maps
    derivation of calibrated maps
    relating vegetation to depth and fluctu-
      ation of water table and other environ-
      mental factors

Drafting
    fine-drafting of vegetation map and
      derived maps

Table 29.   Introductory Course in the Phytosociological Method

In the Field	In the Classroom
	Lecture: phytosociological analysis (analytical features of plant communities)
Demonstration and Exercises: collecting data in the field in several groups of 10–12 participants each	
	Lecture: synthetic features of plant communities the phytosociological system introduction to the table method and techniques with practical exercises in making tables, using data collected in the field
Demonstration: introduction to vegetation mapping	
Exercise: making a simple vegetation map in the field	
	Lecture and Demonstration: phytosociological, economic, and ecological exploitation of the tables discussion and explanation of vegetation maps prepared by the Institute
Demonstration and Exercise: observation of plant communities using vegetation maps	

The students are divided into groups of ten to twelve, and each group works under the guidance of a staff member of the Bureau. The area to be studied in the field is a pasture along the west bank of the Weser River which includes a depression and a ridge, thus assuring adequate contrasts. Each group receives a key for sterile grasses. Stand samples are taken along a line at right angles to the course of the river.

The quadrats along the river and in the depression reveal a relatively uniform vegetation composed of a small number of species. The students sample the stands and on their return to the laboratory prepare a raw table (cf. Chapter 19). Species which occur only in some of the samples, not in all, are entered in a new table, the extract table, revealing groups of the differential species. These groups indicate spring floods of different duration and are distinguished by their location: along the river or in the depression. Eventually, a differentiated table is prepared.

The groups of differential species are local units; their general validity is assured only after a comparison with phytocenoses in similar conditions elsewhere results in the same groups. This is the task of systematic phytocenology. The vegetation of an entire region can thus be classified, using the same method as employed above for finding the groups of differential species.

The student's personal manipulation of the tables which he assembled in the field is important for the beginner, for these reasons: (1) Comparison of the stand samples among themselves and with ecological observations is one of the most basic and fruitful methods of phytocenological research. (2) This method is basic to morphological and systematic phytocenology, permitting the definition of superior categories and hence an entire classification. (3) The participant who himself prepared his directions for mapping, his key, has thus completed the essential preparation for his mapping activities.

Mapping begins along the line of the quadrats. It is most significant that the mapper recognize the vegetation units and can establish them so unequivocally that others can recognize them and delimit them in the same manner. It is therefore specially useful to have the same area mapped by several groups: a sound test that the "experiment" (the vegetation maps) can be repeated with the same results.

The plant communities obtained through abstracting the stand samples become evident by establishing their borders; this reveals their areal extent. By separating one from another with a boundary, the mapper becomes more intimately acquainted with them.

The vegetation map is prepared at the large scale of 1:2,500. The entire area of the map is included as no blank spots are admitted. The map faithfully reproduces the actual conditions without any generalization. Thus everything that the vegetation can reveal directly or by implication is shown on the map.

In a second part of the course, the economic utilization and exploitation of vegetation maps is explained and discussed, largely on the basis of graduated (calibrated) phytocenoses. The purpose of the course is to show how a vegetation map is made at Stolzenau, to show participants how far they can go alone and when they need help from experts.

The University of Kansas Seminar

In the United States, the University of Kansas is at present the only institution of higher learning where formal training in vegetation mapping is available. This consists of a seminar, lasting one semester.

The course comprises lectures and exercises in the laboratory and in the field. It is organized to give the student an insight into the nature and use of vegetation maps and to acquaint him with a broad variety of such maps. The comparative method has been found particularly useful, compelling the student to discover the reasons for analogies and differences. He is taught the compilation of small-scale maps and must produce a compiled vegetation map at 1:1,000,000. Furthermore, the student learns to organize the map content and the legend as well as the use of patterns, symbols, and colors.

In the field, the student learns to analyze vegetation and the particular significances of life forms and of taxa. He uses quadrats, transects, and other means to establish phytocenoses and their boundaries and is trained to observe the relations between plant communities and their sites. He is introduced to the interpretation of aerial photographs, their use in the field, and to the use of stereoscopes. He is expected to produce one large scale vegetation map based on his own field work.

The following outline illustrates some of the work performed during the seminar on vegetation mapping.

1. Lectures on the nature of vegetation, its analysis, and its classification.
2. A study of aerial photographs: recognition and interpretation of vegetation and its divisions; relations between phytocenoses and ecological aspects of the landscape.
3. A study of vegetation maps and their characteristics with the comparative method.

Part I

a. Comparison of vegetation maps all of the same area, but by different authors using different classifications and different scales.
b. Comparison of different vegetation maps with regard to their organization of content and legend, their use of colors, patterns, and symbols.
c. Comparison of vegetation maps of mountainous terrain with vegetation maps of plains regions of the same scale: contrasts in detail and generalization; varying controls; altitude and exposure (climate) in mountains, soils, and geology in plains.
d. Comparison of vegetation maps based on the same classification but on different scales and by different authors.
e. Comparison of vegetation maps of uniform scale but by different authors using different classifications.

Part II

a. Comparison of vegetation maps with soil maps of the same area and the same scale.
b. Comparison of vegetation maps with climatic maps (precipitation, xerothermic index, phenology, etc.) of the same area and the same or similar scales.
c. Comparison of vegetation maps with geological and physiographic maps of the same area and the same or similar scales.

4. Preparation of profiles on topographic maps. How profiles are made and how to show vegetation on them. Study of the distribution of vegetation horizontally (on the map) and vertically (on the profile). Significance of profile changing with latitude. Direction of profiles:

across the maximum number of phytocenoses and across the greatest number of ecological conditions, hence at right angles to sea shores, river banks, contours up and down mountains, etc.

5. Translation of the terminology of a given map (e.g., KÜCHLER, 1964) into that of a different classification (e.g., RÜBEL).

6. Compilation of a vegetation map at the scale of 1:1,000,000 of a state or a sheet of the aeronautical charts, with studies in generalization.

7. Take vegetation map into the field, recognize the portrayed plant communities, note degree of detail and generalization, transitions, etc.

8. Take non-recent vegetation map into field, observe succession and other changes that have occurred since the map was prepared.

9. Relate phytocenoses on a vegetation map to observable sites and site differences in the field. This leads to a study of calibrating vegetation maps to given environmental factors.

10. In the winter, make a large-scale vegetation map, showing only physiognomy and structure of the woody vegetation.

11. In the summer, make a large-scale vegetation map, showing phytocenoses both physiognomically and floristically. Large-scale mapping is based on the use of quadrats and transects from which tables can be derived. The mapping techniques are similar to those described by WALTHER earlier in this chapter and are usually applied on the campus or on the University of Kansas Natural History Reservation.

12. The phytocenoses comprehensively described and recorded on the map and in the tables are then analyzed with regard to individual features of the vegetation (structure, dynamics, formation, periodicity, ecological relations, uses, etc.). The student learns how to exploit vegetation maps that are sharply focused on a given purpose or application.

Several of the points listed above may be dealt with simultaneously as the whole program extends through several months. The amount of time devoted to each of the points varies considerably.

33

Commercial, Engineering, and Fiscal Interests

Industrial enterprises and financial institutions have not much appreciated the utility of vegetation maps, at least, not so far. And yet, such commercial interests may well derive considerable benefit from vegetation maps that have been properly adjusted to their particular purposes and needs.

Investments

All institutions concerned with the investment of funds must do so with an eye on the profits that can be realized and the losses which may possibly be incurred. The amount which a bank may advance for the purchase of a tract of range or forest land is in direct proportion to the productivity of this land and the use to which it is to be put. It is not possible for bankers to be experts in all fields of economic activity with which they come in contact. A good vegetation map with an appropriate commentary will, however, give the banker a sure guidance and protect him against undue losses.

Insurance

Similar considerations apply to the insurance companies, especially where crop insurance is involved, but also fire insurance, especially in forests. It is now a well-known fact that some species of forest trees burn much more readily than others; that a lush herbaceous ground cover hinders the spread of fire; and that the susceptibility of the vegetation to fire varies with the seasons. This seasonal variation is again influenced by the structure and the floristic composition of the vegetation in each season.

A good vegetation map with an appropriate commentary will not only protect the insurance company against losses, but it permits also a more accurate calculation of the minimum premiums.

Insurance of livestock is also a problem directly affected by the nature and condition of the vegetation, i.e., the pastures. Poor, overgrazed land results in low-grade livestock, more susceptible to diseases and of low productivity, whereas a healthy, well-managed range permits the farmer to maintain his animals in good condition. This is to say, the risk of undue losses is minimized, as is the need for high insurance premiums.

Fertilizers

The fertilizer industry ought to appreciate the quality and condition of the land as revealed on vegetation maps. For instance, if the vegetation reveals that a tendency toward a lack of soil moisture exists, then lime may be applied only with caution as it may intensify the effects of a drought. The interests of lumber companies (paper, furniture, etc.) have been mentioned in the section on forestry.

Engineering

Vegetation maps can also be most useful to the engineer concerned with road construction. They will show him what type of vegetation covers the land through which the new road is to lead; such information helps the engineer select the appropriate equipment for preparing the road bed and also just where to place the road. For the vegetation maps will reveal avoidable swamps and other obstacles to road construction. In hilly and mountainous terrain, cuts and fills usually have steep sides that must be protected against undue erosion which will eventually endanger the road. A vegetation map will reveal what types of vegetation should be established on the bare slopes to insure their most effective protection.

In this connection, it is interesting to note that the German Government Railways (Deutsche Bundesbahn) requested the Federal Bureau for Vegetation Mapping to prepare large-scale maps of the potential natural vegetation of its entire rail network! This involves the mapping of about 18,750 miles of right-of-ways extending from the dunes and marshes along the coasts of the North Sea and the Baltic Sea to and into the Alps. This vast work is based on the consideration that the establishment of the potential natural vegetation on the right-of-ways of the Bundesbahn will insure stabilization of the land, especially wherever erosion may be threatening to weaken the dams, fills, and roadbeds. It was pointed out that this order for vegetation maps was by no means a matter of altruism on the part of the railroad administration to help science along. It is rather an expression of self-protection and economy. The gains are expected greatly to outweigh the cost of production of so many vegetation maps (BARZ, 1963).

The great increase in the use of hydroelectric power has stimulated the preparation of vegetation maps appreciably, and for two main reasons.

(1) The construction of dams and the impounding of large amounts of water, together with the establishment of power stations and right-of-ways for power lines, imply a serious, indeed revolutionary, intrusion into an established order. The partial destruction of the landscape, the effect on the entire water economy of the soil and the subsoil, frequently result in damage suits of enormous proportions. It has been found that large-scale maps of the real vegetation are by far the best way to determine accurately just how great the alleged damage is. This requires that vegetation maps be prepared before the power project is begun and again a few years after its completion. The differences revealed by the two sets of maps are then the just and fair basis for calculating indemnities. WAGNER (1963) reports that in Austria maps of the actual vegetation are prepared for this purpose at the very large scale of 1:2,880.

(2) An altogether different relation between the vegetation and the production of hydroelectric power involves the water supply. From the point of view of the power station, it is most desirable to have a uniform and sustained flow of water. This is best assured by keeping the entire watershed covered with natural vegetation. It is therefore useful to prepare detailed maps of the potential natural vegetation and, on the basis of these maps, establish phytocenoses that are natural in the area and hence insure the greatest stability of the vegetation. A stable vegetation, on the other hand, will protect the land most efficiently against erosion, reduce surface runoff to a minimum, promote the percolation of rain and melting snow into the soil, and permit streams to flow evenly. The cost of preparing the maps of the potential natural vegetation is thus returned many times.

The construction of canals for drainage and the regulation of rivers may affect the depth of the water table and its fluctuations considerably. The effect of such constructions on the quality of meadows, fields and pastures has already been mentioned and the usefulness of maps of the real vegetation before construction and again several years later is now well documented (ELLENBERG, 1952; MEISEL, 1963; TÜXEN, 1942a, 1952b, 1954a, 1954b; WALTHER, 1950).

Plant and Plant-Product Industries

Industrial corporations concerned with the manufacture of items derived from plant products such as paper, furniture, etc., often own large holdings of forests and their use of vegetation maps has already been discussed in Chapter 30. Other concerns produce their raw materials agriculturally (cotton, sugar cane, sugar beets, soy beans, etc.). That such companies may have use for vegetation maps may be illustrated by the following example.

BRAUN-BLANQUET (1951) reports that a large industrial concern in southern France produced *Arundo donax* as a fiber crop on an area of modest size. The concern bought the surrounding, mostly uncultivated land for a considerable distance to expand the cultivation of this cane. This expansion failed on all uncultivated land in spite of a costly installation of irrigation and drainage systems. A phytocenologist was consulted. He prepared a detailed vegetation map at 1:5,000 and a report. The map showed that less than one third of the more recently acquired area was adapted to the cultivation of *Arundo donax*, whereas the remainder was too alkaline or too swampy. As a result, the company sold its holdings at a loss. The speculative character of the whole transaction could have been avoided had the vegetation map been prepared before, not after, the purchase was made.

Real Property Appraisal

Both real estate companies and the Bureau of Internal Revenue are interested in the actual value of properties. Where these properties consist of forests, range land, and other non-urban types, vegetation maps can be of great value in assessing the properties fairly.

Port Authorities and Marine Industry

Finally, an altogether different approach to the use of vegetation maps by public works administrations comes from MOLINIER (1963). He points out the utility of maps of marine biocenoses which reveal the gradual choking of river mouths and ports with sand. As the sand accumulates, biocenoses change and the biota shift to other areas or disappear, making room for different species. Such maps are also very useful in connection with the fishing industry. The maps reveal the details of the fishing grounds and their extent, and they can serve as a basis for the protection and management of the grounds.

34

Military Activities

Military men like to consider themselves realists. They must be able to act promptly under emergency conditions and must plan for these. They are concerned with the movement of men and equipment; and such movement must proceed as rapidly as possible even though regular communications may not be available. Furthermore, such movements may have to be concealed. Cross-country movements and the aspects of camouflage and concealment create a vital interest in many aspects of vegetation, especially its physiognomy and structure. Obviously, a forested mountainous terrain presents aspects totally different from those in a vast plain of grasslands. One need only compare the immense distances covered by the campaigns on the Russian steppes or the Libyan deserts during World War II with the bloody and obstinate battles for every yard in the jungles of Guadalcanal or in the Hürtgen Forest on Germany's western frontier.

Planning Field Strategy

From a military point of view, the vegetation map offers the great advantage of allowing an officer to study the vegetational features of the terrain. He can therefore plan his operations with much greater confidence of moving efficiently while avoiding dangerous obstacles and surprises. For instance, lateral visibility is often of significance and can frequently be recognized on vegetation maps with a surprising degree of accuracy because such maps, especially when they show the physiognomy and structure of the vegetation, indicate the height and density of the plant communities, the density of a forest, the amount of undergrowth, how "open" shrub formations are, and the like. An officer also wants to be aware of all kinds of vegetational obstacles in the form of closely growing trees, lianas and vines, swamp vegetation or jungle-like thickets when light or heavy equipment is to be moved; such obstacles to traffic can also be gleaned from a vegetation map.

Survival and Guerilla Warfare

Detailed vegetation maps are useful to guerilla fighters who may be forced to remain self-sufficient for some time. To a considerable degree, they can plan their actions and, indeed, their very survival on the information they gather from a vegetation map. Guerilla troops should therefore be carefully instructed in the use of vegetation maps and be made aware of their military and economic significance.

Designing Maps for Military Use

It has been emphasized repeatedly that vegetation maps must be so designed as to serve their purpose best. The question then arises as to how vegetation must be described to serve military purposes. This question was dealt with in great detail as an essential part of the project "Military Evaluation of Geographic Areas" (MEGA) under the direction of WARREN E. GRABAU. The following paragraphs are based on ADDOR (1963), one of GRABAU's collaborators.

The complexity of vegetation must be related to the complexity of military activities and a system for describing vegetation must be devised which fulfills all requirements of these activities. The requirements of such a system are postulated as follows.

1. It must have predictive value. This implies that it must be universally applicable, either directly or by adaptation; that it must yield consistent results wherever and by whomever applied; and that it should be entirely objective and quantitative.

2. It should include all attributes of the vegetation which are known to, or conceivably could, exert an effect upon any military activity, whether or not those attributes are readily susceptible of quantitative analysis. It is a requirement of the system that a procedure be developed which will render them susceptible, if necessary.

3. It should be designed so that any combination of effect-producing factors could be extracted and evaluated without reference to any other factor, a requirement imposed by the fact that the different activities will be affected differently by different factors.

4. It should be simple, easily learned, and based upon an uncomplicated, rapidly executed sampling technique, since it is not anticipated that all military analysts will be trained botanists, and since the analyst may at times be working under duress of time and/or harassment.

These requirements make it obvious that a floristic approach to vegetation is out of the question. Soldiers cannot be expected to be taxonomists; even with an adequate knowledge of systematics, the vegetation cannot be described in a manner that fulfills the four requirements.

All phytocenoses consist of taxa and of life forms, and if the taxa do not lend themselves to portray a vegetational situation adequately from a military point of view, life forms certainly do. MEGA specialists trained their attention on the existing systems to describe the physiognomy and structure of vegetation with life forms as the basic ingredients. As might have been expected, none of the existing systems was entirely adequate and a new system (Table 30) was devised, specially attuned to military

Table 30. MEGA System of Vegetation Analysis

GROWTH FORM

Crown or *Plant Shape:* leaf and/or branch mass projected upon vertical plane.
DEFINITION:
  a. round: top of crown hemispherical or nearly so, base of crown round or broad.
  b. flat-topped: top of crown flat or nearly so, base of crown rounded or compressed.
  c. pointed: top of crown conical or pointed, base of crown rounded or broad.
  d. spindle: top of crown conical or pointed, base of crown slender or long-tapered toward stem.
  e. irregular: crown shape not classifiable, or undeterminable.
  f. conforming: leaf or branch mass essentially conforms to configuration of ground or to shape of plant used as support; used only when decumbent or twining.
  g. crownless: leaf and branch mass absent.

Crown Diameter: measure crown area by polygon method, normalize area to circular area, determine diameter of resultant circle.
  RANGE OF VALUES:
  a. less than 0.5 m
  b. 0.5 to 2.0 m
  c. 2.0 to 6.0 m
  d. 6.0 to 15.0 m
  e. more than 15.0 m

HEIGHT

CLASS	RANGE OF VALUES	MEASURE STEM DIAMETER AT
VIII	more than 35 m	1.5 m
VII	13 to 35 m	1.5 m
VI	5 to 13 m	1.5 m
V	1.8 to 5 m	1.0 m
IV	0.7 to 1.8 m	0.3 m
III	0.3 to 0.7 m	0.1 m
II	0.1 to 0.3 m	ground level
I	less than 0.1 m	

STEM CHARACTERISTICS

Stem Diameter: see height table for point at which stem diameter is measured.
  RANGE OF VALUES:
  a. less than 2.5 cm
  b. 2.5 to 7.5 cm
  c. 7.5 to 15 cm
  d. 15 to 30 cm
  e. 30 to 60 cm
  f. more than 60 cm

Stem Habit: use only on height classes II to VIII.
  DEFINITION:
  a. erect: stem supports crown by its own strength.

Table 30. (Continued)

b. decumbent: stem supported partially or wholly by ground or other plants; attitude essentially horizontal.
c. twining: stem twines around or adheres to the stems of other plants for support.
d. free: stem free of other plants, but leaf mass supported by other plants.

Stem Hardness: measure at same point as stem diameter is measured.
  DEFINITION:
  a. stem not succulent.
  b. stem succulent and green.
  c. stem succulent and not green (fungi).

BRANCHING HABIT

Type of Branching
  DEFINITION:
  a. horizontal: branches diverge from main stem at approximately right angles.
  b. divergent: branches diverge upward from main stem.

Height of First Branching
  DEFINITION:
  a. less than 0.5 m above ground
  b. 0.5 to 1.0 m
  c. 1.0 to 2.0 m
  d. 2.0 to 3.0 m
  e. more than 3.0 m

ROOT HABIT
(above ground structure only; use only on plants more than 0.7 m tall, i.e., height class IV and up)

Type of Structure
  DEFINITION:
  a. stilt or prop roots (e.g., mangrove).
  b. enlarged base (e.g., bald cypress).
  c. plank buttresses.

Height of Emergence: point at which root modification diverges from stem.
  DEFINITION:
  a. less than 0.3 m
  b. 0.3 to 0.6 m
  c. 0.6 to 2.0 m
  d. more than 2.0 m

Spread: diameter of root modification at ground level.
  DEFINITION:
  a. less than 2 × stem diameter
  b. 2 to 5 × stem diameter
  c. 5 to 15 × stem diameter
  d. 15 to 45 × stem diameter
  e. more than 45 × stem diameter

FOLIAGE CHARACTERISTICS

Leaf Size: area of leaf
  DEFINITION:
  a. less than 1 sq cm
  b. 1 to 150 sq cm
  c. more than 150 sq cm

Leaf Shape
  DEFINITION:
  a. broad and flat: length/width less than or equal to 5.
  b. long and flat: length/width more than 5.

Table 30.　(Continued)

---

c. awl: cross section approximately equidimensional; will not droop if held by
　　one end.
d. threadlike: cross section approximately equidimensional; droops if held by
　　one end.

Leaf Texture
　DEFINITION:
　a. filmy, translucent.
　b. membranous: does not permanently deform when wrapped around a pencil;
　　　place ventral, i.e., "upper" surface next to pencil.
　c. hard: permanently deforms when wrapped around a pencil; place ventral,
　　　i.e., "upper" surface next to pencil.
　d. succulent: more than 2 mm thick.

Leaf Condition
　DEFINITION:
　a. leaves living
　b. leaves dead

ARMATURE

　DEFINITION:
　a. spines more than 5 mm long.
　b. spines less than 5 mm long.
　c. cutting edges.
　d. stinging organs.
　e. poisons.

DISTRIBUTION

　DEFINITION:
　a. random.
　b. aggregated: plants in groups, but mechanically independent; plant shape not
　　　obviously affected by associates.
　c. clumped: plants in close association; stems independent but shapes obviously
　　　affected by associates.
　d. grid: all plants approximately equally distant from the nearest neighbors.
　e. row: plants closely spaced in one direction, much more widely spaced in
　　　another.
　f. strip: elongate patches.

SPECIAL ELEMENTS

　DEFINITION:
　a. epiphytes: plants growing entirely upon other plants, not rooted in soil.
　b. slash: detached plants such as will not rot away within one season; specifically,
　　　larger stems with branches intact; a condition intermediate between vegeta-
　　　tion and microrelief.

needs. Only the concrete physical character of life forms could be considered as it alone affected military activities. From a soldier's point of
view, it makes no difference whether a forest is composed of red oaks
(*Quercus rubra*) or of black oaks (*Quercus velutina*). But it may be imperative for him to know whether the trees are so close that he cannot
move his equipment through the forest, or whether the trees are so young
and small that tanks can knock them down, etc. The new system devised
by the MEGA staff deals therefore exclusively with life forms and structural aspects of vegetation. It ignores all features that have no bearing
on military matters, no matter how significant these features may be in
other respects.

The following basic features of vegetation, called "prime parameters," are considered to have potential military significance:

1. Growth form
2. Height
3. Coverage
4. Stem characteristics
5. Branching habit
6. Root habit
7. Foliage characteristics
8. Armature
9. Distribution
10. Stem spacing

These prime parameters are broken down into classes. Size classes applied to height, stem diameter, leaf size, etc., for instance, are easily established; the only problem is the determination of useful class intervals. In the case of some other parameters such as leaf texture or stem hardness, the problem consists only in establishing adequate definitions. With all class intervals and definitions established, every plant in the world can be described as a structural element in terms of these parameters. It follows that all types of vegetation can similarly be described and identified in terms of the established structural elements.

Although the MEGA system has been tested and improved repeatedly and is now considered efficient, it is recognized that further research is needed for additional and important refinements. One remaining need appears to be a quantified approach to seasonal variations of the vegetation; another need is an improved version of coverage.

Coverage is important in connection with concealment and camouflage. While coverage may reach 100 per cent, the actual cover may be so thin as to provide little concealment from the air. Crown density or resistance to light or other types of wave penetration may promise more satisfactory results.

Other problems include the relation of the vegetation to food supply and health aspects. For instance, some potential food plants have edible leaves and poisonous roots, others have poisonous leaves but edible roots, still others are poisonous when raw. The problems are numerous.

The description of the vegetation based on the above system is designed to serve military interests. In some respects, this leads to some unconventional interpretations. For instance, a large snag (dead tree) is considered equivalent to a deciduous tree during the period of defoliation; a deciduous tree is said to have a leafy crown even though the tree has shed its leaves if it plays host to a large number of evergreen epiphytes; slash is considered a transition between vegetation and microrelief.

The vegetation is recorded in the field with the help of tables. All features of the vegetation which are considered in the MEGA system are listed across the head of the table with one vertical column for each item. The tables can therefore be printed in advance. Each individual stand of the vegetation to be recorded is numbered and is assigned a horizontal line. There remains nothing to do but to mark an X at the intersection of a horizontal stand line with the vertical columns of features that occur in the stand. In this manner the vegetation of a large number of stands can be recorded rapidly on one table.

VI

CONCLUSION

35
Needs for the Future

The problems involved in grasping the nature of phytocenoses in all its complexities are not likely ever to be solved. The same can be said of the sites on which all plant communities are growing. However, it is not necessary to solve these problems completely and partial solutions have already progressed very far. In our efforts to understand the relations between phytocenoses and biotopes, we may therefore hope to produce relatively satisfactory results simply by continuously endeavoring to push the frontiers of our knowledge beyond the horizon. This applies to both basic and applied research.

Uniform Small-Scale Mapping

Small-scale mapping is essential in order to tie the various parts of continents together and establish the bases for detailed research. The scale should be 1:1,000,000 and serious efforts should be made to map all countries at that scale. The base maps are now available for practically all parts of the world and information is rapidly becoming available.

On such maps, regional uniformity would be highly desirable but efforts at standardization should not be pushed too far. For instance, a color scheme for Kansas is not likely to be the same as that for California, but it could well be the same for Oklahoma, Nebraska, and even the Dakotas. On the other hand, the classification of vegetation must be the same throughout any one continent. This is imperative. If the same classification can be used satisfactorily on more than one continent, then this should, of course, be considered seriously. Incidentally, the term continent need not be taken literally. For instance, the Soviet Union is of such a large size that it would be entirely reasonable to consider it a "continent." Conceivably, the same classification of vegetation may be used for the "continent" of the Soviet Union and the continent of Europe. The latter is, in fact, the western part of the Eurasian continent and as such a westward extension of the "Soviet continent." Similarly, North America, north of the Rio Grande, sometimes called Anglo-America, may be regarded as a continent.

Vegetation mapping as a field and all research based on it would benefit immensely if numerous vegetation maps at 1:1,000,000 were to be published in the near future. So far, relatively few vegetation maps are available at this scale and nearly half of the sheets are published in the Soviet Union.

Large-Scale Mapping

Large-scale mapping is needed just as urgently as mapping at small scales or even more so. Detailed maps of relatively small areas permit a great deal of experimentation. Many authors have not yet fully appreciated the value of experiments and graduate students at universities in particular should be encouraged to proceed along such lines, albeit under guidance in order to avoid undue waste. Large-scale vegetation maps are most needed in ecological studies, be these basic or applied to silviculture, range management or land use planning. As vegetation maps have become points of reference for observing changes in the character and quality of the actual vegetation, they have become valuable tools in conservation, the importance of which is now generally recognized.

In discussing small-scale mapping, it was proposed to map every country at the uniform scale of 1:1,000,000. Such an approach is not useful for large-scale maps. On the other hand, while the scale may fluctuate widely, great and persistent efforts should be made to place vegetation maps on a sound scientific basis. This does not at all imply that all authors must conform to one single method and classification. It does imply that vegetation maps in general will attain a higher level of quality and usefulness. Such efforts will certainly be justified by their eventual results.

Vegetation mapping as a field of inquiry is still young. Yet it has already begun to fulfill the hopes of the early pioneers. More mappers will come along filled with eager enthusiasm, continuing the work of their predecessors. They must never forget that a part of that work is to keep an open mind for new or different ideas and methods, to test these in experiments, to compare and improve them and forever try to map the vegetation in such a manner that the resulting maps represent a real service to mankind.

BIBLIOGRAPHY

ABRAMOVA, T. G.   1962.   The importance of a medium scale geobotanical map for the geobotanical subdivison ("rayonization") for agricultural purposes, in VICTOR B. SOCHAVA (1962a), pp. 152–156.

ADDOR, EUGENE E.   1963.   Vegetation description for military purposes, in Military evaluation of geographic areas; report on activities to April 1963. Vicksburg, Miss. U.S. Army Engineer Waterways Experiment Station, Miscellaneous Paper No. 3–610, pp. 98–128.

AICHINGER, ERWIN.   1954.   Statische und dynamische Betrachtung in der pflanzensoziologischen Forschung. Zürich. Geobotanisches Forschungsinstitut Rübel. Veröffentlichungen, Vol. 29.

ALBERTSON, F. W., G. W. TOMANEK, and ANDREW RIEGEL.   1957.   Ecology of drought cycles and grazing intensity on grasslands of the central Great Plains. Ecological Monographs, vol. 27, pp. 27–44.

ALLEN, G. S.   1963.   The role of biology in the forest industry. American Institute of Biological Sciences, Bulletin, August, pp. 31–34.

ANDREWS, H. J., and R. W. COWLIN.   1936.   Forest type maps of Oregon and Washington. Portland, Ore. Pacific Northwest Forest and Range Experiment Station.

APINIS, ARVIDS E.   1963.   Der Wert der Vegetationskarte für die grundlegenden bodenmikrobiologischen Untersuchungen, in REINHOLD TÜXEN (1963a), pp. 185–194.

ARKANSAS STATE GAME AND FISH COMMISSION.   1948.   Wildlife and cover map of Arkansas. Little Rock, Ark.

AUBERT DE LA RÜE, EDGAR, FRANÇOIS BOURLIÈRE, and JEAN-PAUL HARROY.   1957.   The Tropics. New York. Alfred A. Knopf, Inc.

AUBREVILLE, A.   1961.   De la nécessité de fixer une nomenclature synthétique des formations végétales tropicales avant d'entreprendre la cartographie de la végétation tropicale, in HENRI GAUSSEN (1961a), pp. 37–47.

AUGARDE, JACQUES.   1957.   Contribution à l'étude des problèmes de l'homogénéité en phytosociologie. Montpellier. Bulletin du Service de la carte phytogéographique, série B, vol. 2, pp. 11–23.

AYASSE, L., and RENÉ MOLINIER.   1955.   Carte des groupements végétaux des environs de la Motte-du-Caire (B.-A.) au 1/10,000: utilisation de la photo aérienne. Revue forestière française, No. 9–10, pp. 697–707.

BAGNOULS, F., and HENRI GAUSSEN.   1953.   Saison sèche et indice xérothermique. Bulletin de la Société d'Histoire Naturelle de Toulouse, vol. 88, pp. 193–239.

BARZ, WALTER.   1963.   Vegetationsbau bei der Deutschen Bundesbahn, in REINHOLD TÜXEN (1963a), pp. 409–412.

BEADLE, N. C. W., and A. B. COSTIN.   1952.   Ecological classification and nomenclature. *Proceedings of the Linnean Society of New South Wales*, vol. LXVII, pp. 61–82.

BEARD, J. S. 1944. Climax vegetation in tropical America. *Ecology*, vol. 25, pp. 127–158.

BELOW, S. V. 1962. Theoretical bases of spectrozonal aerophotography of vegetation, *in* VICTOR B. SOCHAVA (1962a), pp. 237–243.

BENNETT, CHARLES F. 1963. Notes on the use of light aircraft in mapping the vegetation in the American tropics. *Professional Geographer*, vol. 15, No. 6, pp. 21–24.

BEREZIN, A. M. 1962. On the choice of a scale of aerophotos and of kinds of aerorecords for the deciphering and mapping of forests, *in* VICTOR B. SOCHAVA (1962a), pp. 223–231.

BERTOVIC, STJEPAN. 1963. Pflanzensoziologische Kartierungen in Kroatien und andern Teilen Jugoslawiens, *in* REINHOLD TÜXEN (1963a), pp. 231–243.

BHARUCHA, F. R. 1952. Vegetation cartography. *Indian Forester*, vol. 78, No. 6.

BHARUCHA, F. R. 1955. Les problèmes cartographiques du sud-est asiatique, *in* HENRI GAUSSEN (1955), pp. 189–193.

BILLINGS, W. D. 1952. The environmental complex in relation to plant growth and distribution. *Quarterly Review of Biology*, vol. 27, pp. 251–265.

BLAEU, JOANNIS. 1640–1654. Theatrum Orbis Terrarum. Amsterdam. *Novus Atlas*, vols. 1–6.

BOER, T. A. DE. 1954. Grünlandvegetationskartierung in den Niederlanden. *Festschrift Aichinger*, pp. 1232–1234. Wien. Springer Verlag.

BOER, T. A. DE. 1963. Die Grünlandvegetionskartierung als Grundlage für die landwirtschaftliche Verbesserung ganzer Gebiete in den Niederlanden, *in* REINHOLD TÜXEN (1963a), pp. 441–455.

BORZA, A. 1963. Bibliographie der Vegetationskarten Rumäniens. *Excerpta botanica*, sectio B: Sociologica, vol. 5, pp. 103–107.

BRAUN, E. LUCY. 1950. *Deciduous Forests of Eastern North America*. Philadelphia, Pa. Blakiston Co.

BRAUN-BLANQUET, JOSIAS. 1932. *Plant Sociology*. (Translated by G. D. Fuller and H. S. Conard.) New York. McGraw-Hill Book Co., Inc.

BRAUN-BLANQUET, JOSIAS. 1944. Sur l'importance pratique d'une carte détaillée des associations végétales de la France. Montpellier. Station internationale de géobotanique méditerranéenne et alpine. Communication 86.

BRAUN-BLANQUET, JOSIAS. 1951, 1964. *Pflanzensoziologie*. 2nd and 3rd eds. Wien. Springer Verlag.

BRAUN-BLANQUET, JOSIAS, LOUIS EMBERGER, and RENÉ MOLINIER. 1947. Instructions pour l'établissement de la carte des groupements végétaux. Paris. Centre National de la Recherche Scientifique.

BRAUN-BLANQUET, JOSIAS, G. LEMÉE, and RENÉ MOLINIER. 1963. Gallia. *Excerpta botanica*, sectio B: Sociologica, vol. 5, pp. 40–43.

BRAUN-BLANQUET, JOSIAS, and Y. T. TCHOU. 1947. Carte des groupements végétaux de la France, région nordouest de Montpellier. Montpellier. Station internationale de géobotanique méditerranéenne et alpine.

BROCKMANN-JEROSCH, H. 1935. Vegetation der Erde, *in* H. HAACK, *Physikalischer Wandatlas*. Gotha.

BROMME, TRAUGOTT. 1851. *Atlas zu Alexander von Humboldts Kosmos*. Stuttgart. Krais & Hoffman Verlag.

BUCHWALD, KONRAD. 1951. Vegetationskarten als Grundlage für die Landschaftsplanung. *Pflanze und Garten*, vol. 1, pp. 11–13.

BUCHWALD, KONRAD. 1953. Generalwasserplanung auf Grund natürlicher Standortkartierung am Beispiel des Argengebietes, *in Wirksame Landschaftspflege durch wissenschaftliche Forschung.* Bremen-Horn. Dorn Verlag. Pp. 57–62.

BUCHWALD, KONRAD. 1954. Grünlandkartierung im Rahmen des ERP–Grünlandförderungsprogramms. *Landwirtschaft, angewandte Wissenschaft,* No. 21.

BURKE, T. F., and HAL SHELTON. 1953. *The United States of America.* Denver, Colo. Jeppeson & Co.

BURTT-DAVY, J. 1938. The classification of tropical woody vegetation types. Oxford. Imperial Forestry Institute Paper No. 13.

BUTORINA, T. N. 1962. Principles of compilation of forest-type maps, *in* VICTOR B. SOCHAVA (1962a), pp. 103–109.

CAIN, STANLEY A. 1932. Concerning certain phytosociological concepts. *Ecological Monographs,* vol. 2, pp. 475–508.

CAIN, STANLEY A., and G. M. DE OLIVEIRA CASTRO. 1959. *Manual of Vegetation Analysis.* New York. Harper & Bros.

CALIFORNIA FOREST AND RANGE EXPERIMENT STATION. 1954. Field manual: soil-vegetation surveys in California. Berkeley, Calif. University of California. Revised, October 1954.

CALIFORNIA FOREST AND RANGE EXPERIMENT STATION. 1955a. Legends and supplemental information to accompany timber stand–vegetation cover maps of California. Berkeley, Calif. University of California. Revised, May 1955.

CALIFORNIA FOREST AND RANGE EXPERIMENT STATION. 1955b. Field manual: grassland sampling. Berkeley, Calif. University of California.

CALIFORNIA FOREST AND RANGE EXPERIMENT STATION. 1958. Soil-vegetation surveys in California. Berkeley, Calif. University of California.

CANADIAN FORESTRY SERVICES. 1948. Lac Letondal. Ottawa. Dept. of Mines and Resources.

CANNON, HELEN L. 1960. The development of botanical methods of prospecting for uranium on the Colorado Plateau. Washington, D.C. Geological Survey, Bulletin 1085-A.

CARBIENER, R. 1963. Les sols du massif de Hohneck, leurs rapports avec le tapis végétal. Strasbourg. Association philomathique d'Alsace et de Lorraine.

CHABROL, P. 1961. Méthodes cartographiques et plans forestiers dans l'oeuvre de la Réformation de la Grande Maîtrise des Eaux et Forêts de Toulouse au XVIIe siècle, *in* HENRI GAUSSEN (1961a), pp. 219–226.

CHAMBERLIN, T. C. 1883. Vegetation map of Wisconsin. *Atlas of the Geological Survey,* plate III. Madison, Wis.

CHAMPION, H. G. 1936. A preliminary survey of the forest types of India and Burma. *Indian Forest Records,* N. S. New Delhi.

CHIPP, T. F. 1926. Aims and methods of study in tropical countries, *in* A. G. TANSLEY and T. F. CHIPP, *Aims and Methods in the Study of Vegetation.* London. British Empire Vegetation Committee. Pp. 194–237.

CLEMENTS, FREDERIC E. 1916. *Plant Succession.* Carnegie Institution of Washington, Publication No. 242.

CLEMENTS, FREDERIC E. 1928. *Plant Succession and Indicators.* New York. The H. W. Wilson Co.

COLWELL, ROBERT N. 1964. Aerial photography—a valuable sensor for the scientist. *American Scientist,* vol. 52, pp. 16–49.

Cook, G. H., and J. C. Smock. 1878. Vegetation map of New Jersey. Trenton, N.J. Geological Survey of New Jersey.

Costin, A. B. 1954. Vegetation map of the Monaro region, *in* A. B. Costin, *Study of the Ecosystems of the Monaro Region of New South Wales*. Sydney, N.S.W. Government Printer.

Coupland, Robert T. 1959. Effects of changes in weather conditions upon grasslands in the northern Great Plains, *in Grasslands*. American Association for the Advancement of Science.

Cunningham, R. N., and H. C. Moser. 1939. The distribution of forests in the upper peninsula of Michigan. St. Paul, Minn. Lake States Forest Experiment Station.

Cunningham, R. N., and H. C. Moser. 1940. The distribution of forests in northern Minnesota. St. Paul, Minn. Lake States Forest Experiment Station.

Curtis, John T. 1959. *The Vegetation of Wisconsin*. Madison, Wis. University of Wisconsin Press.

Curtis, John T., and R. P. McIntosh. 1951. An upland forest continuum in the prairie-forest border region of Wisconsin. *Ecology*, vol. 32, pp. 476–496.

Curtis, M. A. 1860. Vegetation map of North Carolina. Raleigh, N.C. *Geological and Natural History Survey of North Carolina*, part III.

Cushman, M., and M. Lusk. 1949. Vegetation-soil and timber stands and vegetation elements: Mendocino County. Berkeley, Calif. California Forest and Range Experiment Station. University of California.

Dansereau, Pierre. 1957. *Biogeography*. New York. The Ronald Press Co.

Dansereau, Pierre. 1958. A universal system for recording vegetation. *Contributions de l'institut botanique de l'Université de Montréal*, vol. 72, pp. 1–58.

Dansereau, Pierre. 1961. Essai de représentation cartographique des éléments structuraux de la végétation, *in* Henri Gaussen (1961a), pp. 233–255.

Daubenmire, Rexford F. 1943. Vegetational zonation in the Rocky Mountains. *Botanical Review*, vol. 9, pp. 352–393.

Davis, John E. 1943. Southern Florida. Florida Geological Survey, Bulletin 25.

Demchenko, L. A. 1962. An essay on the compilation of a medium scale map for a district atlas, *in* Victor B. Sochava (1962a), pp. 211–214.

Devred, R. 1955. Kwango. Brussels. Institut National pour l'Étude Agronomique du Congo belge. Vol. 10.

Devred, R. 1960. La cartographie de la végétation au Congo belge. *Bulletin agricole du Congo belge et du Ruanda-Urundi*, vol. LI, pp. 529–542.

Dice, L. R. 1943. *The Biotic Provinces of North America*. Ann Arbor, Mich. University of Michigan Press.

Doing Kraft, Hendrik. 1963. Eine Landschaftskartierung auf vegetationskundlicher Grundlage im Masstab 1:25,000 in den Dünen bei Haarlem, *in* Reinhold Tüxen (1963a), pp. 297–312.

Doniţa, N., V. Leandru, and E. Puşcaru-Soroceanu. 1960. *Harta Geobotanica R.P.R.* Bucharest. Academia Republicii Populare Romine.

Drude, Oskar. 1890. Über die Prinzipien in der Unterscheidung von Vegetationsformationen. *Englers Botanische Jahrbücher*, vol. XI.

Drude, Oskar. 1905. Die Methoden der speziellen pflanzengeographischen

Kartographie. Wien. 2nd International Botanical Congress. *Wissenschaftliche Ergebnisse.*

DRUDE, OSKAR. 1907. Die kartographische Darstellung mitteldeutscher Vegetationsformationen. Dresden. *Bericht des freien Vereins für systematische Botanik und Pflanzengeographie.*

DRUDE, OSKAR. 1913. *Die Ökologie der Pflanzen.* Braunschweig. Vieweg Verlag.

DUNNING, DUNCAN. 1942. A site classification for the mixed-conifer selection forests of the Sierra Nevada. Berkeley, Calif. California Forest and Range Experiment Station, Research Note 28.

DU RIETZ, G. EINAR. 1931. Life forms of terrestrial flowering plants. *Acta phytogeographica suecica*, vol. 3.

DUVIGNEAUD, PAUL. 1961. Application de la méthode des groupes écologiques à la cartographie au 1/50,000 des forêts de la Lorraine belge, *in* HENRI GAUSSEN (1961a), pp. 83–86.

EGLER, FRANK E. 1942. Vegetation as an object of study. *Philosophy of Science*, vol. 9, pp. 245–260.

EGLER, FRANK E. 1951. A commentary on American Plant ecology. *Ecology*, vol. 32, pp. 673–694.

EGLER, FRANK E. 1954. Vegetation science concepts I: initial floristic composition, a factor in old-field vegetation development. *Vegetatio*, vol. 4, pp. 412–417.

EHWALD, E. 1950. Über das Zusammenwirken von Standortskunde und Pflanzensoziologie bei der forstlichen Standortskartierung. *Allgemeine Forstzeitschrift*, vol. 5, pp. 416–418.

ELLENBERG, HEINZ. 1937. Über die bäuerliche Wohn- und Siedlungsweise in nordwest Deutschland in ihrer Beziehung zur Landschaft, insbesondere zur Pflanzendecke. Hannover. *Mitteilungen der floristisch-soziologischen Arbeitsgemeinschaft in Niedersachsen*, vol. 3.

ELLENBERG, HEINZ. 1950. *Unkrautgemeinschaften als Zeiger für Klima und Boden.* Stuttgart. Ulmer Verlag.

ELLENBERG, HEINZ. 1952. Auswirkungen der Grundwassersenkung auf die Wiesengesellschaften am Seitenkanal westlich Braunschweig. Stolzenau an der Weser. *Angewandte Pflanzensoziologie*, vol. 6.

ELLENBERG, HEINZ. 1953. Physiologisches und ökologisches Verhalten derselben Pflanzenarten. *Berichte der deutschen botanischen Gesellschaft*, vol. 65.

ELLENBERG, HEINZ. 1954a. Über einige Fortschritte der kausalen Vegetationskunde. *Vegetatio*, vol. 5–6, pp. 199–211.

ELLENBERG, HEINZ. 1954b. Zur Entwicklung der Vegetationssystematik in Mitteleuropa. *Festschrift Aichinger*, pp. 134–143. Wien. Springer Verlag.

ELLENBERG, HEINZ. 1955. Südwestdeutschland: Wuchsklimakarte. Stuttgart. Reise- und Verkehrsverlag.

ELLENBERG, HEINZ. 1956. *Aufgaben und Methoden der Vegetationskunde.* Stuttgart. Ulmer Verlag.

ELLENBERG, HEINZ. 1958. Über die Beziehungen zwischen Pflanzengesellschaft, Standort, Bodenprofil und Bodentyp. Stolzenau an der Weser. *Angewandte Pflanzensoziologie*, vol. 15, pp. 14–18.

ELLENBERG, HEINZ. 1960. Können wir eine gemeinsame Plattform für die verschiedenen Schulen in der Waldtypenklassifikation finden? *Silva Fennica*, vol. 105, pp. 26–32.

ELLENBERG, HEINZ, and OTTI ZELLER. 1951. Die Pflanzenstandortskarte des Kreises Leonberg. Hannover. *Forschungs- und Sitzungsbericht der Akademie für Raumforschung und Landesplanung*, vol. II.

EMBERGER, LOUIS. 1939. Carte phytogéographique du Maroc. Zürich. Geobotanisches Forschungsinstitut Rübel. *Veröffentlichungen*, vol. 14.

EMBERGER, LOUIS. 1958. Afrique du nord et Australie méditerranéenne. UNESCO. *Actes du colloque de Canberra (Australia), 1956: Climatologie et microclimatologie*, pp. 141–146.

EMBERGER, LOUIS. 1961. Évolution, principes actuels et problèmes de la technique cartographique pratiqués au service de la carte des groupements végétaux, *in* HENRI GAUSSEN (1961a), pp. 211–217.

EMBERGER, LOUIS. 1962. Rapport de synthèse sur la contribution que la recherche scientifique de base—notamment en écologie—peut apporter pour résoudre des problèmes posés par la montagne. *Bulletin de la fédération française d'économie montagnarde*, n.s. No. 12, pp. 197–207.

EMBERGER, LOUIS, HENRI GAUSSEN, and PAUL REY. 1955. *Service de la carte phytogéographique*. Paris Centre National de la Recherche Scientifique.

EMBERGER, LOUIS, and GILBERT LONG. 1959. Orientation actuelle au service de la C.G.V. de la cartographie phytosociologique appliquée. *Bulletin du service de la carte phytogéographique*, série B, vol. 4, pp. 119–146.

EMBERGER, LOUIS, and GILBERT LONG. 1962. Écologie et agronomie, études de base et mise en valeur des terres; point de vue de l'écologiste. *Bulletin technique d'information des ingénieurs des services agricoles*, No. 172.

EMBERGER, LOUIS, and RENÉ MOLINIER. 1955. *Les couleurs*. Paris. Centre National de la Recherche Scientifique. Service de la carte phytogéographique. Pp. 65–68.

ESKUCHE, ULRICH. 1955. *Vergleichende Standortuntersuchungen an Wiesen im Donauried bei Herbertingen*. Tübingen. Institut für angewandte Botanik der Universität.

ETTER, H. 1947. Vegetationskarte des Sihlwaldes der Stadt Zürich. *Zeitschrift der schweizer Forstverwaltung*, Beiheft 24.

FENTON, E. WYLLIE. 1947. The transitory character of vegetation maps. *Scottish Geographical Magazine*, vol. 63, pp. 129–130.

FERNALD, MERRITT LYNDON. 1950. *Gray's Manual of Botany*, 8th ed. New York. American Book Co.

FIORI, A. 1940. Formazioni vegetali d'Italia. Milano. *in:* Giotto Dainelli, *Atlante fisico-economico d'Italia*, plate 21.

FISHER, J. R., and K. E. BRADSHAW. 1957. Uses of soil-vegetation survey information in road construction. Soil Science Society of America. *Proceedings*, vol. 21, pp. 115–117.

FLAHAUT, CHARLES. 1894. Projet de carte botanique, forestière et agricole de la France. *Bulletin de la Société botanique de la France*, vol. 41.

FLAHAUT, CHARLES, and C. SCHRÖTER. 1910. *Referate und Vorschläge betreffend die pflanzengeographische Nomenklatur*. Brussels. 3rd International Botanical Congress.

FONCIN, MYRIAM. 1961. Représentation de la végétation sur les cartes anciennes, *in* HENRI GAUSSEN (1961a), pp. 147–155.

FOSBERG, F. RAYMOND. 1958. Mapping of vegetation types. UNESCO. *Study of Tropical Vegetation*, pp. 219–220.

FOSBERG, F. RAYMOND. 1961a. What should we map? *in* HENRI GAUSSEN (1961a), pp. 23–35.

FOSBERG, F. RAYMOND. 1961b. The study of vegetation in Europe. *Bulletin,* American Institute of Biological Sciences, June, pp. 17–19.

FOSBERG, F. RAYMOND. 1961c. A classification of vegetation for general purposes. *Tropical Ecology,* vol. 2, pp. 1–28.

FOSBERG, F. RAYMOND, B. J. GARNIER, and A. W. KÜCHLER. 1961. Delimitation of the humid tropics. *Geographical Review,* vol. LI, pp. 333–347.

FRIEDEL, HELMUT. 1934. Boden- und Vegetationsentwicklung am Pasterzenufer. Klagenfurt. *Carinthia,* vol. II, pp. 29–41.

FRIEDEL, HELMUT. 1956. Vegetationskarte der Umgebung der Pasterze, *in* HELMUT FRIEDEL, *Die alpine Vegetation des obersten Mölltales (Hohe Tauern).* Innsbruck. Wagner Verlag.

FUKAREK, PAVLE. 1963. Die Ausarbeitung einer detaillierten Waldkarte Bosniens und der Herzegowina auf pflanzensoziologischer Grundlage, *in* REINHOLD TÜXEN (1963a), pp. 363–386.

FULLER, GEORGE D., and HENRY S. CONARD. 1932. *Plant Sociology.* (Translation.) New York. McGraw-Hill Book Co., Inc.

FURRER, ERNST. 1962. Vegetationsforschung in der Schweiz seit 1900. *Geographica Helvetica,* vol. XVII, pp. 43–57.

GALIANO, EMILIO FERNANDEZ. 1960. Mapa de vegetación de la provincia de Jaén (mitad oriental). Jaén. Instituto de estudios giennenses.

GALIANO, EMILIO FERNANDEZ. 1961. État actuel de la cartographie botanique en Espagne, *in* HENRI GAUSSEN (1961a), pp. 179–186.

GALKINA, E. A. 1962. Special aspects in swamp vegetation mapping, *in* VICTOR B. SOCHAVA (1962a), pp. 121–130.

GAMS, HELMUT. 1918. Prinzipienfragen der Vegetationsforschung. *Vierteljahresschrift der naturforschenden Gesellschaft in Zürich,* vol. 63, pp. 293–493.

GAMS, HELMUT. 1927. Vegetationskarte des unteren Rhonetals, *in* HELMUT GAMS, Von den Follatères zur Dent des Morcles. Bern. *Beiträge zur geobotanischen Landesaufnahme der Schweiz,* vol. 15.

GAMS, HELMUT. 1936. Vegetationskarte der Glocknergruppe. Wien. *Abhandlungen der Zoologisch-Botanischen Gesellschaft,* vol. XVI.

GAMS, HELMUT. 1941. Über neue Beiträge zur Vegetationssystematik unter besonderer Berücksichtigung des floristischen Systems von Braun-Blanquet. *Botanisches Archiv,* vol. 42.

GAMS, HELMUT. 1954. Vegetationssystematik als Endziel oder Verständigungsmittel? Zürich. Geobotanisches Forschungsinstitut Rübel. *Veröffentlichungen,* vol. 29.

GARDNER, J. L. 1961. Vegetation map, Walnut Gulch Experimental Watershed. Tucson, Ariz. Southwest Watershed Research Center, Agricultural Experiment Station, University of Arizona.

GARDNER, ROBERT A. 1955a. Soil-vegetation surveys as an aid in range management. Society of American Foresters. *Proceedings,* pp. 37–39.

GARDNER, ROBERT A. 1955b. Interpretation of soil-vegetation survey data. Berkeley, Calif. California Forest and Range Experiment Station.

GARDNER, ROBERT A., and KENNETH E. BRADSHAW. 1954. Characteristics and vegetation relationships of some podzolic soils near the coast of northern California. Soil Science Society of America. *Proceedings,* vol. 18, pp. 320–325.

GARDNER, ROBERT A., and A. EVERETT WIESLANDER. 1957. The soil-vegetation survey in California. Soil Science Society of America. *Proceedings,* vol. 21, pp. 103–105.

GAUSSEN, HENRI. 1930. Carte des productions végétales, Port Vendres. Paris. Librairie P. Lechevalier.

GAUSSEN, HENRI. 1936. Signes conventionnels pour le travail sur le terrain. Paris. Centre National de la Recherche Scientifique. Service de la carte phytogéographique.

GAUSSEN, HENRI. 1945a. Divisions régionales et éléments floristiques de la France. Paris. Éditions géographiques de France. *Atlas de France*, plate 27.

GAUSSEN, HENRI. 1945b. Tapis végétal de la France. Paris. Éditions géographiques de France. *Atlas de France*, plates 30–33.

GAUSSEN, HENRI. 1948. Carte de la végétation de la France, feuille Perpignan. Toulouse. Service de la carte de la végétation de la France.

GAUSSEN, HENRI. 1949. Projets pour diverses cartes du monde à 1:1,000,000: la carte écologique du tapis végétal. Paris. *Annales agronomiques*, vol. XIX.

GAUSSEN, HENRI. 1953. A proposed ecological vegetation map. *Surveying and Mapping*, vol. 13, pp. 168–173.

GAUSSEN, HENRI (ed.). 1955. *Les divisions écologiques du monde*. Paris. Centre National de la Recherche Scientifique. 59th International Colloquium, 1954.

GAUSSEN, HENRI. 1955a. Expression des milieux par des formules écologiques; leur représentation cartographique, *in* HENRI GAUSSEN (1955), pp. 13–25.

GAUSSEN, HENRI. 1955b. Rapport général sur la cartographie écologique, *in* HENRI GAUSSEN (1955), pp. 221–231.

GAUSSEN, HENRI. 1957a. Integration of data by means of vegetation maps. Bangkok. 9th Pacific Science Congress. *Proceedings.*

GAUSSEN, HENRI. 1957b. Les cartes de végétation. Institut français de Pondichéry. *Travaux de la section scientifique et technique*, vol. 1, pp. 51–87.

GAUSSEN, HENRI. 1958. L'emploi des couleurs en cartographie. *Bulletin du service de la carte phytogéographique*, série A, vol. 3, pp. 5–10.

GAUSSEN, HENRI. 1959. The vegetation maps. Institut français de Pondichéry. *Travaux de la section scientifique et technique*, vol. 1, pp. 155–179.

GAUSSEN, HENRI (ed.). 1961a. *Méthodes de la cartographie de la végétation.* Paris. Centre National de la Recherche Scientifique. 97th International Colloquium, Toulouse, 1960.

GAUSSEN, HENRI. 1961b. L'emploi des couleurs dans la cartographie de la végétation, *in* HENRI GAUSSEN (1961a), pp. 137–145.

GAUSSEN, HENRI. 1963. Le choix des couleurs dans les cartes de végétation, *in* REINHOLD TÜXEN (1963a), pp. 109–118.

GAUSSEN, HENRI, P. LEGRIS, and M. VIART. 1961. Notes on the sheet Cape Comorin. Institut français de Pondichéry. *Travaux de la section scientifique et technique*, hors série No. 1.

GAUSSEN, HENRI, P. LEGRIS, and M. VIART. 1963. Notice de la feuille Madras. Institut français de Pondichéry. *Travaux de la section scientifique et technique*, hors série No. 2.

GAUSSEN, HENRI, GUY ROBERTY, and JEAN TROCHAIN. 1950. Carte de la végétation de l'Afrique occidentale française, feuille Thiès. Paris. Office de la recherche scientifique outre-mer.

GAUSSEN, HENRI, and A. VERNET. 1958. Carte internationale du tapis végétal, feuille Tunis-Sfax. Toulouse. Service de la carte de la végétation de la France.

GIACOMINI, VALERIO. 1961. Le probléme du choix des échelles en cartographie de la végétation, *in* HENRI GAUSSEN (1961a), pp. 127–135.

GILLMAN, CLEMENT. 1949. A vegetation types map of Tanganyika Territory. *Geographical Review*, vol. 39.

GINZBERGER, A., and J. STADLMANN. 1939. *Pflanzengeographisches Hilfsbuch*. Wien. Springer Verlag.

GODRON, M., and H. N. LE HOUÉROU. Vegetation map of the Sologne. Montpellier. Service de la carte des groupements végétaux. Unpublished ms.

GORBACHEV, B. N., and O. S. GOROZHANKINA. 1962. The compilation of maps of natural (reconstructed) vegetational cover using plant indicators, *in* VICTOR B. SOCHAVA (1962a), pp. 77–86.

GOSSWEILER, J. 1939. Carta fitogeografica de Angola. Lisboa. Edição do Governo Geral de Angola.

GOUNOT, MICHEL. 1956. A propos de l'homogénéité et du choix des surfaces des relevés. Service de la carte phytogéographique. *Bulletin*, série B, vol. 1, pp. 7–17.

GOUNOT, MICHEL. 1959. L'exploitation mécanographique des relevés pour la recherche des groupes écologiques. Service de la carte phytogéographique. *Bulletin*, série B, vol. 4, pp. 147–177.

GRISEBACH, AUGUST. 1872. Die Vegetationsgebiete der Erde. *in his Die Vegetation der Erde*. Leipzig. Engelmann Verlag.

GUINET, P. 1953. Carte de la végétation de l'Algérie, feuille Béni Abbès. Toulouse. Service de la carte de la végétation de la France.

HANNIG, E., and H. WINKLER. 1926–1940. *Pflanzenareale*. Jena. Fischer Verlag.

HARE, F. KENNETH. 1959. A photo-reconnaissance survey of Labrador-Ungava. Ottawa. Geographical Branch, Mines and Technical Surveys, Memoir No. 6.

HARPER, L. 1857. Map of the prairie above Tibley creek. Jackson, Miss. *Preliminary Report on the Geology and Agriculture of the State of Mississippi*, plate V.

HARPER, ROLAND M. 1943. Forests of Alabama. Geological Survey of Alabama, Monograph 10.

HAYDEN, FREDERIK V. 1878. Colorado and parts of adjacent territories. Washington, D.C. U.S. Geological and Geographical Survey, 10th Annual Report.

HEIKURAINEN, L. (ed.). 1960. Symposium on forest types and forest ecosystems. *Silva Fennica*, vol. 105.

HEJNY, SLAVOMIL. 1963. Die Wege und Methoden der Vegetationskartierung in Böhmen und Mähren, *in* REINHOLD TÜXEN (1963a), pp. 261–263.

HILDEBRAND, O. 1939. Pflanzensoziologische Reichskartierung. *Mitteilungen des Reichsamts für Landesaufnahme*, No. 1.

HILLS, G. ANGUS. 1952. The classification and evaluation of site for forestry. Ontario Department of Lands and Forests, Research Report No. 24.

HOLDRIDGE, L. R. 1959. Mapa ecológico de Guatemala con la clave de clasificación de vegetales del mundo. San José, Costa Rica. Instituto interamericano de ciencias agrícolas.

HORVÁT, ADOLF OLIVER. 1963. Phytozönologische Waldkartierung im Mecsek Gebirge bei Pecs (Fünfkirchen) in Südungarn, *in* REINHOLD TÜXEN (1963a), pp. 245–259.

HORVAT, IVO. 1958. Carte des groupements végétaux de la Croatie du sudouest. Zagreb. Forest Research Institute.

HORVAT, IVO. 1963a. Leitende Gesichtspunkte für eine pflanzensoziologische Gliederung Europas, in REINHOLD TÜXEN (1963a), pp. 61–94.

HORVAT, IVO. 1963b. Vegetationskarte Europas, in REINHOLD TÜXEN (1963a), pp. 334–346.

HUECK, KURT. 1939. Vegetationskarte des Riesengebirges (nördlicher Teil). in his Botanische Wanderungen im Riesengebirge. Jena. Fischer Verlag.

HUECK, KURT. 1943. Vegetationskarte des Deutschen Reiches, Blatt Berlin. Berlin-Neudamm. Neumann Verlag.

HUECK, KURT. 1950. Natürliche Pflanzendecke von Niedersachsen. Bremen. Dorn Verlag. Atlas von Niedersachsen, p. 19.

HUECK, KURT. 1950–1951. Vegetationskarten aus Argentinien. Die Erde, vol. 2, pp. 145–154.

HUECK, KURT. 1955. Nouvelles cartes de la végétation sud-américaine et leur signification pour l'agriculture et la sylviculture, in HENRI GAUSSEN (1955), pp. 181–188.

HUECK, KURT. 1956. Mapa fitogeográfico do estado de São Paulo. Boletim Paulista de Geografia, No. 22, pp. 19–25.

HUECK, KURT. 1957. Die Ursprünglichkeit der brasilianischen "campos cerrados" und neue Beobachtungen an ihrer Südgrenze. Erdkunde, vol. XI, pp. 193–203.

HUECK, KURT. 1960. Mapa de vegetación de la República de Venezuela. Mérida. Instituto Forestal Latino Americano de Investigación y Capacitación.

HULTÉN, ERIC. 1950. Atlas of the Distribution of Vascular Plants in Northwestern Europe. Stockholm. Generalstabens Litografiska Anstalts Förlag.

HUMBERT, H. 1955. Projet de la carte de végétation de Madagascar, in HENRI GAUSSEN (1955), pp. 49–60.

HUMBOLDT, ALEXANDER VON. 1807. Ideen zu einer Physiognomik der Gewächse. Tübingen.

HUMBOLDT, ALEXANDER VON, and AIMÉ BONPLAND. 1805. Géographie des plantes équinoxiales: tableau physique des Andes et pays voisins, in their Essai sur la géographie des plantes. Paris. Levrault, Schoell & Co.

IGNATIEV, E. I., and O. V. SHKURLATOV. 1962. The importance of geobotanical maps in medico-geographical studies, in VICTOR B. SOCHAVA (1962a), pp. 204–207.

IONESCU, T. 1956. A propos de la cartographie des groupements végétaux des terres cultivées en zone semi-aride. Service de la carte phytogéographique. Bulletin, série B, vol. 1, pp. 19–23.

IONESCU, T. 1958. Maroc, région des Doukkala, in T. IONESCU, Étude phytosociologique et écologique de la plaine des Doukkala. Rabat. Ministère d'Agriculture du Maroc, Division de la mise en valeur et du génie rural.

ISACHENKO, A. G. 1962. Some connections of landscape mapping with geobotanical mapping, in VICTOR B. SOCHAVA (1962a), pp. 169–177.

ISACHENKO, T. I. 1962. Principles and methods of generalization in geobotanical mapping in large, medium and small scale, in VICTOR B. SOCHAVA (1962a), pp. 28–46.

IVANOVA, E. N., and N. N. ROSOV. 1962. Some works on general soil cartography of Siberia and their connection with geobotanical studies, in VICTOR B. SOCHAVA (1962a), pp. 194–199.

JAEGER, H. 1952. Standortserkundung und Standortskartierung als Grundlagen der Forsteinrichtung. Der Wald, vol. 2, pp. 82–85.

JENKS, GEORGE F. and DUANE KNOS. 1961. The use of shading patterns in graded series. Annals of the Association of American Geographers, vol. 51, pp. 316–334.

JENSEN, HERBERT A. 1947. A system for classifying vegetation in California. California Fish and Game, vol. 34, pp. 199–266.

JOHNS, EWART. 1957. The surveying and mapping of vegetation on some Dartmoor pastures. Geographical Studies, vol. IV, No. 1, pp. 129–137.

JOHNSTON, W. B. 1961. Locating the vegetation of early Canterbury: a map and its sources. Transactions of the Royal Society of New Zealand, vol. 1, No. 2, pp. 5–15.

KEAY, R. W. J. (ed.). 1959. Vegetation map of Africa south of the tropic of cancer. London. Oxford University Press.

KELHOFER, ERNST. 1917. Einige Ratschläge für Anfänger in pflanzengeographischen Arbeiten. Zürich. Beiträge zur geobotanischen Landesaufnahme der Schweiz, vol. 3.

KELNER, U. G. 1962. Utilization of complementary data when compiling geobotanical maps for comprehensive district atlases of the U.S.S.R., in VICTOR B. SOCHAVA (1962a), pp. 259–264.

KHAN, M. A. WAHEED. 1954. Sliced maps. Indian Forester, vol. 80, pp. 103–116.

KHARIN, N. G. 1962. New methods of vegetation deciphering on aerophotos, in VICTOR B. SOCHAVA (1962a), pp. 232–236.

KLAPP, E. 1949. Landwirtschaftliche Anwendungen der Pflanzensoziologie. Ludwigsburg.

KLEOPOV, G. N., and E. M. LAVRENKO. 1938. Geobotanical map of the Ukraine. Kiev. Ukrainian Research Institute for Agricultural Botany.

KNAPP, RÜDIGER. 1948. Arbeitsmethoden der Pflanzensoziologie und die Eigenschaften der Pflanzengesellschaften. Stuttgart. Ulmer Verlag.

KNAPP, RÜDIGER. 1949. Angewandte Pflanzensoziologie. Stuttgart. Ulmer Verlag.

KNAPP, RÜDIGER. 1951. Zur Bedeutung pflanzensoziologischer Karten für die Forst- und Landwirtschaft und die Vegetationskartierung in Hessen, in Wirksame Landschaftspflege durch wissenschaftliche Forschung. Akademie für Raumforschung und Landesplanung. Bremen-Horn. Dorn Verlag. Forschungs- und Sitzungsberichte, vol. II, pp. 63–69.

KOLESNIKOV, B. P. 1962. The use of the genetic forest type classification in compiling a forest stand map, in VICTOR B. SOCHAVA (1962a), pp. 92–97.

KÖNEKAMP, A. H., and F. WEISE. 1952. Pflanzensoziologie und Grünlandkartierung im Dienste der Landwirtschaft. Braunschweig-Völkenrode. Schriftenreihe der Forschungsanstalt für Landwirtschaft, Heft 5, pp. 7–21.

KÖPPEN, WLADIMIR. 1931. Grundriss der Klimakunde. Berlin. De Gruyter Verlag.

KOSMAKOVA, O. P. 1960. Editorial work in the representation of vegetation on topographic maps. Geodesy and Cartography, No. 1–2, pp. 27–31.

KRAJINA, VLADIMIR J. 1959. Classification of Ecosystems of Forests. Vancouver, B.C. University of British Columbia.

KRAJINA, VLADIMIR J. 1960. Can we find a common platform for the different schools of forest classification? Silva Fennica, vol. 105, pp. 50–55.

KRAUSE, WERNER. 1950. Über Vegetationskarten als Hilfsmittel kausalanalytischer Untersuchung der Pflanzendecke. Planta, vol. 38, pp. 296–323.

KRAUSE, WERNER. 1952. Das Mosaik der Pflanzengesellschaften und seine Bedeutung für die Vegetationskunde. *Planta*, vol. 41, pp. 240–289.

KRAUSE, WERNER. 1954a. Grünlandkartierung im Rahmen des ERP-Grünlandförderungsprogramms 1951/1953. *Landwirtschaft und Angewandte Wissenschaft*, vol. 21, pp. 1–5.

KRAUSE, WERNER. 1954b. Zur ökologischen und landwirtschaftlichen Auswertung von Vegetationskarten der Allmendweiden im Hochschwarzwald. *Festschrift Aichinger*, pp. 1076–1100. Vienna. Springer Verlag.

KRAUSE, WERNER. 1955. Pflanzensoziologische Luftbildauswertung. Stolzenau an der Weser. *Angewandte Pflanzensoziologie*, vol. 10.

KRAUSE, WERNER. 1956. Zur Kenntnis der Wiesenbewässerung im Schwarzwald. Donaueschingen. Staatliches Forschungs- und Beratungsinstitut für Höhenlandwirtschaft.

KRAUSE, WERNER. 1958. Methoden und Ergebnisse der Vegetationskartierung. *Umschau*, Heft 19, pp. 595–598.

KRAUSE, WERNER. 1962. Die Analyse des Landschaftsbaues in der Luftbildauswertung, erläutert an Beispielen aus dem Südschwarzwald. *Berichte zur deutschen Landeskunde*, vol. 29, pp. 85–98.

KRIPPELOVÁ, TERÉZIA, and ROBERT NEUHÄUSL. 1963. Bibliographie der Vegetationskarten der Tschechoslowakei. *Excerpta botanica*, sectio B: Sociologica, vol. 5, pp. 203–213.

KRYLOV, G. V. 1962. Forest map and forest site map of western Siberia, *in* VICTOR B. SOCHAVA (1962a), pp. 110–113.

KÜCHLER, A. W. 1947a. A geographic system of vegetation. *Geographical Review*, vol. 37, pp. 233–240.

KÜCHLER, A. W. 1947b. Localizing vegetation terms. *Annals of the Association of American Geographers*, vol. 37, pp. 197–208.

KÜCHLER, A. W. 1948. A new vegetation map of Manchuria. *Ecology*, vol. 29, pp. 513–516.

KÜCHLER, A. W. 1949. A physiognomic classification of vegetation. *Annals of the Association of American Geographers*, vol. 39, pp. 201–210.

KÜCHLER, A. W. 1950. Die physiognomische Kartierung der Vegetation. *Petermanns Geographische Mitteilungen*, vol. 94, pp. 1–6.

KÜCHLER, A. W. 1951a. The relation between classifying and mapping vegetation. *Ecology*, vol. 32, pp. 275–283.

KÜCHLER, A. W. 1951b. Vegetation map of the world. *Encyclopaedia Britannica Atlas*, p. 31.

KÜCHLER, A. W. 1952. Toward a solution of the problems in mapping the vegetation of the United States at the scale of 1:1,000,000. Washington, D.C. International Geographical Union, XVIIth Congress. *Proceedings*, pp. 257–260.

KÜCHLER, A. W. 1953a. Vegetation mapping in Europe. *Geographical Review*, vol. XLIII, pp. 91–97.

KÜCHLER, A. W. 1953b. World natural vegetation. *Goode's World Atlas*, pp. 16–17. Chicago, Ill. Rand McNally & Co.

KÜCHLER, A. W. 1953c. Natural vegetation of the United States and southern Canada. *Goode's World Atlas*, pp. 52–53. Chicago, Ill. Rand McNally & Co.

KÜCHLER, A. W. 1954a. Some considerations concerning the mapping of herbaceous vegetation. *Transactions of the Kansas Academy of Science*, vol. 57, pp. 449–452.

KÜCHLER, A. W. 1954b. Vegetation maps at the scale from 1:200,000 to

1:1,000,000. Paris. 8th International Botanical Congress. *Rapports et communications*, section 7, pp. 107–112.

KÜCHLER, A. W. 1955a. A comprehensive method of mapping vegetation. *Annals of the Association of American Geographers*, vol. XLV, pp. 404–415.

KÜCHLER, A. W. 1955b. Projet d'une carte physionomique de la végétation du monde, *in* HENRI GAUSSEN (1955), pp. 163–168.

KÜCHLER, A. W. 1956a. Notes on the vegetation of southeastern Mount Desert Island, Maine. *University of Kansas Science Bulletin*, vol. 38, part 1, pp. 335–392.

KÜCHLER, A. W. 1956b. Classification and purpose in vegetation maps. *Geographical Review*, vol. XLVI, pp. 155–167.

KÜCHLER, A. W. 1957a. Applied phytosociology. *Ecology*, vol. 38, pp. 541–542 (review).

KÜCHLER, A. W. 1957b. The new Soviet vegetation maps. *Ecology*, vol. 38, p. 671 (review).

KÜCHLER, A. W. 1960a. Vergleichende Vegetationskartierung. *Vegetatio*, vol. IX, pp. 208–216.

KÜCHLER, A. W. 1960b. Vegetation mapping in Africa. *Annals of the Association of American Geographers*, vol. 50, pp. 74–84.

KÜCHLER, A. W. 1960c. Mapping tropical forest vegetation. *Silva Fennica*, vol. 105, pp. 60–63.

KÜCHLER, A. W. 1961. Mapping the dynamic aspects of vegetation, *in* HENRI GAUSSEN (1961a), pp. 187–201.

KÜCHLER, A. W. 1963. Die Zusammenstellung von Vegetationskarten kleinen Masstabs, *in* REINHOLD TÜXEN (1963a), pp. 39–46.

KÜCHLER, A. W. 1964. *The Potential Natural Vegetation of the Conterminous United States*. New York. American Geographical Society, Special Research Publication No. 36.

KÜCHLER, A. W. 1966. Analyzing the physiognomy and structure of vegetation. *Annals of the Association of American Geographers*, vol. 56, pp. 112–127.

KÜCHLER, A. W., and JACK MCCORMICK. 1965. *International Bibliography of Vegetation Maps*. Vol. I: North America. Lawrence, Kansas. University of Kansas Library Series.

KUHNHOLTZ-LORDAT, G. 1949. *La cartographie parcellaire de la végétation*. Paris. Institut national de la recherche agronomique.

KUMINOVA, A. V. 1962. Geobotanical mapping during a comprehensive study of pastures and haylands on state and collective farms, *in* VICTOR B. SOCHAVA (1962a), pp. 131–138.

KUZNETSOV, N. I. 1928. Geobotanical map of the European part of the Soviet Union. Leningrad. Central Botanical Garden, Geobotanical Section.

LAASIMER, L. R. 1962. On the connection of geobotanical subdivision ("rayonization") and mapping with agricultural and silvicultural subdivision, *in* VICTOR B. SOCHAVA (1962a), pp. 157–163.

LACLAVÈRE, G., and J. DEJEUMONT. 1961. Sur l'impression des cartes de la végétation, *in* HENRI GAUSSEN (1961a), pp. 265–273.

LAUER, WILHELM. 1952. Humide und aride Jahreszeiten in Afrika und Südamerika und ihre Beziehungen zu den Vegetationsgürteln. *Bonner Geographische Abhandlungen*, Heft 9.

LAVERGNE, DIDIER. 1955. Principes pour un recensement cartographique de l'humus dans le monde, *in* HENRI GAUSSEN (1961a), pp. 95–105.

LAVRENKO, E. M., and L. E. RODIN. 1956. Vegetation map of central Asia. Leningrad. Academy of Sciences, Geobotanical Institute.

LAVRENKO, E. M., and VICTOR B. SOCHAVA. 1956. Vegetation map of the U.S.S.R. Leningrad. Academy of Sciences, Geobotanical Institute.

LEBRUN, JEAN. 1961. La cartographie de la végétation: une méthode de developpement des pays tropicaux (application au Congo belge), *in* HENRI GAUSSEN (1961a), pp. 111–126.

LEBRUN, JEAN, and R. DEVRED. 1961. La cartographie de la végétation au Congo belge, *in Recent Advances in Botany*. Toronto. University of Toronto Press.

LEGRIS, P. 1962. Botanical and ecological cartography in India. Institut français de Pondichéry. *Travaux de la section scientifique et technique*.

LEGRIS, P., and M. VIART. 1959. Documentation and method proposed for vegetation mapping at 1/1,000,000 scale. Institut français de Pondichéry. *Travaux de la section scientifique et technique*, vol. 1, pp. 197–205.

LE HOUÉROU, H. N. 1955. Contribution à l'étude de la végétation de la région de Gabès: notice détaillée de la carte des groupements végétaux de Gabès-Sidi Chemmakh. *Annales du service botanique et agronomique de Tunisie*, vol. 28, pp. 141–180.

LE HOUÉROU, *Contribution à l'étude écologique de l'olivier en Tunisie*. Montpellier. Service de la carte des groupements végétaux.

LEIBERG, J. B. 1899. Vegetation map of Montana. U.S. Geological Survey, Report, part 5 (facing p. 256).

LIBAULT, A. 1961. Occupation du sol et systèmes de culture, *in* HENRI GAUSSEN (1961a), pp. 227–231.

LINKOLA, K. 1941. Die Kartierung der Flora und Vegetation Finlands. Helsinki. *Sitzungsbericht der finnischen Akademie der Wissenschaft*, 1938.

LIPATOVA, V. V. 1962. A contribution towards the bibliography of the problem of vegetation mapping, *in* VICTOR B. SOCHAVA (1962a), pp. 265–266.

LIVINGSTON, BURTON EDWARD. 1903. The relation of soils to natural vegetation in Roscommon and Crawford counties, Michigan. Michigan Geological Survey, Annual Report, pp. 9–30.

LIVINGSTON, BURTON E., and FORREST SHREVE. 1921. *The Distribution of Vegetation in the United States as Related to Climatic Conditions*. Carnegie Institution of Washington, Publication No. 284.

LOHMEYER, WILHELM. 1963. Erfahrungen bei der Verwendung von Luftbildern für die Vegetationskartierung, *in* REINHOLD TÜXEN (1963a), pp. 129–137.

LOHMEYER, WILHELM, and HEINZ ELLENBERG. 1946. Vegetationskarte der Eilenriede bei Hannover. Stolzenau an der Weser. Bundesstelle für Vegetationskartierung.

LONG, GILBERT. 1954. Sbeitla. *Annales du service botanique et agronomique de Tunisie*, vol. 27.

LONG, GILBERT. 1959. Possibilités actuelles d'application pratique de la cartographie phytosociologique et écologique au service de la carte des groupements végétaux. Montpellier. Service de la carte des groupements végétaux.

LONG, GILBERT. 1960. Cartographie de la végétation prairiale et pastorale. *Fourrages*, vol. 4, pp. 53–61.

LONG, GILBERT. 1962. Recherches écologiques de base et aménagement du territoire. Un cas concret: la commune de Vesc (Drôme). *Bulletin de la fédération française d'économie montagnarde,* n.s. vol. 12, pp. 137–152.

Long, Gilbert. 1963. Possibilités actuelles d'application pratique de la cartographie phytosociologique et écologique au service de la carte des groupements végétaux, *in* Reinhold Tüxen (1963a), pp. 353–362.

Louis, Herbert. 1939. Die natürlichen Vegetationsgebiete Anatoliens. *in his: Das natürliche Pflanzenkleid Anatoliens.* Stuttgart. Spemann Verlag.

Lubimova, E. L. 1962. The use of toponyms for the compilation of botanical maps, *in* Victor B. Sochava (1962a), pp. 64–67.

Lüdi, Werner. 1921. Genetisch-dynamische Vegetationskarte des Lauterbrunnentals (Sukzessionskarte). Bern. *Beiträge zur geobotanischen Landesaufnahme der Schweiz,* vol. 9.

Lukicheva, A. N. 1962. Principles of the choice of color designation for small-scale geobotanical maps, *in* Victor B. Sochava (1962a), pp. 244–253.

Maack, Reinhard. 1950. Mapa fitogeografico do estado do Paraná. Curitiba. Serviço de geologia e petrografia do instituto de biologia a pesquisas tecnologicas.

MacConnell, William P., and Lester E. Garvin. 1956. Cover mapping a state from aerial photographs. *Photogrammetric Engineering,* vol. 22, pp. 702–707.

Major, Jack. 1963. Vegetation mapping in California, *in* Reinhold Tüxen (1963a), pp. 195–218.

Malin, James C. 1947. Grassland, "treeless" and "subhumid." *Geographical Review,* vol. XXXVII, pp. 241–250.

Mangenot, Georges. 1955. Écologie et représentation cartographique des forêts équatoriales et tropicales humides, *in* Henri Gaussen (1955), pp. 149–156.

Mangenot, Georges. 1956. *Les recherches sur la végétation dans les régions tropicales humides de l'Afrique occidentale.* Paris. UNESCO, Humid Tropics Research: Study of Tropical Vegetation.

Markgraf, F. 1949. Karte der Waldstufen in Albanien. Zürich. Geobotanisches Forschungsinstitut Rübel, Bericht für das Jahr 1948.

Marres, Paul. 1952. La cartographie parcellaire de la végétation. *Annales de Géographie,* vol. LXI, pp. 363–366.

Marres, Paul. 1955. Phénomènes actuels de surface et l'équilibre du tapis végétal dans la région méditerranéenne, *in* Henri Gaussen (1955), pp. 117–123.

Marschall, Franz. 1963. Vegetationskartierung und Güterzusammenlegung an einem Beispiel aus dem Oberengadin, *in* Reinhold Tüxen (1963a), pp. 473–480.

Martius, Carl Friedrich Philipp. 1858. *Flora brasiliensis.* Leipzig. Oldenburg Verlag.

Matuszkiewicz, Aniela. 1961. Bibliographie der Vegetationskarten Polens. *Excerpta botanica,* sectio B: Sociologica, vol. 3, pp. 68–77.

Matuszkiewicz, Aniela. 1963. La cartographie phytosociologique en Pologne; son état actuel et l'utilisation pratique, *in* Reinhold Tüxen (1963a), pp. 347–352.

Mazing, V. V. 1962. Some problems of large-scale vegetation mapping, *in* Victor B. Sochava (1962a), pp. 47–53.

McArdle, Richard E. 1949. The yield of Douglas fir in the Pacific Northwest. U.S. Dept. of Agriculture, Technical Bulletin 201.

McGee, W. J. 1889. Primeval forests and swamps of northeastern Iowa. Washington, D.C. U.S. Geological Survey, 11th Annual Report, plate XXII.
Meisel, Klaus. 1958. Vergleich zwischen Boden- und Vegetationskarte. Stolzenau an der Weser. *Angewandte Pflanzensoziologie*, vol. 15, pp. 118–130.
Meisel, Klaus. 1963. Die Vegetationskarte als Grundlage für die Beurteilung von Wasserschäden, *in* Reinhold Tüxen (1963a), pp. 423–430.
Mensching, Horst. 1950. Verbreitungskarten von Pflanzengesellschaften als Hilfsmittel für den Morphologen am Beispiel des Wesertales. Stolzenau an der Weser. *Mitteilungen der floristisch-soziologischen Arbeitsgemeinschaft*, N.F., Heft 2.
Merriam, C. Hart. 1898. Life zones and crop zones. Washington, D.C. U.S. Dept. of Agriculture. Division of Biology, Survey Bulletin No. 10.
Meusel, Hermann. 1943. *Vergleichende Arealkunde*. Berlin-Zehlendorf. Bornträger Verlag.
Molinier, René. 1951. La cartographie phytosociologique au service de la prospection agronomique. Association française pour l'avancement des sciences, 70th Congress. *Proceedings*, fasc. 4.
Molinier, René. 1952. Carte des groupements végétaux de la France, feuille Aix S.O. Montpellier. Service de la carte des groupements végétaux.
Molinier, René. 1957. *L'intérêt pédagogique de la carte des groupements végétaux*. Paris. Centre National de la Recherche Scientifique.
Molinier, René. 1958. Le massif de la Sainte Baume: considérations d'ensemble d'après la nouvelle carte de 1/20,000me. Marseille. Musée d'Histoire Naturelle, *Bulletin*, vol. XVIII, pp. 45–104.
Molinier, René, Roger Molinier, and H. Paliot. 1951. Cartes phytogéographiques à diverses échelles de la forêt domaniale de la Sainte Baume (Var). Association française pour l'avancement des sciences, 70th Congress. *Proceedings*, fasc. 4.
Molinier, Roger. 1954. Île du Grand Ribaud (Var): carte des groupements végétaux terrestres et des peuplements marins superficiels. Montpellier. Service de la carte des groupements végétaux.
Molinier, Roger. 1954. Étude des biocénoses marines du Cap Corse. *Vegetatio*, vol. 9, pp. 121–192 and 217–312.
Molinier, Roger. 1961. Carte des associations végétales terrestres et des biocénoses marines dans le sud-est de la France, *in* Henri Gaussen (1961a), pp. 157–170.
Molinier, Roger. 1963. La cartographie des biocénoses marines et ses applications, *in* Reinhold Tüxen (1963a), pp. 103–107.
Molinier, Roger, and J. Picard. 1959. Délimitation et cartographie des peuplements marins benthiques de la mer Méditerranée. Service de la carte phytogéographique. *Bulletin*, série B, vol. 4, pp. 73–84.
Moor, Max, and Urs Schwarz. 1957. Die kartographische Darstellung der Vegetation des Creux-du-Vent Gebietes (Jura des Kantons Neuenburg). Bern. *Beiträge zur geobotanischen Landesaufnahme der Schweiz*, vol. 37.
Moore, C. W. E. 1953. Vegetation map of the southeastern Riverina, New South Wales. *Australian Journal of Botany*, vol. 1, No. 3.
Mráz, K., and V. Samek. 1963. Beiträge zum Problem der Vegetationskartierung mit besonderer Rücksicht auf ihre forstliche Anwendung, *in* Reinhold Tüxen (1963a), pp. 385–393.
Muller, Cornelius H. 1937. Plants as indicators of climate in northeast Mexico. *American Midland Naturalist*, vol. 18, pp. 986–1000.

MULLER, CORNELIUS H. 1939. Relations of the vegetation and climatic types in Nuevo Leon, Mexico. *American Midland Naturalist*, vol. 21, pp. 687–729.
MULLER, CORNELIUS H. 1947. Vegetation and climate of Coahuila, Mexico. *Madroño*, vol. IX, pp. 33–57.
MUNZ, PHILIP A., and DAVID D. KECK. 1959. *A California Flora.* Berkeley. University of California Press.

NASONOVA, O. N. 1962. Pasture and hayland maps and principles of their compilation, in VICTOR B. SOCHAVA (1962a), pp. 145–151.
NEUHÄUSL, ROBERT. 1963. Vegetationskarte von Böhmen und Mährens, Zürich. Geobotanisches Institut Rübel. Bericht No. 34, pp. 107–121.
NEUHÄUSL, ROBERT. 1963. Kartierung der natürlichen Vegetation Mährens, in REINHOLD TÜXEN (1963a), pp. 265–278.
NOIRFALISE, ALBERT. 1961. La cartographie des végétations en Belgique. *Natura monsana*, vol. 14, pp. 45–49.
NOIRFALISE, ALBERT. 1963. Objectifs et problèmes de la cartographie des végétations en Belgique, in REINHOLD TÜXEN (1963a), pp. 95–101.
NOMOKONOV, L. I. 1962. The vegetation map in the comprehensive atlas of the Irkutsk region, in VICTOR B. SOCHAVA (1962a), pp. 208–210.

OBERDORFER, ERICH. 1950. Eine pflanzensoziologische Kartierung im Freiburger Stadtwaldgebiet als Grundlage waldbaulicher Arbeit. Stolzenau an der Weser. *Mitteilungen der floristisch-soziologischen Arbeitsgemeinschaft*, N.F., vol. 2, pp. 54–59.
OBERDORFER, ERICH. 1957. Eine Vegetationskarte von Freiburg im Breisgau. Freiburg. *Berichte der Naturforschenden Gesellschaft*, vol. 47, p. 2.
OEFELEIN, HANS. 1960. Vegetationskartierung: Helvetia. *Excerpta botanica*, sectio B: Sociologica, vol. 2, pp. 215–218.
OLENIN, A. S. 1962. The present state and prospects in the development of peat deposits mapping, in VICTOR B. SOCKAVA (1962a), pp. 114–120.
OZENDA, PAUL. 1961a. La publication de coupures provisoires: raison d'être, techniques possibles; le cas des Alpes du sud, in HENRI GAUSSEN (1961a), pp. 257–264.
OZENDA, PAUL. 1961b. La représentation cartographique de la végétation à moyenne échelle à l'aide de trames. Comité français de techniques cartographiques. *Bulletin*, fasc. 11, pp. 177–182.
OZENDA, PAUL. 1962. Bulletin des laboratoires de biologie végétale de Grenoble et du Lautaret. Grenoble. Faculté des Sciences.
OZENDA, PAUL. 1963. Documents pour la carte de la végétation des Alpes. Grenoble. Laboratoires de biologie végétale de Grenoble et du Lautaret.
OZENDA, PAUL. 1964. *Biogéographie végétale.* Paris. Éditions Doin, Deren & Cie.

PALLMANN, H. 1948. Über die Zusammenarbeit von Bodenkunde und Pflanzensoziologie. St. Gallen. *Verhandlungen der schweizer naturforschenden Gesellschaft.*
PÉRÈS, J. M., and J. PICARD. 1955. Biotopes et biocenoses de la Méditerranée occidentale comparés à ceux de la Manche et de l'Atlantique nord-oriental. *Archives de zoologie experimentale*, vol. 92, No. 1.
PINA MANIQUE E ALBUQUERQUE, J. DE. 1954. Carta ecológica de Portugal. Lisboa. Direcção Geral dos serviços agricolas; serviço editorial da repartição de estudos, informação e propaganda.

PREISING, E. 1956. Erläuterungen zur Karte der natürlichen Vegetation der Umgebung von Göttingen. Stolzenau an der Weser. *Angewandte Pflanzensoziologie*, vol. 13.

RAMAN, K. G. 1962. Classification of geographical complexes in Latvia and the possible use of these principles in geobotanical mapping, *in* VICTOR B. SOCHAVA (1962a), pp. 178–185.

RAUNKIAER, C. 1934. *The Life Forms of Plants and Statistical Plant Geography.* Oxford. Clarendon Press.

REGEL, C. V. 1949. Landschaft und Pflanzenverein. *Geographia Helvetica*, vol. IV, pp. 243–254.

RENAUD, PAUL. 1949. Cartographie parcellaire appliquée à l'apiculture. *in* G. KUHNHOLTZ-LORDAT, *La cartographie parcellaire de la végétation.* Paris. Institut national de la recherche agronomique.

RETZER, JOHN L. 1953. Soil-vegetation survey of wild-lands. *Journal of Forestry*, vol. 51, pp. 615–619.

REY, PAUL. 1955. Recensement cartographique des milieux et analyse écologique des cartes de la végétation, *in* HENRI GAUSSEN (1955), pp. 169–180.

REY, PAUL. 1956. Les cartes de la végétation des Pyrénées au 200,000ᵉ. Toulouse. 2ᵉ congrès international d'études pyrénéennes 1954. *Actes*, vol. 3, section 11, pp. 17–22.

REY, PAUL. 1957a. L'interpretation des photographies aériennes. Service de la carte phytogéographique. *Bulletin*, série A, vol. 2, pp. 5–44.

REY, PAUL. 1957b. Initiation à l'utilisation scientifique et pédagogique des cartes de la végétation. Service de la carte phytogéographique. *Bulletin*, série A, vol. 2, pp. 73–86.

REY, PAUL. 1958. La cartographie, botanique en couleurs. Service de la carte phytogéographique. *Bulletin*, série A, vol. 3, pp. 11–19.

REY, PAUL. 1961. De la clarté en toute chose, même en cartographie de la végétation, *in* HENRI GAUSSEN (1961a), pp. 283–288.

REY, PAUL. 1962a. Écologie et agronomie: la cartographie de la végétation à l'épreuve de l'agronomie. *Bulletin technique d'information des services agricoles*, No. 172, pp. 1–3.

REY, PAUL. 1962b. Les perspectives fondamentales de la cartographie de la végétation. *Comité français de techniques cartographiques*, vol. 14, pp. 69–73.

REY, PAUL. 1962c. Généralisation cartographique de la végétation. Toulouse. Service de la carte de la végétation. *Notes et Documents*, N. 5.

REY, PAUL. 1962d. Recherche biogéographique, carte de la végétation et aménagement de l'espace rural. Toulouse. Service de la carte de la végétation. *Notes et Documents*, No. 6.

RICHARDS, PAUL W., A. G. TANSLEY, and A. S. WATT. 1940. The recording of structure, life form and flora of tropical forest communities as a basis of their classification. *Journal of Ecology*, vol. 28, pp. 224–239.

RITCHIE, J. C. 1958. A vegetation map from the southern spruce forest zone of Manitoba. Ottawa. *Geographical Bulletin*, No. 12.

ROBERTY, GUY. 1961. La végétation des régions dépourvues de tradition agricole précisément définie et sa représentation cartographique, *in* HENRI GAUSSEN (1961a), pp. 103–110.

ROSENBERG, V. A., 1962. Principles of the compilation of forest maps, *in* VICTOR B. SOCHAVA (1962a), pp. 98–102.

Roussine, N., and C. Sauvage. 1961. Afrique du Nord. *Excerpta botanica*, sectio B: Sociologica, vol. 3, pp. 48–50.
Rowe, J. S. 1959. Forest regions of Canada. Ottawa. Dept. of Northern Affairs and National Resources, Forestry Branch.
Rowe, J. S. 1961. The level-of-integration concept and ecology. *Ecology*, vol. 42, pp. 420–427.
Rübel, Eduard. 1916. Vorschläge zur geobotanischen Kartographie. Bern. *Beiträge zur geobotanischen Landesaufnahme der Schweiz*, vol. 1.
Rübel, Eduard. 1930. *Die Pflanzengesellschaften der Erde.* Bern. Huber Verlag.

Salisbury, E. J. 1931. The standardization of descriptions of plant communities. *Journal of Ecology*, vol. 19, pp. 177–189.
Sappa, Francesco and Giovanni Charrier. 1949. Carta della vegetazione della val Sangone (Alpi Cozie). Florence. *Nuovo Giornale botanico italiano*, N.S. vol. LVI.
Sargent, C. S. 1884a. Map showing the position of the forests, prairie and treeless regions of North America exclusive of Mexico. *10th Census of the United States*, vol. 9. Washington, D.C.
Sargent, C. S. 1884b. Vegetation maps of individual states. *10th Census of the United States*, vol. 9. Washington, D.C. Includes the following states (with the pages they face given in parentheses): Alabama (524), Arkansas (544), Florida (522), Georgia (519), Louisiana (536), Maine (496), Michigan (550), Minnesota (558), North Carolina (514), South Carolina (519), Texas (541), West Virginia (512), Wisconsin (554).
Sayago, Marcelino. 1957. La cartografía botánica en colores. Córdoba, Argentina. *Revista de la facultad de ciencias exactas físicas y naturales*, vol. XIX, pp. 1–16.
Saxton, W. T. 1924. Phases of vegetation under monsoon conditions. *Journal of Ecology*, vol. 12, pp. 1–38.
Scamoni, Alexis. 1950. Kriterien bei der Standortskartierung im Bereich des Dilluviums von Mecklenburg, Brandenburg und Sachsen-Anhalt. *Allgemeine Forstzeitschrift*, vol. 5, pp. 435–438.
Scamoni, Alexis. 1954. *Waldgesellschaften und Waldstandorte.* Berlin. Akademie Verlag.
Scamoni, Alexis. 1956. Vegetationsstudien im Waldschutzgebiet "Fauler Ort" und in den angrenzenden Waldungen. *Feddes Repertorium*, Beiheft 137, pp. 55–109.
Scamoni, Alexis. 1958a. Karte der natürlichen Vegetation der Deutschen Demokratischen Republik. *Klimaatlas der Deutschen Demokratischen Republik*, vol. 1, Ergänzungsband. Berlin.
Scamoni, Alexis. 1958b. Zur Karte der natürlichen Vegetation der Deutschen Demokratischen Republik. Remagen. *Berichte zur deutschen Landeskunde*, vol. 21, pp. 53–74.
Scamoni, Alexis. 1963. Prinzipien der Karte der natürlichen Vegetation der Deutschen Demokratischen Republik, *in* Reinhold Tüxen (1963a), pp. 47–59.
Scharfetter, Rudolf. 1932. Die kartographische Darstellung der Pflanzengesellschaften, *in* Emil Abderhalden, *Handbuch der biologischen Arbeitsmethoden*, Abteilung XI, Teil 5, 1. Hälfte, pp. 77–164. Berlin. Urban & Schwarzenberg.
Scharfetter, Rudolf. 1954. Erläuterungen zur Vegetationskarte der

Steiermark. Naturwissenschaftlicher Verein für Steiermark. *Mitteilungen*, vol. 84, pp. 121–158.

SCHIMPER, A. F. W. 1898. *Pflanzengeographie auf physiologischer Grundlage*. Jena. Fischer Verlag.

SCHIMPER, A. F. W., and F. C. VON FABER. 1935. *Pflanzengeographie auf physiologischer Grundlage*, 3rd ed. Jena. Fischer Verlag.

SCHLENKER, G. 1950. Forstliche Standortskartierung in Württemberg. *Allgemeine Forstzeitschrift*, vol. 5, pp. 418–422.

SCHMID, EMIL. 1940. Die Vegetationskartierung der Schweiz im Masstab 1:200,000. Zürich. Geobotanisches Forschungsinstitut Rübel. Bericht für das Jahr 1939, pp. 76–85.

SCHMID, EMIL. 1942. Über einige Grundbegriffe der Biozoenologie. Zürich. Geobotanisches Forschungsinstitut Rübel. Bericht für das Jahr 1941.

SCHMID, EMIL. 1944. Kausale Vegetationsforschung. Zürich. Geobotanisches Forschungsinstitut Rübel. Bericht für das Jahr 1943.

SCHMID, EMIL. 1948. *Vegetationskarte der Schweiz*. Bern. Huber Verlag.

SCHMID, EMIL. 1949. *Vegetation des Mediterrangebiets*. Zürich. Orell-Füssli A.G.

SCHMID, EMIL. 1954. Anleitung zu Vegetationsaufnahmen. *Vierteljahresschrift der naturforschenden Gesellschaft in Zürich*, vol. 99, Beiheft 1.

SCHMID, EMIL. 1955. Principes de cartographie mondiale aux échelles du 200,000ᵉ et du 1,000,000ᵉ basés sur les unités biocénologiques, *in* HENRI GAUSSEN (1955), pp. 157–161.

SCHMID, EMIL. 1961. Erläuterungen zur Vegetationskarte der Schweiz. Bern. *Beiträge zur geobotanischen Landesaufnahme der Schweiz*, vol. 39.

SCHMITHÜSEN, JOSEF. 1942. Vegetationsforschung und ökologische Standortslehre in ihrer Bedeutung für die Geographie der Kulturlandschaft. *Zeitschrift der Gesellschaft für Erdkunde zu Berlin*, pp. 113–157.

SCHMITHÜSEN, JOSEF. 1959. *Allgemeine Vegetationsgeographie*. Berlin. De Gruyter & Co.

SCHMITHÜSEN, JOSEF. 1963. Der wissenschaftliche Inhalt der Vegetationskarten verschiedener Masstäbe, *in* REINHOLD TÜXEN (1963a), pp. 321–334.

SCHOUW, JOACHIM FREDERIK. 1823. *Grundzüge einer allgemeinen Pflanzengeographie (mit Atlas)*. Berlin.

SCHOUW, JOACHIM FREDERIK. 1838. Pflanzengeographische Karte der Erde. Leipzig. *Berghaus' physikalischer Atlas*.

SCHRÖTER, CARL. 1910. Über pflanzengeographische Karten. Brussels. 3rd International Botanical Congress. *Proceedings*, vol. 2, pp. 97–154.

SCHULZ, G. E. 1962. Phenological maps and their use in geobotany, *in* VICTOR B. SOCHAVA (1962a), pp. 87–91.

SCHWEINFURTH, ULRICH. 1957. Verbreitung der Vegetationstypen im Himalaya, *in* ULRICH SCHWEINFURTH, Die horizontale und vertikale Verbreitung der Vegetation im Himalaya. *Bonner Geographische Abhandlungen*, vol. 20.

SCHWEINFURTH, ULRICH. 1958. Über kartographische Darstellungen der Vegetation des Himalaya. *Erdkunde*, vol. XII, pp. 120–125.

SCHWICKERATH, MATHIAS. 1954. *Die Landschaft und ihre Wandlung auf geobotanischer und geographischer Grundlage entwickelt und erläutert im Bereich des Messtischblattes Stolberg*. Aachen. Georgi Verlag.

SCHWICKERATH, MATHIAS. 1963. Assoziationsdiagramme und ihre Bedeutung für die Vegetationskartierung, *in* REINHOLD TÜXEN (1963a), pp. 11–38.

SEIBERT, PAUL. 1954. Vegetationskarte des Graf Görtzischen Forstbezirks Schlitz. Stolzenau an der Weser. *Angewandte Pflanzensoziologie*, vol. 9.

SEIBERT, PAUL. 1958. Die Pflanzengesellschaften im Naturschutzgebiet "Pupplinger Au." München. Bayrische Landesstelle für Gewässerkunde. *Landschaftspflege und Vegetationskunde*, Heft 1.

SEIBERT, PAUL. 1963. Pflanzensoziologische und bodenkundliche Untersuchungen im Naturschutzgebiet "Pupplinger Au" als Grundlage für die Massnahmen der Wasserwirtschaft, *in* REINHOLD TÜXEN (1963a), pp. 431–439.

SENDTNER, OTTO. 1854. Karte der Filze bei Rosenheim, *in* OTTO SENDTNER, *Die Vegetationsverhältnisse Südbayerns nach den Grundsätzen der Pflanzengeographie und mit Bezugnahme auf die Landescultur geschildert*. Müchen.

SHANTZ, HOMER LEROY. 1911. Natural vegetation as an indicator of the capabilities of land for crop production in the Great Plains area. U.S. Dept. of Agriculture, Bureau of Plant Industry, Bulletin 201.

SHANTZ, HOMER LEROY. 1923. The natural vegetation of the Great Plains region. *Annals of the Association of American Geographers*, vol. 13, pp. 81–107.

SHANTZ, HOMER LEROY, and R. L. PIEMEISEL. 1924. Indicator significance of the natural vegetation of the southwestern desert region. *Journal of Agricultural Research*, vol. 28, No. 8.

SHANTZ, HOMER LEROY, and RAPHAEL ZON. 1923. Natural vegetation of the United States. U.S. Dept. of Agriculture. *Atlas of American Agriculture*.

SHCHELKUNOVA, R. P. 1962. The use of aerophotography in the compilation of geobotanical pasture maps in the Far North, *in* VICTOR B. SOCHAVA (1962a), pp. 164–168.

SHREVE, FORREST. 1914. *A Montane Rain Forest*. Carnegie Institution of Washington, Publication No. 199.

SHREVE, FORREST. 1915. *The Vegetation of a Desert Mountain Range as Conditioned by Climatic Factors*. Carnegie Institution of Washington, Publication No. 217.

SHREVE, FORREST. 1917. Vegetation areas of the United States. *Geographical Review*, vol. 3, facing p. 124.

SHREVE, FORREST. 1942. The desert vegetation of North America. *Botanical Review*, vol. 8, pp. 199–246.

SHUMILOVA, L. V. 1962. Vegetation mapping as a basis of phytogeographical subdivision (rayonization), *in:* VICTOR B. SOCHAVA. (1962a), pp. 68–71.

SIGAFOOS, ROBERT S. 1958. Vegetation of northwestern North America as an aid in interpretation of geologic data. Geological Survey, Bulletin 1061-E.

SISSINGH, G., and P. TIDEMAN. 1960. Een vegetatiekartering van het kaartblad Zevenaar, 1:25,000. *Mededelingen Landbouwhoogeschool Wageningen*, vol. 60, No. 13.

SOBOLEV, L. N. 1962. Principles in the compilation of a pasture and hayland map, *in:* VICTOR B. SOCHAVA, (1962a), pp. 139–144.

SOCHAVA, VICTOR B. 1954. Les principes et les problèmes de la cartographie géobotanique, *in Essais de botanique*. Leningrad. Éditions de l'Académie des Sciences de l'U.R.S.S., pp. 273–288.

SOCHAVA, VICTOR B. 1958. The most significant achievements in mapping the vegetation of the U.S.S.R. in the past 40 years. *Izvestia of the All-Union Geographical Society*, vol. 90, pp. 109–117.

SOCHAVA, VICTOR B. 1961. Quelques conclusions méthodiques d'après les travaux sur la cartographie de la végétation de l'U.R.S.S., in HENRI GAUSSEN, (1961a), pp. 203–210.

SOCHAVA, VICTOR B. (ed.)   1962a.   *Principles and Methods of Vegetation Mapping.* Leningrad. Academy of Sciences of the U.S.S.R. (In Russian).

SOCHAVA, VICTOR B.   1962b.   Mapping problems in geobotany, *in* VICTOR B. SOCHAVA (1962a), pp. 5–27.

SOCHAVA, VICTOR B., and T. I. ISACHENKO (eds.). 1963 to present. *Geobotanical Mapping.* Leningrad. Komarov Botanical Institute, Academy of Sciences of the U.S.S.R. Annual.

SOCIETY OF AMERICAN FORESTERS.   1954.   Forest cover types of North America (exclusive of Mexico). Washington, D.C.

SOLOVEI, I. N.   1962.   Vegetation mapping during large-scale soil mapping in Belo-Russia, *in* VICTOR B. SOCHAVA (1962a), pp. 200–203.

SOÓ, REZSÖ VON.   1954.   Angewandte Pflanzensoziologie und Kartierung in Ungarn. *Festschrift Aichinger,* pp. 337–345. Wien. Springer Verlag.

SOÓ, REZSÖ VON.   1960.   Bibliographia phytosociologica: Hungaria. Vegetationskartierung. *Excerpta botanica,* sectio B: Sociologica, vol. 2, pp. 120–121.

SOUGNEZ, N., and ALBERT NOIRFALISE.   1954.   Significance and practical application of a phytosociological grassland chart. Paris. European Grassland Conference.

SOUGNEZ, N., and R. TOURNAY.   1963.   Cartographie de la végétation (Belgium). *Excerpta botanica,* sectio B: Sociologica, vol. 5, pp. 250–257.

SPEIDEL, BERTHOLD.   1963.   Vegetationskartierung als Grundlage zur Melioration salzgeschädigter Wiesen an der Werra, *in* REINHOLD TÜXEN (1963a), pp. 457–468.

SPURR, STEPHEN H.   1960.   *Photogrammetry and Photo-Interpretation.* New York. The Ronald Press Co.

STAMP, L. DUDLEY.   1934.   Vegetation formulae. *Journal of Ecology,* vol. 22, pp. 299–303.

STAMP, L. DUDLEY.   1961.   The world land-use survey, *in* HENRI GAUSSEN (1961a), pp. 75–81.

STEENIS, C. G. G. J. VAN.   1958.   Vegetation map of Malaysia. Paris. United Nations Educational, Scientific and Cultural Organization.

STEUBING, LORE.   1963.   Ergebnisse einer Vegetationskartierung in Windschutzgebieten, *in* REINHOLD TÜXEN (1963a), pp. 469–472.

STEWART, ROBERT E., and JOHN W. BRAINERD.   1945.   Patuxent Research Refuge. Washington, D.C. U.S. Fish and Wildlife Service.

SUKACHEV, V. N.   1947.   The bases of forest biogeocenology. Moscow. Jubilee Sbornik of the Academy of Sciences of the U.S.S.R.

SUKACHEV, V. N.   1954.   Quelques problèmes théoriques de la phytocénologie, *in Essais de botanique.* Leningrad. Academy of Sciences of the U.S.S.R. Pp. 310–330.

SUKACHEV, V. N.   1960.   The correlation of the concept "forest ecosystem" and "forest biogeocenose" and their importance for the classification of forests. *Silva Fennica,* vol. 105, pp. 94–97.

SUZUKI, TOKIO.   1963.   Schneetälchen-Gesellschaften des Gassan Gebirges in Japan, *in* REINHOLD TÜXEN (1963a), pp. 219–230.

TANSLEY, A. G.   1935.   The use and abuse of vegetational concepts and terms. *Ecology,* vol. 16, pp. 284–307.

TANSLEY, A. G., and T. F. CHIPP.   1926.   *Aims and Methods in the Study of Vegetation.* London. British Empire Vegetation Committee.

TERECHOV, N. M. 1962. Coordination of geobotanical maps with physiographic and other maps, *in* VICTOR B. SOCHAVA (1962a), pp. 254–258.

THILL, A. 1961. La cartographie des végétations et ses applications forestières. *Bulletin de la Société Royale Forestière de Belgique.* Juillet.

TIDEMAN, P. 1963. Vegetationskartierung als Grundlage für Verwaltungspläne in Naturschutzgebieten in den Niederlanden, *in* REINHOLD TÜXEN (1963a), pp. 481–490.

TIVY, JOY. 1954. Reconnaissance vegetation survey of certain hill grazings in the Southern Uplands. *Scottish Geographical Magazine,* vol. 70, pp. 21–33.

TOMASELLI, RUGGERO. 1958. *Plant Communities of the Western Half of the University of Kansas Natural History Reservation.* Pavia, Italy. Casa Editrice Renzo Cortina.

TOMASELLI, RUGGERO. 1961. Relations entre réalisateurs et utilisateurs de cartes de végétation en Italie, *in* HENRI GAUSSEN (1961a), pp. 275-282.

TOMASELLI, RUGGERO. 1963–1964. Interpretazione e rappresentazione cartografica della vegetazione. *La Scuola in Azione,* vol. 6, pp. 58-76.

TRAPNELL, C. G. 1948. Vegetation-soil map of Northern Rhodesia. Lusaka. Dept. of Agriculture, Forestry Branch.

TRAUTMANN, WERNER. 1963. Methoden und Erfahrungen bei der Vegetationskartierung der Wälder und Forsten, *in* REINHOLD TÜXEN (1963a), pp. 119–127.

TROCHAIN, JEAN L. 1940. *Contribution à l'étude de la végétation du Sénégal.* Dakar. Institut français d'Afrique noire.

TROCHAIN, JEAN L. 1957. Accord interafricain sur la définition des types de végétation de l'Afrique tropicale. Brazzaville. *Bulletin de l'Institut d'Études Centrafricaines,* N.S., No. 13–14, pp. 55–93.

TROCHAIN, JEAN L. 1961. Représentation cartographique des types de végétation intertropicaux africains, *in* HENRI GAUSSEN (1961a), pp. 87–102.

TROLL, CARL. 1936. Termiten-Savannen. Stuttgart. *in: Länderkundliche Forschung: Festschrift Norbert Krebs,* pp. 275–312.

TROLL, CARL. 1939. Vegetationskarte der Nanga Parbat Gruppe. Leipzig. Deutsches Museum für Länderkunde. *Wissenschaftliche Veröffentlichungen,* N.S., No. 7.

TROLL, CARL. 1941. Studien zur vergleichenden Geographie der Hochgebirge. Bonn. Friedrich Wilhelms Universität, Bericht 23, pp. 49–96.

TROLL, CARL. 1943. Die Frostwechselhäufigkeit in den Luft- und Bodenklimaten der Erde. *Meteorologische Zeitschrift,* vol. 60, pp. 161–171.

TROLL, CARL. 1948. Der asymmetrische Aufbau der Vegetationszonen und Vegetationsstufen auf der Nord- und Südhalbkugel. Zürich. Geobotanisches Forschungsinstitut Rübel. Bericht für das Jahr 1947, pp. 46–83.

TROLL, CARL. 1950. Die geographische Landschaft und ihre Erforschung. *Studium Generale,* vol. 3, pp. 163–181.

TROLL, CARL. 1951. Das Pflanzenkleid der Tropen in seiner Abhängigkeit von Klima, Boden und Mensch. Remagen. Verlag des Amtes für Landeskunde.

TROLL, CARL. 1955. Der jahreszeitliche Ablauf des Naturgeschehens in den verschiedenen Klimagürteln der Erde. *Studium Generale,* vol. 8, pp. 713–733.

TROLL, CARL. 1956. Der Klima- und Vegetationsaufbau der Erde im Lichte neuer Forschungen. Mainz. Akademie der Wissenschaften und Literatur. *Abhandlungen,* pp. 216–229.

Tüxen, Jes. 1963. Vegetationskarten als Hilfsmittel der Altlandschafts-forschung am Beispiel des Messtischblattes Stolzenau an der Weser, *in* Reinhold Tüxen (1963a), pp. 313–319.

Tüxen, Reinhold. 1937. Die Pflanzengesellschaften Nordwestdeutschlands. Stolzenau an der Weser. *Mitteilungen der floristisch-soziologischen Arbeits-gemeinschaft*, vol. 3.

Tüxen, Reinhold. 1942a. Über die Verwendung pflanzensoziologischer Untersuchungen zur Beurteilung von Schäden des Grünlandes. *Deutsche Wasserwirtschaft*, vol. 37, No. 10/11.

Tüxen, Reinhold. 1942b. Aus der Arbeitsstelle für theoretische und ange-wandte Pflanzensoziologie der tierärztlichen Hochschule Hannover. Han-nover. Jahresbericht der naturhistorischen Gesellschaft.

Tüxen, Reinhold. 1950a. Neue Methoden der Wald- und Forstkartierung. Stolzenau an der Weser. *Mitteilungen der floristisch-soziologischen Arbeits-gemeinschaft*, N.F., vol. 2.

Tüxen, Reinhold. 1950b. Grundriss einer Systematik der nitrophilen Un-krautgesellschaften in der eurosibirischen Region Europas. Stolzenau an der Weser. *Mitteilungen der floristisch-soziologischen Arbeitsgemeinschaft*, N.F., vol. 2, pp. 94–175.

Tüxen, Reinhold. 1952a. Hecken und Gebüsche. Hamburg. *Mitteilungen der geographischen Gesellschaft*, vol. 50, pp. 85–117.

Tüxen, Reinhold. 1952b. Ein einfacher Weg zur nachträglichen Fest-stellung von Entwässerungsschäden. Stolzenau an der Weser. *Mitteilungen der floristisch-soziologischen Arbeitsgemeinschaft*, N.F., vol. 3.

Tüxen, Reinhold. 1954a. Pflanzengesellschaften und Grundwasserganglinien. Stolzenau an der Weser. *Angewandte Pflanzensoziologie*, vol. 8.

Tüxen, Reinhold. 1954b. Die Wasserstufenkarte und ihre Bedeutung für die nachträgliche Feststellung von Änderungen im Wasserhaushalt einer Landschaft. Stolzenau an der Weser. *Angewandte Pflanzensoziologie*, vol. 8.

Tüxen, Reinhold. 1954c. Über die räumliche, durch Relief und Gestein bedingte Ordnung der natürlichen Waldgesellschaften am nördlichen Rande des Harzes. *Vegetatio*, vol. V–VI, pp. 454–478.

Tüxen, Reinhold. 1956a. Baltrum. Stolzenau an der Weser. Bundesanstalt für Vegetationskartierung.

Tüxen, Reinhold. 1956b. Die heutige potentielle natürliche Vegetation als Gegenstand der Vegetationskartierung. Stolzenau an der Weser. *Ange-wandte Pflanzensoziologie*, vol. 13, pp. 5–42.

Tüxen, Reinhold. 1957a. Wegweiser durch die pflanzensoziologisch-syste-matische Abteilung, Botanischer Garten, Bremen. Bremen, Gartenbauamt.

Tüxen, Reinhold. 1957b. Die heutige natürliche potentielle Vegetation als Gegenstand der Vegetationskartierung. Remagen. *Berichte zur deutschen Landeskunde*, vol. 19, pp. 200–246.

Tüxen, Reinhold. 1958. Die Eichung von Pflanzengesellschaften auf Torf-profiltypen. Stolzenau an der Weser. *Angewandte Pflanzensoziologie*, vol. 15, pp. 131–141.

Tüxen, Reinhold. 1959. Bibliographie der Verbreitungs- und Arealkarten von Pflanzengesellschaften. *Excerpta botanica*, sectio B: Sociologica, vol. 1, pp. 227–261.

Tüxen, Reinhold. 1961. Bemerkungen zu einer Vegetationskarte Europas, *in* Henri Gaussen (1961a), pp. 61–73.

Tüxen, Reinhold (ed.). 1963a. *Bericht über das internationale Symposium für Vegetationskartierung vom 23.–26.3. 1959 in Stolzenau an der Weser.* Weinheim. Cramer Verlag.

TÜXEN, REINHOLD. 1963b. Typen von Vegetationskarten und ihre Erarbeitung, *in* REINHOLD TÜXEN (1963a), pp. 139–154.

TÜXEN, REINHOLD, and G. HENTSCHEL. 1954. Bibliographie der Vegetationskarten Deutschlands. Stolzenau an der Weser. *Mitteilungen der floristischsoziologischen Arbeitsgemeinschaft,* N.F., vol. 5.

TÜXEN, REINHOLD, and H. MEISSNER. 1959. Vegetationskartierung. *Excerpta botanica,* sectio B: Sociologica, vol. 1, pp. 50–51.

TÜXEN, REINHOLD, and E. PREISING. 1950. Zentralstelle für Vegetationskartierung: Geschichte, Aufbau und Aufgaben. Stolzenau an der Weser. Zentralstelle für Vegetationskartierung.

TÜXEN, REINHOLD, and E. PREISING. 1951. Erfahrungsgrundlagen für die pflanzensoziologische Kartierung des nordwestdeutschen Grünlandes. Stolzenau an der Weser. *Angewandte Pflanzensoziologie,* vol. 4.

U.S. FOREST SERVICE. 1934. Areas characterized by major forest types, states of Alabama, Florida, Georgia, Louisiana and Mississippi. New Orleans, La. Southern Forest Experiment Station.

U.S. FOREST SERVICE. 1940. Areas characterized by major forest types, states of North and South Carolina. Asheville, N.C. Appalachian Forest Experiment Station.

U.S. FOREST SERVICE. 1941. Areas characterized by major forest types, Virginia. Asheville, N.C. Appalachian Forest Experiment Station.

U.S. FOREST SERVICE. 1952. The timber supply situation in Florida. Washington, D.C. Forest Resource Report No. 6.

VEATCH, J. O. 1953. *Soils and Land of Michigan.* East Lansing, Mich. Michigan State College Press.

VICTOROV, S. V. 1962. Geobotanical indication maps and methods of their compilation, *in* VICTOR B. SOCHAVA (1962a), pp. 72–76.

VICTOROV, S. V., A. VOSTOKOVA, and D. D. VISHIVKIN. 1964. *A Short Guide to Geobotanical Mapping.* New York. The Macmillan Co.

VINOGRADOV, B. V. 1962. The major problems of desert vegetation mapping using aerophotos, *in* VICTOR B. SOCHAVA (1962a), pp. 215–222.

VORONOV, A. G., and A. M. CHELTSOV-BEBUTOV. 1962. On the methods of biogeographical mapping of open landscapes, *in* VICTOR B. SOCHAVA (1962a), pp. 186–193.

WAGNER, HEINRICH. 1948. Die Bedeutung der Vegetationskartierung für Forschung und Praxis. Wien. *Jahrbuch der Hochschule für Bodenkultur,* vol. 2, pp. 23–26.

WAGNER, HEINRICH. 1961a. Die Fassung der Gesellschaftseinheiten auf Grund der grossmasstäbigen Vegetationskartierung, *in* HENRI GAUSSEN (1961a), pp. 171–178.

WAGNER, HEINRICH. 1961b. Bibliographie der Vegetationskarten Osterreichs. *Excerpta botanica,* sectio B: Sociologica, vol. 3, pp. 305–315.

WAGNER, HEINRICH. 1963. Vegetationskartierung im Dienste der Beweissicherung von Flusskraftwerken in Österreich, *in* REINHOLD TÜXEN (1963a), pp. 413–422.

WAGNER, PHILIP L. 1957. A contribution to structural vegetation mapping. *Annals of the Association of American Geographers,* vol. 47, pp. 363–369.

WAIBEL, LEO. 1943. Place names as an aid in the reconstruction of the original vegetation of Cuba. *Geographical Review,* vol. XXXIII, pp. 376–396.

WALLACE, A. R. 1876. *The Geographic Distribution of Animals.* London. Macmillan & Co.

WALTER, HEINRICH. 1951. *Grundlagen der Pflanzenverbreitung.* Stuttgart. Ulmer Verlag.

WALTER, HEINRICH. 1955. Le facteur eau dans les régions arides et sa signification pour l'organisation de la végétation dans les contrées subtropicales, *in* HENRI GAUSSEN (1955), pp. 27–39.

WALTHER, KURT. 1950. Unkraut-Herden als Zeiger grundwassergeschädigter Grünlandgesellschaften auf Niedermoorböden. Stolzenau an der Weser. *Mitteilungen der floristisch-soziologischen Arbeitsgemeinschaft,* N.F., vol. 2.

WALTHER, KURT. 1957. Vegetationskarte der deutschen Flusstäler: mittlere Elbe oberhalb Damnatz. Stolzenau an der Weser. Bundesstelle für Vegetationskartierung.

WALTHER, KURT. 1960. Pflanzensoziologie und Kulturtechnik. *Zeitschrift für Kulturtechnik,* vol. 1, pp. 65–76.

WALTHER, KURT. 1963. Die Vegetationskartierung in den einführenden pflanzensoziologischen Lehrgängen der Bundesstelle für Vegetationskartierung, *in* REINHOLD TÜXEN (1963a), pp. 155–165.

WANGERIN, WALTER. 1915. Vorläufige Beiträge zur kartographischen Darstellung der Vegetationsformationen im norddeutschen Flachland unter besonderer Berücksichtigung der Moore. *Berichte der deutschen botanischen Gesellschaft,* vol. 33, pp. 168–199.

WEIDEMANN, DORRIT. 1950. Vegetationskartierung—eine wichtige Grundlage der deutschen Forstwirtschaft. *Forst und Holz,* vol. 5, pp. 27–39.

WEISE, F. 1952. Pflanzensoziologische Grünlandkartierung 1951. Braunschweig-Völkenrode. *Landbauforschung Völkenrode,* vol. 2, pp. 44–45.

WELLS, PHILIP V. 1962. Vegetation in relation to geological substratum and fire in the San Luis Obispo quadrangle, California. *Ecological Monographs,* vol. 32, pp. 79–103.

WENZEL, ALFRED. 1963. Technische Erfahrung in der Vegetationskartographie, *in* REINHOLD TÜXEN (1963a), pp. 167–172.

WESTHOFF, V. 1954. Die Vegetationskartierung in den Niederlanden. Wien. *Festschrift Aichinger,* pp. 1223–1231. Springer Verlag.

WESTHOFF, V. 1958a. Boden- und Vegetationskartierung von Wald- und Forstgesellschaften im Quercion robori-petraeae-Gebiet der Veluwe (Niederlande). Stolzenau an der Weser. *Angewandte Pflanzensoziologie,* vol. 15.

WESTHOFF, V. 1958b. Een gedetaillerde vegetatiekartering van een deel van het bosgebied van Middachten. Wageningen. Publicatie L.E.B.–Fonds.

WESTHOFF, V. 1961. Bibliographia phytosociologica; Neerlandia: Vegetationskartierung. *Excerpta botanica,* sectio B: Sociologica, vol. 3, pp. 140–141.

WESTVELD, MARINUS. 1951. Vegetation mapping as a guide to better silviculture. *Ecology,* vol. 32, pp. 508–517.

WESTVELD, MARINUS. 1952. A method of evaluating forest site quality. Upper Darby, Pa. Northeastern Forest Experiment Station, Station Paper No. 48.

WESTVELD, MARINUS. 1954. Use of plant indicators as an index to site quality. Boston. Society of American Foresters, New England Section.

WIESLANDER, A. EVERETT. 1934. Vegetation types of California, Ramona quadrangle. Berkeley, Calif. California Forest and Range Experiment Station.

WIESLANDER, A. EVERETT. 1935. A vegetation type map of California. *Madroño,* vol. 3, pp. 140–144.

WIESLANDER, A. EVERETT. 1937. Vegetation types of California, Tujunga quadrangle. Berkeley, Calif. California Forest and Range Experiment Station.

WIESLANDER, A. EVERETT. 1944. Forest survey type maps. Berkeley, Calif. California Forest and Range Experiment Station.

WIESLANDER, A. EVERETT. 1949. The timberstand and vegetation-soil maps of California. Berkeley, Calif. California Forest and Range Experiment Station.

WIESLANDER, A. EVERETT. 1955. California cooperative soil-vegetation surveys. Berkeley, Calif. California Forest and Range Experiment Station.

WIESLANDER, A. EVERETT. 1956. Uses of soil-vegetation survey information, California Cooperative Soil-Vegetation Survey. Berkeley, Calif. California Forest and Range Experiment Station.

WIESLANDER, A. EVERETT, and R. E. STORIE. 1952. The vegetation-soil survey in California and its use in the management of wild lands for yield of timber, forage and water. *Journal of Forestry*, vol. 50, pp. 521–526.

WIESLANDER, A. EVERETT, and R. E. STORIE. 1953. Vegetational approach to soil surveys in wild land areas. Soil Science Society of America, *Proceedings*, vol. 17, pp. 143–147.

WIESLANDER, A. EVERETT, and R. C. WILSON. 1942. Classifying forest and other vegetation from air photographs. *Photogrammetric Engineering*, vol. 8, pp. 203–215.

WILLIAMS, R. J. 1955. Vegetation regions (of Australia). Canberra, Australia. Dept. of National Development. *Atlas of Australian Resources.*

WITTICH, W. 1950. Die Auswertung der Standortskartierung durch die Forsteinrichtung. *Allgemeine Forstzeitschrift*, vol. 5, pp. 413–416.

WOOSTER, L. C. 1876. Vegetation map of the lower St. Croix district, Wisconsin. *in:* T. C. CHAMBERLIN, *Geology of Wisconsin*, p. 146. Madison, Wis. 1882.

WORLD METEOROLOGICAL ORGANIZATION. 1956. *International Cloud Atlas.* Geneva.

WRABER, MAKS. 1963. Allgemeine Orientierungskarte der potentiellen natürlichen Vegetation im slowenischen Küstenland als Grundlage für die Wiederbewaldung der degradierten Karst- und Flyschgebiete, *in* REINHOLD TÜXEN (1963a), pp. 369–384.

WYATT-SMITH, J. 1962. Some vegetation types and a preliminary vegetation map of Malaya. Kuala Lumpur. Regional Conference of Southeast Asian Geographers.

YOUNG, ROBERT N., and PAUL F. GRIFFIN. 1957. Recent land-use changes in the San Francisco Bay area. *Geographical Review*, vol. XLVII, pp. 396–405.

ZIANI, PETAR. 1963. Die Vegetationskarte als Grundlage der Verbesserung der degradierten Bodenflächen im Ost-Mittelmeergebiet, *in* REINHOLD TÜXEN (1963a), pp. 395–407.

ZOHARY, M. 1947. A vegetation map of western Palestine. *Journal of Ecology*, vol. 34, pp. 1–18, map facing p. 18.

ZONNEVELD, I. S. 1960. *De Brabantse Biesbosch.* Wageningen. Centrum voor Landbouwpublikaties.

ZONNEVELD, I. S. 1963. Vegetationskartierung eines Süsswassergezeitendeltas (Biesbosch), *in* REINHOLD TÜXEN (1963a), pp. 279–296.

APPENDIX

Classification of Vegetation by Drude (Cain and Castro, 1959)

I.   CLOSED LAND FORMATIONS

    A.   Forests

        1.   Equatorial rainforests
        2.   Monsoon forests
        3.   Savanna forests and thorn forests
        4.   Subtropical-temperate rainforests
        5.   Sclerophyll woodlands
        6.   Summergreen broadleaf forests
        7.   Needleleaf forests

    B.   Shrub formations

        1.   Evergreen scrub
        2.   Light low scrub
        3.   Thorn scrub
        4.   Low scrub of high mountains
        5.   Heath
        6.   Evergreen alpine scrub
        7.   Prostrate dwarf shrubs

    C.   Grasslands

        a.   With adequate and continuous soil moisture
            1.   Meadows
            2.   Peat meadows and meadow moors
            3.   Prairies
            4.   Savannas
        b.   With inadequate soil moisture during summer
            5.   Grass meadows
            6.   Grass steppes

    D.   Formations of forbs, mosses, and lichens

II. OPEN LAND FORMATIONS

    E.   Desert steppes and deserts
    F.   Formations on rock, scree, and gravel

III. AQUATIC FORMATIONS

    G.   Littoral formations of halophytes

    H.   Freshwater formations of lakes, rivers, and streams
        1.   Alluvial, swamp, and shrub formations along banks
        2.   Formations of shallow water, reed swamps
        3.   Formations of deep water and limnoplankton

Classification of Vegetation by Rübel (1930)
LIGNOSA
Pluviilignosa
1. Pluviisilvae—Regenwälder—rainforest
2. Pluviifruticeta—Regengebüsche—rainbush
Laurilignosa
3. Laurisilvae—Lorbeerwälder—laurel forest
4. Laurifruticeta—Lorbeergebüsche—laurel bush
Durilignosa
5. Durisilvae—Hartlaubwälder—broadleaf sclerophyll forest
6. Durifruticeta—Hartlaubgebüsche—broadleaf sclerophyll bush
Ericilignosa
7. Ericfruticeta—echte Heiden—true heath
Aestilignosa
8. Aestisilvae—Sommerwälder—broadleaf summergreen forest
9. Aestifruticeta—Sommergebüsche—summergreen bush
Hiemilignosa
10. Hiemisilvae—regengrüne Wälder—monsoon or raingreen forest
11. Hiemifruticeta—regengrüne Gebüsche—monsoon bush
Aciculilignosa
12. Aciculisilvae—Nadelwälder—needleleaf sclerophyll forest
13. Aciculifruticeta—Nadelgebüsche—needleleaf bush
HERBOSA
Terriherbosa
14. Duriherbosa—Hartwiesen, Steppenwiesen—prairie and steppe
15. Sempervirentiherbosa—immergrüne Wiesen—evergreen grassland
16. Altherbosa—Hochstaudenwiesen—tall herbaceous vegetation
Aquiherbosa
17. Emersiherbosa—Sumpfwiesen—marsh or aquatic grassland
18. Submersiherbosa—submerse Wasserwiesen—submerged aquatic vegetation
19. Sphagniherbosa—Hochmoor—Sphagnum or high moor
DESERTA
20. Siccideserta—Trockeneinöden—dry desert
21. Frigorideserta—Kälteeinöden—cold desert or tundra
22. Litorideserta—Strandsteppen—strand grassland
23. Mobilideserta—Wandereinöden—shifting dunes vegetation
24. Rupideserta—Felsfluren—vegetation of screes, talus, etc.
25. Saxideserta—Stein- und Holzfluren—vegetation of rocks, tree trunks, etc.
SPECIAL GROUPS
26. Phytoplankton—free aquatic organisms, mostly microscopic
27. Phytoedaphon—terrestrial organisms, mostly microscopic and subterranean

Classification of Vegetation by Fosberg (1961c).

I. MAJOR STRUCTURAL GROUP: CLOSED VEGETATION. (*Crowns or peripheries of plants touching or overlapping.*)

    I-A. Formation Class: Forest. (*Closed woody vegetation 5m or more tall.*)

        I-A-1. Formation Group: Evergreen forest. (*At least the canopy layer with no significant leafless period.*)

        F. Multistratal evergreen forest (rainforest). (*Tall, multistratal, orthophyllous; epiphytes and lianas usually common; shrub layers usually sparse.*)

        F. Evergreen swamp forest. (*Bases of trees or root systems adapted to lengthy or permanent submergence; multistratal or unistratal; peat development often notable.*)

        F. Gnarled evergreen forest. (*Low, trunks and branches tending to be twisted or gnarled, usually with one tree layer, usually more or less sclerophyllous.*)

        F. Evergreen hardwood orthophyll forest. (*One or two woody layers, irregular canopy, medium to low stature, much-branched trees.*)

        F. Evergreen softwood orthophyll forest. (*Usually unistratal, of fast-growing trees, tangled with lianas.*)

        F. Evergreen broad sclerophyll forest. (*Leaves hard, stiff, or coriaceous.*)

        F. Evergreen narrow sclerophyll forest (needleleafed forest). (*Leaves [or equivalent] linear or scale-like, hard.*)

        F. Evergreen bamboo forest. (*Dominant layer of large bamboo or giant reed.*)

        F. Microphyllous evergreen forest. (*Frequently but not always of compound-leafed trees, sometimes thorny.*)

        I-A-2. Formation Group: Deciduous forest. (*At least canopy layer bare of leaves for a period during cold or dry season.*)

        F. Winter-deciduous orthophyll forest (hardwood forest).

        F. Deciduous swamp forest.

        F. Dry-season deciduous forest. (*Orthophyllous; thick herb or shrub layer.*)

        F. Microphyllous deciduous forest. (*Trees mostly thornless or spineless.*)

        F. Deciduous thorn forest. (*Trees mostly armed with thorns, spines, or prickles, usually microphyllous.*)

    I-B. Formation Class: Scrub. (*Closed woody vegetation 5 m or less tall.*)

        I-B-1. Formation Group: Evergreen scrub.

        F. Evergreen orthophyll scrub.

        F. Evergreen bamboo or reed brake. (*Dominant layer of dwarf bamboo, cane or woody reeds, may be strictly erect or tangled.*)

        F. Evergreen swamp scrub. (*Composed of shrubs with adaptations to stand lengthy or permanent submergence of root systems; peat development may be notable.*)

F. Evergreen broad sclerophyll scrub. (*Stiff shrubs, leaves generally rather small.*)

F. Mossy evergreen sclerophyll scrub. (*Stiff shrubs, leaves generally rather small; with abundant epiphytes—scrub equivalent of mossy forest.*)

F. Gnarled evergreen narrow sclerophyll scrub (krummholz).

F. Straight evergreen narrow sclerophyll scrub. (*Not especially gnarled.*)

F. Microphyllous evergreen scrub. (*Often thorny.*)

I-B-2. Formation Group: Deciduous scrub. (*Shrubs periodically bare of leaves, usually in dry season or winter.*)

F. Deciduous orthophyll scrub.

F. Deciduous swamp scrub. (*Root systems adapted to prolonged submergence.*)

F. [Deciduous sclerophyll scrub.]

F. Deciduous thorn scrub (thornbush). (*Usually microphyllous, cacti often abundant. Rare in this closed form.*)

I-C. Formation Class: Dwarf scrub. (*Closed predominantly woody vegetation less than 0.5 m tall.*)

I-C-1. Formation Group: Evergreen dwarf scrub.

F. Evergreen orthophyll dwarf scrub.

F. Evergreen broad sclerophyll dwarf scrub.

F. Evergreen shrub bog. (*Dwarf scrub with significant peat accumulation, root systems of plants adapted to constant immersion.*)

I-C-2. Formation Group: Deciduous dwarf scrub.

F. Deciduous orthophyll dwarf scrub.

I-D. Formation Class: Open forest with closed lower layers. (*Trees with crowns not touching, mostly not separated by more than twice their diameter.*)

I-D-1. Formation Group: Evergreen open forest with closed lower layers.

F. Open evergreen orthophyll forest.

F. Open evergreen swamp.

F. Open evergreen broad sclerophyll forest.

F. Open evergreen narrow sclerophyll forest.

F. Open microphyllous evergreen forest. (*May be somewhat thorny.*)

I-D-2. Formation Group: Open deciduous forest with closed lower layers.

F. Open deciduous orthophyll forest.

F. Open deciduous swamp.

F. Open deciduous narrow sclerophyll forest.

F. [Open deciduous broad sclerophyll forest.] (*Possibly does not exist.*)

F. Open microphyllous deciduous forest.

I-E. Formation Class: Closed scrub with scattered trees.

I-E-1. Formation Group: Closed evergreen scrub with scattered trees. (*At least shrub layer evergreen.*)

F. Evergreen orthophyll scrub with trees.

F. Evergreen sclerophyll scrub with trees.

F. Microphyllous scrub with trees.

I-E-2. Formation Group: Closed deciduous scrub with scattered trees.
F. Deciduous orthophyll scrub with trees.
F. [Deciduous sclerophyll scrub with trees.] (*Perhaps does not exist.*)
F. [Microphyllous deciduous scrub with trees.] (*Perhaps does not exist.*)

I-F. Formation Class: Dwarf scrub with scattered trees.
I-F-1. Formation Group: Evergreen dwarf scrub with scattered trees.
F. Microphyllous evergreen dwarf scrub with trees. (*Without significant peat formation.*)
F. Microphyllous evergreen heath with trees. (*With peat accumulation.*)
I-F-2. Formation Group: Deciduous dwarf scrub with trees.
F. Deciduous heath with trees. (*With significant peat accumulation.*)

I-G. Formation Class: Open scrub with closed ground cover.
I-G-1. Formation Group: Open evergreen scrub with closed ground cover.
F. Open evergreen orthophyll scrub.
F. Open evergreen broad sclerophyll scrub.
F. Open gnarled evergreen narrow sclerophyll scrub or open krummholz.
I-G-2. Formation Group: Open deciduous scrub with closed ground cover.
F. Open deciduous orthophyll scrub with closed ground cover.

I-H. Formation Class: Open dwarf scrub with closed ground cover.
I-H-1. Formation Group: Open evergreen dwarf scrub with closed ground cover.
F. Open evergreen orthophyll dwarf scrub.
F. Open evergreen shrub bog.
F. Open evergreen microphyllous dwarf scrub.
I-H-2. Formation Group: Open deciduous dwarf scrub with closed ground cover.
F. Open deciduous orthophyll dwarf scrub. (*Without significant peat accumulation.*)
F. Open deciduous orthophyll heath. (*With significant accumulation of peat.*)

I-I. Formation Class: Tall savanna. (*Closed grass or other herbaceous vegetation 1 m tall or more with scattered trees.*)
I-I-1. Formation Group: Evergreen savanna. (*Trees evergreen.*)
F. Evergreen orthophyll savanna.
F. Evergreen broad sclerophyll savanna.
F. Evergreen broad sclerophyll swamp savanna.
F. Evergreen narrow sclerophyll savanna.
F. Microphyllous evergreen savanna.
I-I-2. Formation Group: Deciduous tall savanna. (*Trees deciduous.*)
F. Deciduous orthophyll savanna.
F. Deciduous microphyll savanna.
F. Deciduous thorn savanna.

I-J. Formation Class: Low savanna. (*Herbaceous vegetation less than 1 m tall, with scattered trees.*)

  I-J-1. Formation Group: Evergreen low savanna. (*Trees evergreen.*)
    F. Evergreen orthophyll low savanna.
    F. Evergreen broad-sclerophyll low savanna.
    F. Evergreen narrow sclerophyll low savanna.
    F. Evergreen narrow sclerophyll lichen savanna.
    F. Evergreen narrow sclerophyll swamp savanna.
  I-J-2. Formation Group: Deciduous low savanna.
    F. Deciduous orthophyll savanna.
    F. [Deciduous broad sclerophyll low savanna.]
    F. Deciduous lichen savanna.
    F. Deciduous swamp savanna.

I-K. Formation Class: Shrub savanna. (*Closed grass or other herbaceous vegetation with scattered shrubs.*)

  I-K-1. Formation Group: Evergreen shrub savanna.
    F. Evergreen orthophyll shrub savanna.
    F. Evergreen broad sclerophyll shrub savanna.
    F. Evergreen narrow sclerophyll shrub savanna.
    F. Evergreen microphyll shrub savanna.
  I-K-2. Formation Group: Deciduous shrub savanna.
    F. Deciduous orthophyll shrub savanna.
    F. [Deciduous broad sclerophyll shrub savanna.]
    F. [Microphyllous deciduous shrub savanna.]
    F. Mesophyllous deciduous thorn shrub savanna.
    F. Microphyllous deciduous thorn shrub savanna.

I-L. Formation Class: Tall grass. (*Closed herbaceous vegetation exceeding 1 m in height, predominantly graminoid.*)

  I-L-1. Formation Group: Evergreen tall grass. (*Shoots remaining green the year round.*)
    F. Evergreen orthophyll tall grass.
    F. Evergreen orthophyll tall tussock grass.
    F. Evergreen sclerophyll tall grass.
  I-L-2. Formation Group: Seasonal tall grass. (*Turning brown in dry season or in winter, often burned.*)
    F. Seasonal orthophyll tall grass.
    F. Seasonal sclerophyll grass.

I-M. Formation Class: Short grass. (*Closed herbaceous vegetation, less than 1 m tall, predominantly graminoid.*)

  I-M-1. Formation Group:Evergreen short grass.
    F. Evergreen orthophyll short grass.
    F. Evergreen orthophyll short tussock grass.
    F. Evergreen short grass and sedge bog. (*Growing from a mass of grass- and sedge-peat.*)
  I-M-2. Formation Group: Seasonal short grass.
    F. Seasonal orthophyll meadows (short grass).
    F. Seasonal sclerophyll short grass meadow.

I-N. Formation Class: Broadleafed herb vegetation. (*Closed vegetation, predominantly of broadleafed herbaceous plants.*)
  I-N-1. Formation Group: Evergreen broadleafed herb vegetation.
    F. Evergreen broadleafed weedy vegetation.
    F. Evergreen fern meadow.
    F. Evergreen giant herb thicket.
  I-N-2. Formation Group: Seasonal broadleafed herb vegetation.
    F. Seasonal broadleafed meadow.
I-O. Formation Class: Marsh. (*Closed vegetation of herbaceous plants, the roots of which are adapted to lengthy or permanent immersion, the upper parts to emersion.*)
  I-O-1. Formation Group: Evergreen marsh.
    F. Evergreen orthophyll graminoid marsh.
    F. Tall evergreen graminoid marsh.
    F. Evergreen broadleafed marsh.
  I-O-2. Formation Group: Seasonal marsh.
    F. Seasonal orthophyll marsh.
    F. Seasonal sclerophyll marsh.
I-P. Formation Class: Submerged meadows. (*Vegetation of rooted aquatic herbs, adapted for permanent complete submersion except in some cases for floating leaves.*)
  I-P-1. Formation Group: Evergreen submerged meadows.
    F. Evergreen watergrass.
    F. Macrophyllous evergreen submerged meadows.
    F. Megaphyllous evergreen submerged meadows.
  I-P-2. Formation Group: Seasonal submerged meadows. (*Plants disappearing, at least their shoots, in winter.*)
    F. Seasonal watergrass.
    F. Broadleafed seasonal submerged meadows. (*Leaves of ordinary size, not narrowly linear or grasslike.*)
    F. Macrophyllous seasonal submerged meadows. (*Water lilies and similar plants dominant.*)
I-Q. Formation Class: Floating meadows. (*Closed vegetation of aquatic herbs, adapted to floating conditions, not rooted in bottom.*)
  I-Q-1. Formation Group: Evergreen floating meadows.
    F. Broadleafed evergreen floating meadows.
    F. Evergreen floating grass.
    F. Thalliform evergreen floating vegetation.
    F. Microphyllous evergreen floating meadows.
  I-Q-2. Formation Group: Seasonal floating meadow.
    F. Thalliform seasonal floating meadow.
    F. Microphyllous seasonal floating meadow.

II. PRIMARY STRUCTURAL GROUP: OPEN VEGETATION. (*Plants or tufts of plants not touching but crowns not separated by more than twice their diameter; plants, not substratum, dominating landscape.*)

II-A. Formation Class: Steppe forest (often called woodland or woodland-savanna. (*Tree layer and lower layers open, lower layers may be open or sparse.*)

    II-A-1. Formation Group: Evergreen steppe forest. (*Tree layers, at least, evergreen.*)

        F. [Evergreen orthophyll steppe forest]. (*Possibly does not exist with open lower layers*).

        F. Evergreen broad sclerophyll steppe forest.

        F. Open evergreen sclerophyll swamp.

        F. Evergreen narrow sclerophyll steppe forest.

        F. Microphyllous evergreen steppe forest.

    II-A-2. Formation Group: Deciduous steppe forest.

        F. Deciduous orthophyll steppe forest.

        F. Microphyllous deciduous steppe forest.

        F. Deciduous bamboo steppe forest.

        F. Open deciduous thorn (steppe) forest.

II-B. Formation Class: Steppe scrub. (*Like steppe forest, but with shrubs [over 0.5 m tall] instead of trees.*)

    II-B-1. Formation Group: Evergreen steppe scrub.

        F. Evergreen broad sclerophyll steppe scrub.

        F. Gnarled evergreen narrow sclerophyll steppe scrub (open krummholz).

        F. Microphyllous evergreen steppe scrub.

        F. Evergreen succulent steppe scrub.

        F. Evergreen saltbush steppe scrub. (*Shrubs with gray scurfy leaves*).

    II-B-2. Formation Group: Deciduous steppe scrub.

        F. Deciduous orthophyll steppe scrub.

        F. [Deciduous sclerophyll steppe scrub.]

        F. Microphyllous deciduous steppe scrub.

        F. Deciduous thorn steppe scrub (thornbush).

II-C. Formation Class: Dwarf steppe scrub. (*Open predominantly woody vegetation less than 0.5 m tall.*)

    II-C-1. Formation Group: Evergreen dwarf steppe scrub.

        F. Evergreen orthophyll dwarf steppe scrub.

        F. Evergreen broad sclerophyll dwarf steppe scrub.

        F. Evergreen narrow sclerophyll dwarf steppe scrub.

        F. Microphyllous evergreen dwarf steppe scrub.

    II-C-2. Formation Group: Deciduous dwarf steppe scrub. (*Perhaps does not exist.*)

II-D. Formation Class: Steppe savanna. (*Steppe with scattered trees.*)

    II-D-1. Formation Group: Evergreen steppe savanna. (*Trees evergreen.*)

        F. Evergreen orthophyll steppe savanna.

        F. Evergreen sclerophyll steppe savanna.

        F. [Evergreen microphyll steppe savanna.]

    II-D-2. Formation Group: Deciduous steppe savanna.

        F. Deciduous orthophyll steppe savanna.

F. [Deciduous broad sclerophyll steppe savanna.] (*Perhaps does not exist.*)

F. Microphyllous deciduous steppe savanna.

F. Deciduous thorn steppe savanna.

II-E. Formation Class: Shrub steppe savanna.

II-E-1. Formation Group: Evergreen shrub steppe savanna.

F. Evergreen orthophyll shrub steppe savanna.

F. Evergreen sclerophyll shrub steppe savanna.

F. Evergreen microphyll shrub steppe savanna.

F. Evergreen succulent shrub steppe savanna.

II-E-2. Formation Group: Deciduous shrub steppe savanna.

F. Deciduous orthophyll shrub steppe savanna.

F. [Deciduous sclerophyll shrub steppe savanna.] (*Possibly does not exist.*)

F. Microphyllous deciduous shrub steppe savanna.

F. Deciduous thorn shrub steppe savanna.

II-F. Formation Class: Dwarf shrub steppe savanna.

II-F-1. Formation Group: Evergreen dwarf shrub steppe savanna.

F. [Evergreen orthophyll dwarf shrub steppe savanna.] (*Possibly does not exist.*)

F. Evergreen narrow sclerophyll dwarf shrub steppe savanna.

F. Succulent dwarf shrub steppe savanna.

II-F-2. Formation Group: Seasonal dwarf shrub steppe savanna.

F. Seasonal sclerophyll dwarf shrub steppe savanna.

II-G. Formation Class: Steppe. (*Open herbaceous vegetation, tufts or plants discrete, yet close enough to dominate the landscape.*)

II-G-1. Formation Group: Evergreen steppe.

F. Evergreen saltbush steppe.

F. Evergreen succulent steppe.

F. Evergreen cushion plant steppe.

II-G-2. Formation Group: Seasonal steppe.

F. Seasonal grass steppe.

F. Annual herb steppe.

III. PRIMARY STRUCTURAL GROUP: SPARSE VEGETATION OR DESERT. (*Plants so scattered that substratum dominates landscape.*)

III-A. Formation Class: Desert forest. (*Scattered trees, subordinate shrub or herb layers very sparse, or absent.*)

III-A-1. Formation Group: Evergreen desert forest. (*May be evergreen because of persistent leaves or because of green stems.*)

F. Evergreen non-succulent desert forest.

F. Evergreen succulent desert forest.

III-A-2. Formation Group: Deciduous desert forest.

F. Microphyllous deciduous desert forest.

III-B. Formation Class: Desert scrub. (*Scattered shrubs in an otherwise bare or only ephemerally vegetated landscape, not here differentiated into shrub and dwarf shrub classes.*)

III-B-1. Formation Group: Evergreen desert scrub.
  F. Evergreen sclerophyll desert scrub.
  F. Microphyllous evergreen desert scrub.
  F. Saltbush desert.
  F. Evergreen desert thorn-scrub. (*Dominated by rigid green-stemmed, spinose, leafless or ephemerally leafy plants.*)
  F. Evergreen succulent desert scrub.
III-B-2. Formation Group: Deciduous desert scrub.
  F. Microphyllous deciduous desert scrub.
  F. Deciduous desert thorn-scrub.
III-C. Formation Class: Desert herb vegetation. (*Scattered herbaceous plants only.*)
III-C-1. Formation Group: Evergreen desert herb vegetation.
  F. Evergreen succulent herb desert.
  F. Evergreen psammophyte desert. (*Plants with special adaptations enabling them to survive in shifting sand.*)
  F. Lichen tundra.
III-C-2. Formation Group: Seasonal desert herb vegetation.
  F. Seasonal desert grass.
  F. Ephemeral herb desert. (*Vegetation principally of ephemeral annuals and geophytes, appearing only for short periods after infrequent rains.*)

Description of Vegetation Structure by Dansereau (1961)

1. LIFE FORM
   W   erect woody plants
   L   climbing or decumbent
       woody plants
   E   epiphytes and crusts
   H   herbs
   M   bryoids

2. STRATIFICATION
   7   more than 25 m
   6   10–25 m
   5   8–10 m
   4   2–8 m
   3   0.5–2 m
   2   0.1–0.5 m
   1   0.0–0.1 m

3. COVERAGE
   b   barren or very sparse
   i   interrupted,
       discontinuous
   p   in patches, tufts, clumps
   c   continuous

4. FUNCTION
   d   deciduous or ephemeral
   s   semideciduous
   e   evergreen
   j   evergreen-succulent or
       evergreen-leafless

5. LEAF SHAPE AND SIZE
   o   leafless
   n   needle, spine, scale or
       subulate
   g   graminoid
   a   medium or small
   h   broad
   v   compound
   q   thalloid

6. LEAF TEXTURE
   o   leafless
   f   filmy
   z   membranous
   x   sclerophyll
   k   succulent or fungoid

Description of Vegetation Structure by Küchler

L I F E   F O R M   C A T E G O R I E S

BASIC LIFE FORMS

Woody Plants:

Broadleaf evergreen	B
Broadleaf deciduous	D
Needleleaf evergreen	E
Needleleaf deciduous	N
Aphyllous	O
Semideciduous (B+D)	S
Mixed (D+E)	M

Herbaceous Plants:

Graminoids	G
Forbs	H
Lichens, mosses	L

SPECIAL LIFE FORMS

Climbers (lianas)	C
Stem succulents	K
Tuft plants	T
Bamboos	V
Epiphytes	X

LEAF CHARACTERISTICS

hard (sclerophyll)	h
soft	w
succulent	k
large (> 400 cm^2)	l
small (< 4 cm^2)	s

S T R U C T U R A L   C A T E G O R I E S

HEIGHT (STRATIFICATION)

8 =	> 35 meters
7 = 20 - 35	"
6 = 10 - 20	"
5 = 5 - 10	"
4 = 2 - 5	"
3 = 0.5 - 2	"
2 = 0.1 - 0.5	"
1 = < 0.1	"

COVERAGE

c = continuous (> 75%)

i = interrupted (50-75%)

p = parklike, in patches (25-50%)

r = rare (6-25%)

b = barely present, sporadic (1-5%)

a = almost absent, extremely scarce (<1%)

Legend, Based on Physiognomic System of A. W. Küchler, from "Vegetation of Southeastern Mount Desert Island, Maine (1:25,000)"—I

1. Needleleaf evergreen trees, medium tall
2. Needleleaf evergreen trees, medium tall and low
3. Needleleaf evergreen trees, low
4. Needleleaf evergreen trees, medium tall, with patches of medium tall broadleaf deciduous trees
5. Needleleaf evergreen trees, medium tall, with patches of low broadleaf deciduous trees
6. Needleleaf evergreen trees, medium tall with low broadleaf deciduous trees and shrubs
7. Needleleaf evergreen trees, medium tall, with broadleaf deciduous shrubs and dwarf shrubs
8. Needleleaf evergreen low trees with patches of low broadleaf deciduous trees
9. Needleleaf evergreen low trees with low broadleaf deciduous trees and shrubs
10. Needleleaf evergreen low trees with broadleaf deciduous shrubs and dwarf shrubs
11. Broadleaf deciduous trees, medium tall, with patches of low needleleaf evergreen trees
12. Broadleaf deciduous trees, medium tall, with patches of shrubs and needleleaf evergreen trees
13. Broadleaf deciduous low trees with patches of needleleaf evergreen low trees
14. Broadleaf deciduous medium tall and low trees and shrubs with patches of needleleaf evergreen medium tall and low trees
15. Broadleaf deciduous low trees with patches of shrubs and needleleaf evergreen trees
16. Broadleaf deciduous shrubs and dwarf shrubs with patches of needleleaf evergreen trees
17. Broadleaf deciduous low trees and shrubs with patches of medium tall and low needleleaf evergreen trees
18. Broadleaf deciduous trees, medium tall
19. Broadleaf deciduous trees, medium tall and low
20. Broadleaf deciduous trees, medium tall and shrubs
21. Broadleaf deciduous trees, medium tall and patches of shrubs
22. Broadleaf deciduous trees, medium tall and low, and patches of shrubs
23. Broadleaf deciduous low trees
24. Broadleaf deciduous low trees and shrubs
25. Broadleaf deciduous low trees and patches of shrubs
26. Broadleaf deciduous shrubs
27. Broadleaf deciduous dwarf shrubs
28. Broadleaf deciduous shrubs and dwarf shrubs with patches of medium tall and low broadleaf deciduous trees
29. Broadleaf deciduous shrubs and dwarf shrubs

30. Grass
31. Grass with patches of broadleaf deciduous shrubs and dwarf shrubs
32. Grass with patches of broadleaf deciduous shrubs and needleleaf evergreen trees
33. Water
34. Urban and agricultural
35. Barren rock with patches of broadleaf deciduous and broadleaf evergreen dwarf shrubs, grass, forbs and needleleaf evergreen dwarf shrubs and occasional low trees

Additional physiognomic information given in 8 physiognomic symbols.

**Legend, Based on Floristic System of K. Hueck, from
"Vegetation of Southeastern Mount Desert Island, Maine (1:25,000)"—II**

LEGEND

1. White pine forest	11. Birch forest
2. Pitch pine forest	12. Deciduous shrubs
3. White cedar forest	13. Blueberries-sweet fern
4. Red spruce forest	14. Sweet gale-leatherleaf
5. Black spruce forest	15. Grassland
6. White spruce forest	16. Sedges
7. Balsam fir forest	17. Summit type
8. Oak forest	18. Barren
9. Beech forest	19. Urban and agricultural
10. Red maple forest	20. Water

Additional information given by 14 symbols for broadleaf trees and shrubs, 10 symbols for needleleaf trees, and 14 symbols for dwarf shrubs and herbaceous types.

**Legend, Based on Physiognomic-Floristic System of A. E. Wieslander, from
"Vegetation of Southeastern Mount Desert Island, Maine (1:25,000)"—III**

1. Barren	9. Grassland-woodland-conifers
2. Urban-agricultural	10. Woodland-conifers
3. Grassland-meadow	11. Miscellaneous conifer types
4. Grassland-shrubs	12. Commercial conifers
5. Dwarf shrubs	13. Shrubs-conifers
6. Shrubs	14. Subalpine
7. Shrubs-woodland	15. Water
8. Woodland	

Additional floristic information given by 15 letter symbols for woodland tree species, 5 letter symbols for commercial conifer species, 15 letter symbols for shrub and dwarf shrub species, and 15 letter symbols for herbaceous species.

Index

453